McGRAW-HILL SERIES IN GEOGRAPHY

V. C. Finch, *Consulting Editor*

ECONOMIC GEOGRAPHY

OF

SOUTH AMERICA

McGRAW-HILL SERIES
IN GEOGRAPHY

SOUTH AMERICA

Scale of Miles
0   200   400   600   800

Economic Geography
of
South America

By
R. H. WHITBECK
Late Professor of Geography
University of Wisconsin

and

FRANK E. WILLIAMS
Professor of Geography
University of Pennsylvania

ASSISTED BY
WILLIAM F. CHRISTIANS
Assistant Professor of Geography
University of Pennsylvania

THIRD   EDITION

McGRAW-HILL BOOK COMPANY, Inc.
NEW YORK AND LONDON
1940

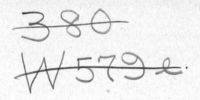

THE MAPLE PRESS COMPANY, YORK, PA.

Preface to the Third Edition

The present book is more than a revision. Not only has the subject matter been brought as nearly up to date as available information permits, but large portions of the book have been entirely rewritten and much of it has been rearranged.

In rewriting the text the junior author has attempted, in so far as possible, to retain the philosophy of his senior. At the same time he has tried to make it conform to a definite pattern of presentation. Other changes have been necessitated by recent economic and political developments. Some illustrations that were in the former text have been omitted and many new ones have been added.

The junior author has received valuable help and suggestions from Professor V. C. Finch of the University of Wisconsin, Professor Preston E. James of the University of Michigan, and Dr. Otis P. Starkey of the University of Pennsylvania. He is greatly indebted to Professor Glenn Trewartha of the University of Wisconsin and Professor G. H. Smith of Ohio State University for the use of maps. Mrs. William F. Christians has rendered valuable aid in typing and reading and Frank C. Williams made a large number of the new maps and graphs. The junior author is particularly indebted to Professor William F. Christians for his untiring help in revising and rewriting.

The junior author is also greatly indebted to many friends, officials, and acquaintances in various parts of South America who gave him information during the trips he made to that continent.

The junior author feels keenly his responsibility in attempting to rewrite this text. The senior author's reputation was so high that nothing should be done that would in any way mar the contribution he made in the earlier text. The senior author's long experience in writing and teaching, his facility for expression, and his knowledge of the South American continent made him peculiarly fitted to write the original. Any changes that have been made are the responsibility of the junior author. Had the senior author lived to collaborate there would surely have been many improvements. It is hoped that the book as now presented will not fall below the standards set by the original author.

FRANK E. WILLIAMS.

PHILADELPHIA, PA.,
    June, 1940.

Preface to the First Edition

This book has grown out of the writer's course in the Geography of South America given at the University of Wisconsin, and out of visits to Venezuela, Peru, Bolivia, Chile, Argentina, Uruguay, and Brazil.

The subject matter of the book is organized on the basis of countries and of geographical regions. The student of South American geography desires to know something of the South American countries as countries; something about the people, resources, industries, and commerce of each country as a whole. In the world's doings, Chile, Argentina, Peru, Colombia, and the other countries are units. Countries are the geographical regions about which people read, in which they are interested, and with which international affairs deal. Countries as political entities are, in many ways, the most significant of geographical units.

But, within each of the larger countries, and often overlapping national boundaries, are natural regions which are also geographically important. The basins of the Amazon and of the Rio de la Plata, for example, overlap national boundaries; yet these great river basins possess a degree of economic unity which ought to be recognized, and, in the following chapters, is recognized. In most of the South American countries there are distinct natural regions such as the Central Valley of Chile, the Pampa of Argentina, and the Eastern Highland of Brazil, and such natural regions are made special units of study.

The characteristics of the people who have come into possession of South America, and the sort of governments which they maintain, are no less important than the physical character of the regions. In economic geography, the human element is of large significance. Physical and climatic features and natural

ix

resources determine, to a degree, what man *may* do in a given region; but many non-geographical factors, primarily man himself, decide what actually shall be done in transforming opportunities into realization.

Obviously the bibliographies at the ends of chapters and at the end of the book are not intended to be exhaustive. They include the more readily accessible primary and secondary sources in English, with additions, mostly from official sources, in Spanish and Portuguese.

For various kinds of assistance, I am indebted to many people both in South America and in the United States. From Dr. Julius Klein, Director of the Bureau of Foreign and Domestic Commerce, I received letters of introduction to United States commercial attachés, trade commissioners and consuls in various South American countries. These officials and their staffs were of very great service, and I desire to acknowledge my obligations to them; they include Mr. Walter N. Pearce, Lima; Mr. Dale C. Macdonough, La Paz; Mr. George A. Makinson, Valparaiso, Mr. Ralph Ackerman, Santiago; Mr. Edward F. Feeley and Mr. George Brady, Buenos Aires; Mr. R. M. Connell, São Paulo; and Mr. W. E. Embry and Mr. M. E. Cremer, Rio de Janeiro. Courtesies were received from the representatives of Grace and Company, and from representatives of the Chile Copper Company, from Señor Rafael Larco Herrera, Lima; Professor D. S. Bullock, Angol, Chile; Señor Ing. Carlos Vallejo, and Señor Alejandro Bunge, Buenos Aires, and Mr. Justus Wallerstein, Rio de Janeiro.

From Professor W. H. Haas of Northwestern University, Professor Preston E. James of the University of Michigan, Mr. E. C. Le Fort and Dr. Glenn Trewartha of the University of Wisconsin, and Dr. Selma Schubring of Madison, I received helpful assistance and suggestions. In the preparation of drawings, Mr. G. H. Smith of the University of Wisconsin and Miss Florence Whitbeck of the University of Rochester rendered valuable service, which it is a pleasure to acknowledge.

R. H. WHITBECK.

THE UNIVERSITY OF WISCONSIN,
MADISON, WIS.

Contents

xi

ECONOMIC GEOGRAPHY
OF SOUTH AMERICA

Chapter I. The Continent of South America

South America, as a continent, has seemed remote to most people of the United States; but recent events have made many North Americans more conscious of their southern neighbors. Part of this change toward closer relationship and enlivened interest is due to economic conditions, but more important have been air-travel developments, rise of industralism in South American countries, and ramifications of the politico-economic revolutions in Europe into Latin American republics. This interest is still confined to a relatively small number, and as late as the year 1935–1936 only 12,000 people from the United States left for South America as contrasted with 250,000 who went to Europe.

The settlement of South America had begun before the middle of the sixteenth century, and Brazil was exporting sugar to Europe before the English landed at Plymouth Rock. But South America has developed slowly and has been greatly exceeded in economic development by North America. Why is it that South America has but little over eighty million people while North America has more than twice that number? Why has South America, with about one-seventh of the land of the earth, only about one-thirtieth of the world's people? With several areas of the world overpopulated and suffering from lack of resources, why are there large areas of South America undeveloped? The answer is not a simple one. Position, topography, climate, resources, types of people, historical development, governmental conditions—all have exerted their influences in varying degrees. As a result of all these different factors, South America is a continent having great diversity in its cultural patterns and manifold stages of economic development.

3

LEGEND

EACH DOT REPRESENTS
20,000 PERSONS

PRINCIPAL CITIES

●   100,000 - 250,000

▲   250,000 - 500,000

■   500,000 - 1,000,000

◈   1,000,000 OR MORE

0 200 400
SCALE OF MILES

Fig. 1.—Distribution of population and larger cities of South America.

PATTERN OF MAJOR ECONOMIC ACTIVITIES

With few exceptions, the major concentrations of population have developed near the sea (Fig. 1). Some favorable environmental conditions, often accompanied by historic accidents, have led to economic development where there was an easy outlet—at the seashore or along a navigable river. Economic activity has tended to develop in a few important regions and in a considerable number of more or less isolated centers (Fig. 2). Communication between these partly developed areas is often difficult, and hence a large part of the trade of South America is with the industrialized portions of North America and Europe rather than with other centers on the South American continent. Furthermore, the trade that is confined to the continent is apt to be coastal, often between parts of the same country. Climatic and other natural conditions have made it profitable to produce goods that are in demand in the progressive countries of the Northern Hemisphere. This has further accentuated the growth of unrelated, or at least only partly related, communities.

As shown by the map of economic activities (Fig. 2), most of South America is still in the extractive stage of economic development. Agriculture, pastoral pursuits, lumbering, and mining take up the energies of most of the people. Though manufacturing is of some importance, on the continent as a whole it is relatively undeveloped. With the exception of two or three districts, manufacturing consists in the preparation of products for local consumption. The principal products are: meat and meat by-products, cotton textiles, beverages, flour, leather, lumber, boots and shoes, and furniture. The chief centers that have developed manufacturing are the larger cities of Argentina, Plateau of Brazil, central Chile, coastal Peru, and the environs of Bogotá and Medellín in Colombia.

EVOLUTION OF THE PATTERN

Discovery of South America.—When the Turks took Constantinople in 1453 and closed the accustomed trade routes between South Europe and the East, an impelling reason was created for someone to undertake a voyage westward across the Atlantic in search of a sea route to the Orient. The Mediterranean peoples were the first to suffer from the closing of the

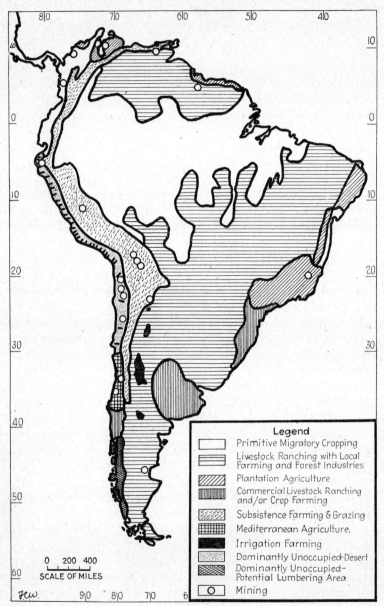

Fig. 2.—Dominant economic activities of South America.

eastern trade routes to India, and the first to suffer are likely to be the first to bestir themselves to find a remedy. It was logical that a Venetian or a Genoese—representing the foremost of trading peoples of the period—should be the first to seek a new route to the East. It was equally logical that Columbus, a Genoese, should find a sympathetic hearing in Spain, a land whose location on the extreme western margin of Europe and at the western gate of the Mediterranean made it a convenient and natural place of departure.

Another factor influencing the course that the little fleet commanded by Columbus should follow was the northern belt of trade winds. These winds blow steadily toward the southwest, and they carried the sailing ships of Columbus across the Atlantic well to the south of the latitude of Spain. The first land encountered was in the West Indies, in latitude 24°N. The trade winds in a measure determined that the Spanish colonial empire in the New World should begin in Middle America, whither the early exploring ships carried their explorers, and then should spread out toward the north and south. The direction of these winds in an age of sailing vessels made it easier for the ships sailing from Spain and Portugal to the New World to sail in the tropics rather than in the more northerly belt of westerlies with their buffeting winds adverse to westward voyages from Europe. Thus it came about that Spain's approach to her future American possessions lay in the path of the trades through West Indian waters to Mexico and the Isthmus of Panama.

In a measure, the trade winds were responsible for the independent discovery of the eastern mainland of South America by the Portuguese and the later control of Brazil by that nation. In 1500, Portuguese ships under the command of Pedro Alvares de Cabral, while sailing southward on a voyage around Africa, were carried westward by the southeast trade winds and touched the eastern coast of South America, and their commander laid claim to the territory in the name of the king of Portugal (Fig. 3).

Thus did a series of geographical and other circumstances influence historical events so that South America and southern North America became Spanish and Portuguese, while other circumstances were leading to British domination of the eastern coast of North America and later made most of that continent essentially Anglo-Saxon in its type of civilization. One cannot help speculating what might have been the results if South America had fallen to the Anglo-Saxons and North America to the Spanish and Portuguese.

Significance of the Location of the Continent of South America. The strong and advanced nations of the world, for some reason, have always been those of the north temperate (north inter-

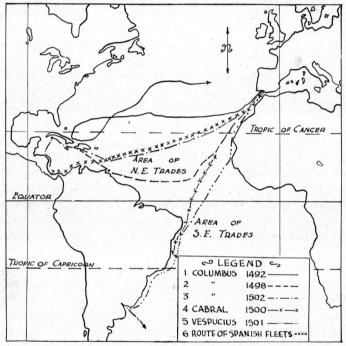

FIG. 3.—Early exploration and trade routes between Europe and South America.

mediate) zone, which includes very nearly all of Europe, Asia, and North America. Modern civilization has grown up in this zone, especially in Europe. The great colonizing and trading nations have been European. The peoples who occupied and initiated the development of the Americas, Africa, Australia, and the islands of the sea went out from Europe; these newer lands were long joined to Europe by political ties, and some of them are still so joined. All are united to Europe by ties of race, language, culture, and commerce. During the last quarter of the eighteenth century and the first quarter of the nineteenth, nearly all the

European colonies in the Americas broke away from their mother countries and set up independent governments. Prior to this separation, the geographical location of South America was deemed little, if any, less favorable than that of North America. Spain and Portugal maintained close relations with their American colonies, and the fact that some of them were a long way off did not prevent the mother countries from actively participating in their economic life. In short, so long as political ties bound the South American colonies to Europe, their out-of-the-way location was little felt. But when these colonies separated from the mother countries and the latter ceased to participate actively in their development, then the location of South America in the Southern Hemisphere gradually revealed itself as something of a disadvantage. Distance is always a factor with which to reckon. Moreover, the loss of their American colonies hastened the decline of Spain and Portugal to unimportant places in world affairs; and they were unable, in other parts of the world, to make good their losses, as Great Britain did. Severed from Spain and Portugal and too weak and inexperienced in self-government to do much for themselves, the South American countries suffered, among other handicaps, the full disadvantage of their location off the great east-west routes along which the currents of commerce, emigration, and development have flowed most freely. These currents are strongest in the Northern Hemisphere where the great land masses, with their invigorating cyclonic climate, have brought forth numerous and vigorous peoples. It would be easy, however, to emphasize unduly this out-of-the-way location of most of South America. Though it unquestionably has somewhat retarded the development of the continent, it has been a minor rather than a major influence.

The Isolation of the West Coast.—Soon after the discovery of America, Spain and Portugal accepted a division of their spheres of activity in the New World, and the Pope established a Line of Demarcation, which gave eastern South America to Portugal and the western portion to Spain (Fig. 4). However, the actual landing of Cabral in eastern South America, already referred to, gave Portugal her real claim to this part of the continent and forced the Spanish conquerors to devote themselves mainly to the northern and western portions of South America. But the land barrier formed by the Isthmus of Panama prevented the

Spanish fleets from directly reaching the west coast and compelled the laborious transfer of cargoes across the isthmus by men and animals. So long as Spain held her vast colonial possessions in America and maintained regular connection with them by her fleets and galleons, even the west coast of South America felt no serious handicap because of its geographical isolation. But after the colonies broke away from Spain and set up independent governments, this isolation became, for a century, a seriously retarding influence upon European immigration to these lands and a hindrance to their commerce. True, ships from Europe rounded Cape Horn and reached the ports of the west coast, but it was a long trip. The southerly location of Chile and its rich nitrate deposits gave that country frequent steamship connections with Europe and eastern North America and broke down its geographical

FIG. 4.—The two lines of demarcation originally intended to separate the colonizing activities of Spain and Portugal in the New World.

isolation in a degree; but, for the other west-coast countries, that isolation continued until the opening of the Panama Canal in 1914.

Framework and Dimensions of the Continent.—The shape of any continent is due largely to the distribution of the mountain systems that make up its framework. This continental framework usually consists of a major mountain system and one or more minor mountain systems. If the major axis extends north and south, the long dimension of the continent is north-south, as it is in both North America and South America. If the main axis extends east and west, as it does in Eurasia, then the long dimension of the continent is east-west. The width of a continent in its various parts is determined mainly by the distance between the principal mountain systems that constitute its framework. In South America, the major axis is the Andes system in the west,

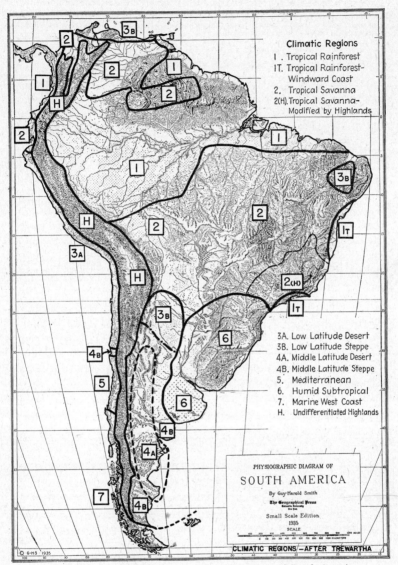

Climatic Regions
1. Tropical Rainforest
IT. Tropical Rainforest-
    Windward Coast
2. Tropical Savanna
2(H).Tropical Savanna-
    Modified by Highlands

3A. Low Latitude Desert
3B. Low Latitude Steppe
4A. Middle Latitude Desert
4B. Middle Latitude Steppe
5. Mediterranean
6. Humid Subtropical
7. Marine West Coast
H. Undifferentiated Highlands

PHYSIOGRAPHIC DIAGRAM OF
SOUTH AMERICA
By Guy-Harold Smith
The Geographical Press
Columbia University
New York
Small Scale Edition
1935
SCALE

CLIMATIC REGIONS—AFTER TREWARTHA

FIG. 5.—Major relief features and climatic regions of South America.

and the secondary axis is the highland of eastern Brazil (Fig. 5). These two axes converge toward the south. In fact, the Brazilian, or minor, axis becomes progressively lower toward the south and disappears under the plains of the River Plata, leaving only the Andes to continue 25 degrees farther to the south, tapering to a point at Cape Horn.

South America is broad in its northern portion because there the mountain systems are far apart. It is somewhat narrower in the extreme north because there the Guiana Highlands, the third element of the continental framework, is not so far from the Andes as the Brazilian Highlands. The continent is very narrow in the south because into this portion only the single major axis extends. Between these three mountain systems—the Andes, the Brazilian Highlands, and the Guiana Highlands—are the vast plains, built up mainly of the sediments which ages of weathering and erosion have removed from the elevated lands and deposited in the shallow seas between and which have later been moderately uplifted into plains. It happens, in the case of South America, that the extent of *coastal* plains is small, while that of *interior* plains is large. In fact, there is only an extremely narrow coastal plain along the entire western side of the continent, and only a narrow strip along the coast of Brazil until the Amazon basin is approached. The absence of broad, easily occupied coastal lowlands in South America has been a retarding factor in the conquest of the continent. In contrast, the presence of a broad plain on the eastern coast of North America greatly aided the early development of that continent.

South America has a length of approximately 4,500 miles, a width of about 3,000 miles in the widest part, and an area not accurately known, but computed at slightly more than 7 million square miles, or 80 per cent of that of North America. It is a continent of emphatic contrasts in topography, with an exceptionally large proportion of lowland; 40 per cent of the area is less than 600 feet in elevation, and about 65 per cent is below 1,000 feet. On the other hand, 6 per cent of the area is about 10,000 feet in elevation. It is probably true of South America, as of no other continent, that its highlands are of more significance to the people than are the lowlands. About three-fourths of South America lies within the tropics; and, in most of that great area, the people choose to live in the highlands to escape the tropical heat. Were it not for the highlands, the greater part of the continent would be like the Tropical Rain Forest of the Amazon. In the United States, over three-fourths of the people live on plains less than 1,000 feet in elevation, while in South America only one-third so live. The only plains of importance that lie in middle latitudes in South America are those of the River Plata (Argentina and Uruguay) and the Central Valley of Chile. Since the economic activities in which men engage are pursued more easily on the plains than in the mountains or on the plateaus, it follows that a continent where men must go to the highlands to escape the enervating climate is unfavorable to these economic activities.

Physical Features of South America.—The evolution of the economic pattern of South America is related in many ways to the physical character of the country (Figs. 2 and 5). Certain associations between the human-use pattern and the highlands, the river basins, and the coast lines are helpful in understanding the South American continent.

The Andes Mountains.—Nowhere else is there a mountain system of such length, continuity, and altitude as the Andes. This stupendous barrier, rising almost out of the Pacific, is 100 to 400 miles broad and for 3,500 miles has few passes as low as 12,000 feet. In the extreme south, the passes are lower, but even these are thousands of feet in elevation. Usually, this massive system is made up not of a single range, but of several ranges often complexly knotted and, near the middle, expanded into the second loftiest plateau of the world, exceeded only by the great Plateau of Tibet in Asia. From Cape Horn to central Chile, there is a main mountain range. A minor range extends along the coast; and, in the south where a pronounced sinking of the land has occurred, this coast range becomes a chain of islands. Between the major and minor range lies the beautiful and fertile Valley of Chile, which in the south dips beneath the ocean.

The coastal chain of hills and low mountains extends nearly the entire length of the continent; but it is rarely a formidable barrier, though the barren slopes and summits give the west coast an inhospitable aspect all the way from southern Ecuador to Valparaiso, a distance of nearly 2,500 miles.

The middle and northern Andes consist in places of three complex ranges, but more commonly of two. Between these are great intermontane valleys, plateaus, detached mountain groups, volcanic peaks, saline basins, and at least two large lakes; the largest, Lake Titicaca, lies at an altitude of 12,500 feet and has an area of 3,200 square miles. Throughout the greater part of their length, the Andes are surmounted by a chain of towering volcanic peaks, both active and quiescent, for intense volcanic activity has attended the growth of this huge mountain system. A number of the peaks rise to altitudes of nearly 4 miles, and in

FIG. 6.—View of the High Andes. Mount Aconcagua in the background.
(*Courtesy of Grace Line.*)

many places the lowest passes through the ranges are in the neighborhood of 15,000 feet high—higher than the summit of Pikes Peak or any other in the United States (not including Alaska) (Fig. 6). The highest peaks are perpetually snow-capped even within the tropics, and one may see hot vapors rising from volcanic vents that are shrouded in snow.

So formidable is the Andean barrier that only one railway directly crosses it, well to the south where it is narrow and provides a pass at 10,452[1] feet in elevation. The few railroads

[1] By completing rail connections between Argentina and Bolivia in 1925, a second railway route from the Atlantic to the Pacific was established. From Oruro and La Paz, branches extend to Antofagasta, Arica, and by way of Lake Titicaca to Mollendo.

that cross one or more of the main ranges do so at elevations ranging from 10,452 to 15,665 feet. The loftiest railroads that man has attempted anywhere in the world are those of the Andes. On no other continent does a wall of mountains so high and so defiant lift itself almost from the ocean's edge and challenge man to conquer it if he can. Had these mountains not been rich in minerals, it is doubtful if the white man would even yet have seriously attempted the conquest of the more rugged portions. There is a vast extent of fertile land that lies beyond the Andes (east) in Colombia, Peru, Bolivia, and Brazil and at no really great distance from the Pacific; but it is barely explored and lies mainly unclaimed and unused. This region is 2,000 miles or more from the Atlantic, and the barrier of the Andes renders the cost of transportation to the Pacific almost prohibitive. The result is that now, after nearly four centuries of white occupation of these mountains, the Atlantic slope of the Andes has been but slightly touched by Europeans.

DIFFICULTIES OF TRANSPORTATION IN THE ANDES.—The use of railways and of steam locomotives dates back over 100 years; yet, as already mentioned, only one railway has been built entirely across the Andean system. In North America, 10 trunk lines cross the full width of the Western Cordillera, which averages much wider than the Andean system but is less abrupt and less lofty. For example, the Great Northern Railroad crosses the Cascade range at about 3,000 feet elevation and the continental divide at about 5,000 feet. The Central-Union Pacific crosses the Sierra Nevada range at 7,000 feet and the continental divide at 8,000 feet. Contrast these figures with the altitudes at which railroads cross ranges of the Andes:

	Feet
Guayaquil and Quito Railroad, Ecuador	11,841
Central Railroad of Peru	15,665
Southern Railroad of Peru	14,688
Arica-La Paz Railroad in Chile and Bolivia	13,986
Antofagasta and Bolivia Railroad	13,000
Chile-Argentine Transandean Railroad	10,452

The last-mentioned road cost upward of $300,000 a mile, is very expensive to maintain, and is operated at a loss in spite of high rates. On certain of the Andean lines, the grades are so steep that trains can ascend and descend only by a special cogwheel device—the rack and pinion. The Central Railroad of Peru employs 16 switchbacks in a difficult portion of its route; and, in places, five track levels, one above the other, are in sight at one time. On most of these lines, the trains go in opposite directions on alternate days. Where roads are so costly to build, maintain, and operate, freight rates must be high, which in turn hinders the use of the railroads and restricts their earnings. The generally low earnings of these roads discourage capital from going into other similar enterprises, and thus the railway conquest of the Andes proceeds very slowly.

The central route from Lima to the city of Iquitos, the chief rubber-collecting center on the Amazon in Peru, well illustrates the conditions of travel in the Peruvian Andes. From Lima to Oroya, one travels by railroad 1 day and crosses the main range of the Andes at an elevation of 15,665 feet. He then may travel by automobile 1 day over the eastern range. Then follow eight relays of pack mules along narrow trails, occupying 8 days; and then 7 days on the river in canoes and on a small steamer. This journey of 1,200 miles requires 18 to 20 hard days and involves about a dozen changes. Yet this is along a main, established route over which a great deal of travel takes place.

Very little that is produced in eastern Peru or Bolivia is sent to the distant Atlantic or to the much nearer Pacific; for, in the case of most products, the cost of transportation exceeds the value of the articles. Rubber has been the chief product of this isolated region, but the low price of rubber has made even this traffic unprofitable.[1] Coffee produced in eastern Peru costs more to transport to Oroya in central Peru than from that city to California. Examples need not be multiplied to impress the fact that a mountain barrier of such magnitude as the Andes, rising along the entire coast of a continent, must retard the whole economic development of that side of the continent.

CLIMATIC INFLUENCES OF THE ANDEAN CORDILLERA.—From Venezuela southward through Colombia, Ecuador, Peru, Bolivia, and into northern Chile, the Andean system lies within the tropics. Its varying elevations give varying temperatures; those of areas between 4,000 and 9,000 feet are mild or cool, and at these alti-

---

[1] The rise in rubber prices that came in 1925, partly revived this traffic; but lower prices soon returned, and South American production reached bottom in 1932. A very slight revival has again begun.

tudes the greater part of the people (north of Chile) make their homes. Because of the cooling influence of the Humboldt Current, the irrigated coastal valleys of Peru are only mildly warm. At certain altitudes, the temperature is that of perpetual spring, for each 330 feet of ascent reduces the temperature 1°F. The change of temperature from day to night is usually greater than the seasonal change. In Venezuela, Colombia, and Ecuador, the rainfall on the mountains is very heavy, for this region is in the equatorial rain belt a large part of the year. Farther south, the rainfall is progressively lighter except on the eastern slope of the mountains, and much of the highland in these countries is dry or even desert. This is due to the fact that the region lies in part in the belt of southeast trade winds which precipitate their moisture on the eastern (windward) side of the Andes,[1] and in part in the belt of horse latitudes where the air is descending from higher altitudes and is dry (compare Figs. 5 and 7). Where the rainfall is sufficient, the chief agricultural lands are at elevations of several thousand feet. This is notably true of the coffee lands of Colombia and Venezuela.

Though it is true that the high elevations provided by the Andes give cool temperatures, the climate is quite unlike that of the temperate zones with their pronounced change of seasons. A uniform, mild climate like that of Quito, for example, tends to breed easygoing habits and procrastination, whereas the wide variation of temperature of the intermediate zones, their alternations of summer and winter, and the passing of their cyclonic storms stimulate energy and make activity enjoyable. The fact that the tropical countries of northern and western South America contain land of high elevation is of immeasurable benefit to them, but it does not make intermediate-zone countries of them. In the southern third of Chile, the prevailing westerly winds, heavily laden with moisture from the Pacific, are forced upward by the Andes, cooled, and made to precipitate this moisture. This gives southern Chile very heavy rainfall but makes western Argentina and Patagonia dry.

EFFECT OF THE LOCATION OF THE ANDES UPON THE RIVERS OF THE CONTINENT.—The Andean chain forms the Great Divide of

[1] For detailed treatment of this subject, see Bowman, Isaiah, "The Andes of Southern Peru," published by the American Geographical Society of New York, 1916.

South America, and from it rivers flow to the Atlantic and to the
Pacific. In no other continent is the main water parting so un-

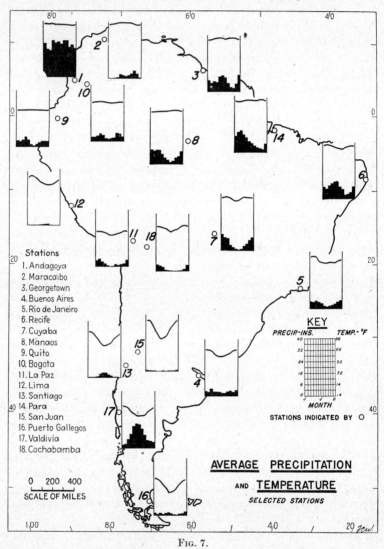

Stations

1. Andagoya
2. Maracaibo
3. Georgetown
4. Buenos Aires
5. Rio de Janeiro
6. Recife
7. Cuyaba
8. Manaos
9. Quito
10. Bogota
11. La Paz
12. Lima
13. Santiago
14. Para
15. San Juan
16. Puerto Gallegos
17. Valdivia
18. Cochabamba

KEY

PRECIP.-INS.   TEMP.- °F

MONTH

STATIONS INDICATED BY ○

AVERAGE   PRECIPITATION
AND   TEMPERATURE
SELECTED STATIONS

0   200   400
SCALE OF MILES

FIG. 7.

symmetrically placed (Fig. 5). Not one river of any size in all
South America flows into the Pacific. The west-flowing streams
are scarcely larger than creeks. Practically none of them is of

any use for navigation, and few are large enough or steady enough to be harnessed for power, except in the southern half of Chile. Rivers and river valleys are nature's avenues into the continents, but no such gateways or avenues lead into South America from the west.

The great rivers all flow to the Atlantic. The headwaters of the Amazon rise within 100 miles of the Pacific but discharge at the opposite side of the continent, nearly 3,000 miles away. Practically all the rubber that was gathered in Peru and Bolivia found its way to market by way of the Amazon. So far to one side of the continent is the main divide that the Amazon has the largest drainage basin of any river in the world; and Brazil, which controls the mouth of this great river, has been able to gain control of most of its vast basin. Such parts of the Amazon basin as are controlled by the Andean countries are of little value to them and remain almost unused.

The Coast Line of Western South America.—It is well known that the surface of the earth undergoes, throughout long periods of time, upward and downward movements. If a coastal region that has hills or mountains sinks somewhat, the ocean backs up into the coast valleys, some of which may become deep and spacious bays; such, for example, are those on the coast of southern Chile. The drowned mouths of the Hudson and Delaware rivers form New York Bay and Delaware Bay. In fact, the majority of the fine harbors of the world are drowned valleys. If, however, the coastal lands are uplifted without deformation, then a strip of the adjacent ocean bottom is brought above the sea and is added to the previously existing coastlands; the river mouths become shallower, the coast line is made more regular, and such indentations of the coast line as do exist are shallow. A rising coast of this sort has few, if any, good harbors.

If the uplift produces a mountain range along the shore, as is the case along the west coast of South America, then a mountain-walled coast results; rivers are few and short, and their mouths make only small bays, if, indeed, deltas are not built. If the mountain chain is relatively uniform, with few or no spurs projecting off into the sea, as again is true along the west coast of South America, then a relatively even coast line is produced; there are few offshore islands, few projecting headlands, and few indentations of the coast line. Along such a coast, large protected harbors are lacking. Such is the case along about four-fifths of the west coast of South America. From Panama to middle Chile, there is only one indentation of any size—the Gulf of Guayaquil in Ecuador. Elsewhere, the ports are mostly located where a small headland, or small inbending of the coast, affords on one side a slight protection from winds and waves. But from Guayaquil to southern Chile, western South America has not one harbor at which large ocean vessels regularly unload their cargoes directly upon piers or moles. Only vessels of light draft can do this; larger vessels anchor offshore and discharge or receive cargo by the aid of lighters. This is another consequence of the great mountain uplift that brought the Andes into existence.

The Brazilian and Guiana Highlands.—As a mountain system, the Andes are geologically young, but the Brazilian Highlands are old, very old, dating from an early period in the history of the earth. So long have these ancient mountains been subjected to the action of weather and streams that their highest summits now rarely reach one-third of the altitude of the Andean summits, and almost the entire area of the Brazilian Highlands stands at elevations of 2,000 to 4,000 feet. What is equally significant, they present a subdued and rounded topography; most of the elevations are broad, most of the slopes are gentle, and the residual soil is deep. The valleys are usually open rather than gorgelike, and their slopes can generally be cultivated without wasteful soil wash taking place. In a few places, notably along the coast from Rio de Janeiro to Santos and southward, steep-faced ranges rise abruptly from the sea to a few thousand feet. In fact, the principal stream divide, or water parting, in southeastern Brazil extends parallel to the coast and close to it. Streams flowing westward into the Paraná River system rise within 20 miles of the Atlantic coast and flow away from it toward the interior. The highlands of Brazil are partly in the intermediate zone, but a much larger area lies within the tropics. These highlands make up about one-fourth the area of Brazil and, with the narrow coastal strip that lies between them and the sea, contain fully 90 per cent of the population and wealth of that country. In the highlands, the summer days are hot, but the nights are usually comfortable. In winter, frosts occasionally occur in the south and damage the coffee trees. Rainfall is ample for agriculture except in a small area in the northeast. The winter temperature is delightful. The southern third of the Brazilian Highlands, with its industrious population and its inflow of European immigrants, constitutes the heart of Brazil and its hope for the future.

The Guiana Highland is the smallest in area and importance of the three highlands that form the mountain framework of South America. It is included partly in the Guianas and partly in Venezuela and is a main directing agent in determining the course of the Orinoco River. In age and elevation, the Guiana Highland is similar to the Brazilian, but it is far less important. It lies in the very heart of the tropics, a considerable distance inland from the coast, is densely forested, and is practically unexplored. It has little present economic significance.

The Coast Line and Coastlands of Eastern South America.—The eastern coast of South America is wholly unlike the western. For the most part, plains and low mountains face the shore, and at no point are such serious topographic difficulties encountered in entering the continent as are found on the west coast. For 1,000 miles along the coasts of Argentina and Uruguay, plains meet the sea. Along a large part of the coast of eastern Brazil, as already pointed out, mountains skirt the coast, but they are not difficult to cross in comparison with the Andes on the west coast. Still farther north, 1,000 miles of the coastlands of Brazil are low plains, mainly belonging to the Amazon Lowland.

Although the east coast of South America has few islands, no prominent peninsulas, and few large indentations, it nevertheless has good harbors in many places. One of the most perfect harbors in the world is that of Rio de Janeiro. The broad estuary of the Rio de la Plata, with its two world ports of Buenos Aires and Montevideo, is shallow, but it is made to serve the needs of a large commerce. Taken as a whole, the east coast of South America is favorable to the penetration of the continent, to commerce, and to economic development.

The Great River Basins.—South America has three great river systems draining three extensive plains, which make up the larger part of the continent and merge one into the other. These river systems are the Amazon, the Plata, and the Orinoco. The area drained by the Amazon is approximately $2\frac{1}{2}$ million square miles, equal to five-sixths of the area of the United States without Alaska. That drained by the River Plata system is less than one-half as large, and the Orinoco basin is still smaller. As a rule, valley plains in the intermediate zones are the most attractive places for human habitation. The greater part of such land is level or nearly so, the soil is fertile, movement from place to place is easy, and the occupations in which men engage are carried on easily. But such are not the conditions within the tropics. The continuous heat and the usually copious rainfall produce such abundant vegetation that man can make little headway in conquering it, and weeds or the forests hold their own.

THE AMAZON BASIN.—In the vast basin of the Amazon, man has scarcely made an impression. The river is not the longest, but it is the largest in the world. Its headwaters reach almost to the western margin of the continent. The main river with its windings is approximately 4,000 miles in length and carries a huge volume of water and silt to the sea. It has a score of tributaries which are themselves great and navigable rivers. No less than 14 of them are as long as the Rhine, or longer, and are greater in size. Their total navigable length exceeds 25,000 miles.

Lying in the belt of heavy equatorial rains, the precipitation over most of the basin is 70 to 100 inches a year, as compared with an average of scarcely 30 inches in the Mississippi basin. The heat and moisture give rise to a dense tropical forest that clothes the greater part of the land, broken here and there by open grasslands. So rapidly and luxuriantly does wild vegetation grow that man finds it next to impossible to keep it removed while a cultivated crop is growing. It is an uneven contest; man usually gives up the struggle, and the forest triumphs.

PLAINS OF THE RIVER PLATA SYSTEM.—Second in area but first in importance among the three great plains of South America are the plains of the River Plata. The river is merely a broad and shallow estuary which receives the water of the Paraná and Uruguay rivers. These plains have an area equal to that of the United States east of the Mississippi River, or about 1 million square miles. The highly important fact about them is that they lie mainly in the intermediate zone and include one of the great agricultural regions of the world. The southern part of this region does not drain into the River Plata but belongs to the same great plain. Included in the region are (1) all of Paraguay, (2) nearly all of Uruguay, (3) the larger and better part of Argentina, (4) one-quarter of Bolivia, and (5) a minor part of Brazil. The Bolivian and Brazilian parts and a third of Paraguay lie within the tropics. Owing to the stimulating quality of the climate, the fertility of the land, and the relatively good means of transportation, the cooler portion of these plains is attracting an enterprising class of immigrants and is making notable progress. It is the only large area in all South America where one finds extensive agricultural lowlands in middle latitudes. It may be regarded as economically the most important part of the continent.

The Paraná is one of the world's great rivers, longer and larger than the Mississippi, navigable for ocean steamers as far up as the city of Rosario; and its main tributary, the Paraguay, carries steamship navigation 1,300 miles into the heart of southern Brazil. The Pampa of Argentina with its millions of acres of fertile land, its enormous crops of cereals, its herds of cattle and flocks of sheep; the great stock-raising interests of Uruguay; the modern railway systems; the great ports of Buenos Aires and Montevideo; the rapidly growing wealth of this region—all combine to make this the outstanding section of South America.

PLAINS OF THE ORINOCO RIVER.—In the extreme northern part of South America—mainly in Venezuela—is the third of the major river plains of the continent. The Orinoco itself is about 1,500 miles in length; and the area of the Llanos, as its grass-covered plains are called, is approximately 120,000 square miles, or equal to that of two states like Illinois. Lying between the parallels of 5 and 10°N., the Llanos have high temperatures, with a wet season during which the low plains are inundated and a dry season, when the parching trade winds blow up the valley, the grass turns brown, and the cattle have scarcely enough feed to keep them alive.

The Orinoco and its main branches are navigated by a few river steamers, but the small population and a few products cannot support frequent steamship service. The only city of even moderate size (Ciudad Bolívar) is a few hundred miles up the river and may be reached by river boats of 10- or 12-foot draft. It is believed that fewer people now live in the Orinoco valley than lived there 400 years ago when the Spaniards came. The raising of cattle, still the chief occupation, was formerly much more extensive than it is now. So far as their effect upon the economic development of South America is concerned, the Llanos are of little importance.

PATTERN OF CLIMATIC REGIONS

The Andes and other highlands of South America combined with latitude, prevailing winds, and ocean currents bring about a great complexity of climatic conditions on the continent. In order that climatic conditions in various parts of the continent may be better understood, a brief discussion of the larger climatic regions is given here. In an area as large and diversified as South America, a great number of climatic regions might be defined, but here only the larger and simpler areas are described. Climate depends on the combination of four atmospheric elements— temperature, pressure, winds, and moisture. The general phases of climate are related to the great wind and pressure belts of the earth. The migration of these belts and other factors bring about a variation in seasonal distribution and in intensity of the atmospheric elements that account for different climates. "Any portion of the earth's surface over which the climatic elements, and therefore the broad climatic characteristics, are essentially similar (not identical), is called a climatic region."[1] The continent of South America is divided into the following climatic regions (Fig. 5):

1. **Tropical Rain Forest.**—The Tropical Rain Forest is found for the most part in the Amazon valley with extensions along the northeastern coast and a narrow belt along the northwestern coast. These are areas having uniformly high temperatures and heavy precipitation with no well-marked dry season (Figs. 8 and 9). The result is a vegetation consisting of luxuriant forests which may or may not have an accompanying dense undergrowth. The areas "1T" which are found along the coast of Brazil have similar forests but depend, for the most part, upon the onshore winds striking near-by highlands for their precipitation.

2. **Tropical Savannas.**—The savannas, in general, have much less rainfall than the Tropical Rain Forest and a long dry season varying generally in length with distance from the equator. The resulting vegetation is apt to be open forests with grasslands near the tropical rain forests, which gradually changes to grass-covered area with a few stunted trees as the poleward margins are approached.

[1] Trewartha, Glenn T., "Climates of the World," The Geographical Press, Columbia University, New York, 1929.

3a. Low-latitude Desert.—The true desert is found only in the western side of the continent as a result of the combined

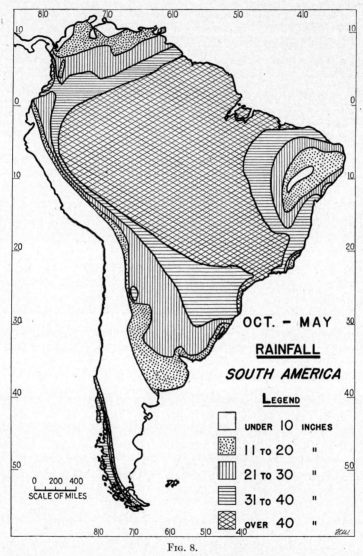

Fig. 8.

influence of the Andes and the air currents from over the Humboldt Current. Few areas in the world are as nearly rainless as this.

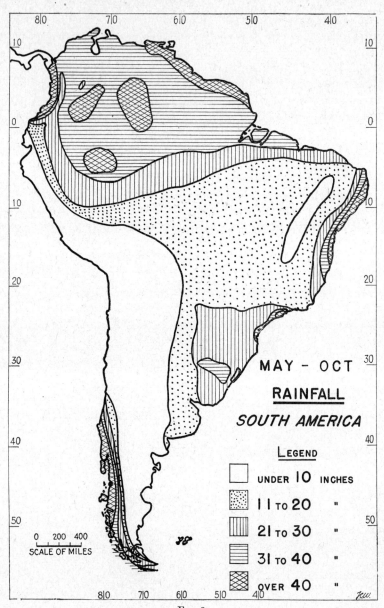

MAY – OCT

RAINFALL

SOUTH AMERICA

LEGEND

UNDER 10 INCHES

11 TO 20   "

21 TO 30   "

31 TO 40   "

OVER 40   "

0   200   400
SCALE OF MILES

FIG. 9.

3*b*. **Low-latitude Steppe.**—The rainfall here is slight with great variability and nondependability. The vegetation is scanty and much of it thorny scrub.

4*a*. **Middle-latitude Desert.**—This area differs from 3*a* in that it has more rainfall and, due to its higher latitude, greater variability in temperature. Much of it has scanty vegetation.

4*b*. **Middle-latitude Steppe.**—These middle-latitude transitional areas often have enough rainfall for grazing and hence are better fitted for human settlement. The rainfall is variable and unreliable, however, and better years may lead to agricultural expansion which invariably leads to economic catastrophe.

5. **Mediterranean.**—The Mediterranean area of South America is confined to the Central Valley of Chile. It has a moderate amount of precipitation in winter with dry summers. Winters are mild and summers warm to hot. Since water for irrigation is available, this is one of the best developed agricultural areas of South America.

6. **Humid Subtropical.**—This area has a climate somewhat similar to that of the southeastern United States but, in general, has less rainfall and is not subject to so many violent drops in temperature which sometimes affect the region of similar climate in the United States. Owing to climate, soil, and other factors, the natural vegetation tends to grass rather than trees as in the United States.

7. **Marine West Coast.**—This region has a high rainfall which, except in the northern part, is well distributed throughout the year. Rough topography, poorly drained soils, and heavy precipitation preclude a high economic development in much of this area.

H. **Highlands.**—It is impossible to make a generalized statement concerning the climate of the highlands. A "mountain" type of climate, in the same sense as a "Mediterranean" or "marine west coast" type, does not exist. Variations in temperature and precipitation are great because of differences in altitude, in wind exposure, and in exposure to sunlight.

PROBLEMS PECULIAR TO TROPICAL ENVIRONMENTS

Certain dreaded diseases are prevalent in tropical lowlands, and this fact retards the economic conquest of these regions.

Among the most important of such diseases in South America are malaria, yellow fever, tropical dysentery, and the hookworm disease.

Malaria is widely prevalent in the tropical lowlands of South America. The germ is carried by mosquitoes of the genus *Anopheles* that have bitten persons having malaria. The disease is pernicious and is one of the chief obstacles to the occupation of the lowland tropics by white people. The ignorant natives cannot be induced to take the necessary precautions, and disease-carrying mosquitoes cannot be eliminated. Whites and nonwhites suffer from the disease. It does not, as a rule, kill its victims quickly but saps their vitality. The following account pertaining to the lowlands of Venezuela would apply equally well to the tropical lowlands of other parts of South America:

"The best-developed agricultural region, around Lake Valencia, is also hot, and tropical diseases are rife. Workmen from the higher towns of the western interior or from Caracas are difficult to obtain and hold in this region on account of the prevalence of malaria. The sugar plantations of the Maracaibo basin are noted in the country for the extreme tropical climate and tropical conditions. Even the Goajira Indians, natives of the region to the west of the lake, suffer from regular epidemics of malaria during the latter part of the rainy season. Any extensive development in agriculture, such as cotton or sugar-cane planting, would have to be undertaken with full attention to sanitation and medical service on a scale with the work contemplated. This expense must be taken into consideration, as well as the prevalent anemia, which detracts from efficiency in all lines of work. The investment in sanitation and medical educational methods is, of course, high, but it has proved necessary in the tropics and is more than repaid by the maintenance of a sufficient working force and the generally increased physical ability of the men engaged in the field work. The natives of the country, born and raised in the same tropical regions, are not immune to malaria, but suffer from it in latent form. Neither is West Indian labor (negro) immune, although less subject to the more pronounced form of malarial fever. In connection with the effect of climatic conditions on labor in general, it may be well to add here that measures taken to improve the diet of persons engaged in heavy labor in the tropics have resulted in increased efficiency. The principal needs are fresh vegetables and cereals and improvements in methods of preparing food."[1]

[1] Bell, P. L. "A Commercial and Industrial Handbook of Venezuela," p. 16, U.S. Dept. of Commerce, Washington, D.C., 1922.

Yellow fever, which at times has made certain parts of South America veritable pestholes, is now nearly under control. It has been proved that a mosquito of the genus *Stegomyia fasciata* is the carrier of the germ of this disease. By biting a sufferer from yellow fever, the mosquito becomes the host of the fever parasite and may introduce it into the system of any person whom it afterward bites. Thus the disease spreads. By getting rid of

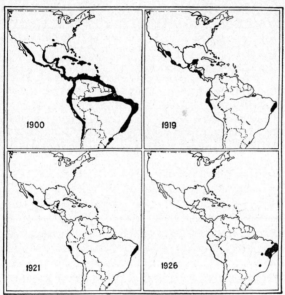

Fig. 10.—The retreat of yellow fever. It has now nearly disappeared from tropical America. (*Rockefeller Foundation.*)

stagnant water in which mosquitoes breed and by using screens on doors and windows, the spread of the disease is retarded, and in many cities (Habana, New Orleans, Santos, Panama, and others), it has been eliminated. The fact that Negroes enjoy almost complete immunity from the disease is one reason for their predominance along these tropical coasts (Fig. 10).

Tropical dysentery arises from an intestinal infection. It is most severe in hot, wet regions and diminishes with increasing distance from the equatorial belt. It is transmitted by germs but may be largely avoided by care in the use of drinking water and by a generally temperate and hygienic mode of life. The ignorant and careless Negroes seldom take these precautions, and the disease spreads as much because of neglect as because of climate.

The hookworm disease is due to an intestinal parasite and is confined chiefly to warm and hot climates. The parasite breeds in human filth and enters the intestinal tract in various ways. Its effect upon the sufferer is pernicious, robbing the red blood cells of their vitality, producing anemia, breaking down the bodily resistance to other diseases, and rendering the victim listless, pale, weak, and unambitious. It affects mainly those who live in unsanitary conditions in hot climates, and its victims in tropical America are numbered by the millions, although conditions there are no worse than in many other warm countries. Where the disease is prevalent, economic progress is slow or stagnant; for the sufferers themselves usually are content with a bare living, and laborers are thus necessarily inefficient. Happily, the disease is readily curable when the patient can be induced to cooperate with the medical authorities. Great service is being performed by the Rockefeller Sanitary Commission for the Eradication of Hookworm Disease.

Indirect Relations of Tropical Climate to Diseases.—The so-called "tropical diseases" also exist outside the tropics, but rarely to a menacing extent. The abundant heat and moisture of the tropics are favorable to the multiplication of microorganisms. Moreover, tropical races include a high proportion of illiterate people who cannot be reached and enlightened through printed advice. They are careless and unsanitary and too poor to have proper medical attention. Frequently, they are undernourished and low in disease resistance. The municipal governments in tropical cities usually lack the funds, knowledge, and energy necessary to fight the unsanitary conditions that breed diseases. Where a determined fight, backed by knowledge and money, has been maintained, tropical diseases have been reduced or eliminated, but this is an expensive undertaking and cannot be carried out over large areas at once. Steady progress is being made, however, and there are those who believe that in time the tropics may become relatively free from the worst diseases. At present, the bad health conditions in most tropical lowlands are an effective reason why white men shun them and leave them largely to the tropical races. The initiative and energy necessary to develop the tropics must come mainly from cooler climes.

Climate and Negro Slavery.—The white man cannot safely do hard, out-of-door labor in the tropics, nor does he feel like doing it. The Negroes of tropical Africa were brought to the West Indies, Brazil, and the southern United States soon after the discovery of America. Negro slavery never gained a hold in the cool lands where the white man is accustomed to manual labor. It was essentially an outgrowth of the white man's attempt to develop hot regions. Slaves became numerous in both Americas and finally were liberated during the nineteenth century. Their peculiar fitness for living in low latitudes and the general reluctance of whites to live in communities where negroes greatly predominate have brought it about that the islands and coast lowlands of the Caribbean and a part of Brazil are occupied largely by Negroes and mulattoes. In Peru, Bolivia, Ecuador, Mexico, and Central America, Indian laborers have held their own, and very few Negroes are found. Climatic and social considerations have made the white man the master and the colored man the worker. This relationship perpetuates in the white man a sense of superiority and a feeling that the colored man must be "kept in his place" and be made to do the distasteful kinds of work.

Tropical White Man's Attitude toward Labor.—Although this attitude is explainable and probably inevitable, it is the curse of tropical countries. The reaction upon the white man is bad. His constant contact with people whom he regards as menials and his own feeling that those who labor belong to an inferior order of society and that a gentleman should not work with his hands kill initiative and create easygoing habits. Such is the price that the white man pays for the easy life of the tropics and for the Negro slavery of the past.

Happily, no South American country consists wholly of tropical lowlands. All the countries that lie within the tropics include highlands upon which people of European stock may live in health and may preserve at least some of the vigor that characterizes the dwellers in cool latitudes. Here, the beneficial effects of the cooler temperature are partly offset by the presence of the Indian peons and half-breed laborers who do the manual labor and thus create the same class distinction between master and servant that exists where Negroes are numerous. The price that is paid for this attitude toward labor is seen in the effect upon

European immigration into parts of Latin America where this attitude exists, for white immigrants from Europe avoid these lands. They prefer to go where laborers are respected and where they do not have to compete with low-paid Negro labor. In South America, they go to the uplands of southern Brazil, to Uruguay, to Argentina, and in smaller numbers to Chile. They shun the tropical lowlands and leave their economic development to inefficient native workers or to imported Orientals who are but little more efficient under the same climatic conditions.

Low Productive Power and Low Purchasing Power of Tropical Peoples.—In addition to malnutrition, disease, ignorance, and lack of ambition already discussed, another cause for the backward economic state of the tropical peoples should be pointed out. Employers declare that more work cannot be secured by paying higher wages, for the native worker will simply work fewer days in the week. If 2 days' work a week will earn enough to supply his simple wants, why go to the trouble of working more? In a hot climate, little clothing is needed; a quickly made hut furnishes shelter; a few banana trees and a patch of corn, beans, and manioc supply food; loafing is the most agreeable of luxuries. In his opinion, the greatest luxury is ease; why sacrifice this to secure something less desired? Thus, the great majority of these people produce little more than they consume.

Social wealth is created mainly by labor, by producing more than one consumes, and by saving something to be contributed to social capital or to be employed in building railways, factories, ships, and public utilities, which in turn become agencies for creating more wealth. In this way, economic life is quickened, productivity is stimulated, purchasing power is increased, and a nation rises in the scale of economic well-being. But in a society where, for climatic or other reasons, men do not practice industry and thrift, progress is slow or retrogression may occur.

The Problem of the Development of the American Tropics.— Several of the West Indies have attained a considerable degree of economic development, mainly agricultural, for they have had the aid of leadership and capital from cooler lands. Cuba, Puerto Rico, Trinidad, and, to a certain degree, other islands have made much progress, and their people, colored or white, enjoy something of prosperity, have acquired some education, and are fairly healthy and happy. But the republics of tropical America are finding their problems of development difficult, partly because the solution of these problems requires greater funds than they can command. However great the potential resources of these countries may be, money is needed to develop them; but most of these countries are not creating capital nearly so fast as they need it. They are constantly seeking loans abroad; and when these are obtained, they are not always used wisely. Interest charges grow and sometimes go unpaid with disastrous effects upon national credit. In order to secure foreign capital for the development of resources, these resources are frequently turned over to foreign corporations, which are allowed to build and operate railroads, docks, and public utilities. Banking and foreign trade are largely in foreign hands, with the result that the earnings of the country are steadily flowing out into foreign lands. Yet the alternative is economic stagnation. A large part of these difficulties arises from the lack of national capital, due to social and political deficiencies for which a tropical climate is partly accountable. Any large and permanent development of the hot tropics seemingly must get its impetus, funds, and leadership from the cooler climates.

SUMMARY OF CLIMATIC AND ECONOMIC CONDITIONS IN SOUTH AMERICA

1. Half of South America suffers from too much heat, as half of North America does from too little.

2. The continent suffers from too much rainfall in most of the tropical lowlands; too little on the west-coast highlands (from southern Ecuador to middle Chile) and too little in western and southern Argentina.

3. In the tropical latitudes, the highlands provide regions of considerable size in which white people may live and retain their energy. It is the influence that the location of South America exerts upon its *climate* rather than its out-of-the-way commercial location that merits emphasis.

4. Because of narrowness in the south, the continent affords only a relatively small area of middle-latitude lowlands.

5. The Negro population is found chiefly where high temperature makes the white man unwilling to do manual labor.

6. For climatic reasons, the highlands of southeastern Brazil, the plains of the River Plata, and the Valley of Chile must be the chief regions of power and progress in South America.

7. The secondary centers of progress are in the highlands of the Andes, where altitude offsets latitude, and on the irrigated coastlands of Peru, where the cool Humboldt Current favorably affects the temperature.

8. The great areas of potential production are in the tropical lowlands; these are the regions which will supply an increasing part of South America's economic products, but probably under leadership supplied from cooler lands.

Chapter II. Colombia

Effective utilization of the resources of Colombia depends, in large measure, on the solution of two major problems, problems that are closely associated with the natural environment of the country. If Colombia is to get the most from her varied resources, she must find ways for the economic utilization of her tropical lowlands, and she must link these lowlands with the more hospitable highland sections and with the outside world through the development of an efficient transportation system.

The location of the country imposes upon much of it the handicap of a humid, enervating, tropical climate with all the attendant problems that such a climate implies. Only in the highlands, where elevation ameliorates the steaming, fever-infested heat of the lowlands, is there a climate suitable for white occupancy. Most of the eight million people of Colombia are concentrated in the Andean section, this despite the fact that many resources, which might enter world trade and add to the economic well-being of the country, are located in the tropical lowlands. Unfortunately, the Andean ranges, which occupy the western third of the country and afford a refuge from the climate of the lowlands, is a region difficult of access (Fig. 11). The rugged relief presents barriers to transportation development, retards economic expansion, and restricts trade. Not only is contact between the Highland Heart and other portions of the country difficult, but access to the sea lanes of world commerce is handicapped by a low, malarial, and largely harborless coast line. Colombia is well located for international trade. It has 460 miles of waterfront on the Pacific and 640 miles on the Caribbean. In addition, almost all parts of the coast are within a day's sailing of the Panama Canal. Unfortunately, the advantage of favorable

35

situation for trade is largely offset by difficult access to the coast from the interior and by the unfavorableness of the coast itself for harbor development.

A better understanding of Colombia's two major problems (the development of tropical lowlands and the extension of trans-

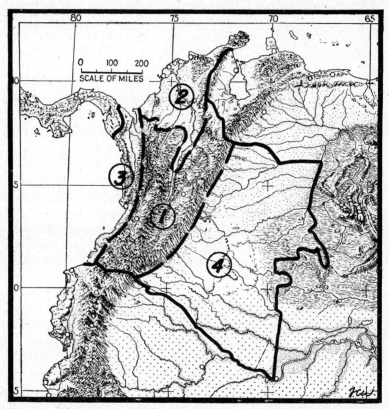

FIG. 11.—Major regions of Colombia. 1, Highland Heart; 2, Caribbean Coastal Margin; 3, Pacific Coast and Atrato Valley; 4, Eastern Tropical Lowlands.

portation facilities), and of other minor and related problems, is gained from a more detailed analysis of the distribution of certain cultural and natural items as well as the association of these patterns.

One of the most important features of the natural environment of Colombia is the topography, for it is largely on the basis of topography that the regions of the country are delimited, and it is with it that many of the natural and cultural patterns are closely associated.

The outstanding feature of Colombia's topography is the great Andean system which traverses the western portion of the country from north to south in three massive ranges known as the Western, Central, and Eastern Cordilleras (Fig. 11). In the south, these three cordilleras merge in a complex mountain knot. Northward, they spread out fanwise and extend like three great fingers toward the Caribbean. Elevated river valleys, high table-lands, and lofty mountain peaks, some in excess of 18,000 feet, characterize this highland portion of the country which has come to be "white man's Colombia." Eastward and southeastward of the Eastern Cordillera is a vast tropical lowland, grassy in the north where it is drained by the Orinoco system, and covered by a tropical forest in the southern Amazonian portion. Along the Caribbean coast, tropical lowlands are also characteristic, except in the northeastern section where a less lofty extension of the main Andean system reaches the coast. On the Pacific side of the Andean system, a low coastal range extends from the Panama boundary southward to Bahía del Chocó where it gives way to a tropical lowland. Between the coastal ranges and the Western Cordillera is the 300-mile-long, lowland, tropical valley of the Atrato River, which drains northward to the Caribbean (Fig. 11).

THE TRANSPORTATION PATTERN

The highland section of the country is drained by two impor-tant rivers, the Magdalena and its chief tributary, the Cauca. The former separates the Eastern and Central Cordilleras, and the latter flows between the Central and Western ranges. These rivers, together with the Atrato, are the principal thoroughfares of the country. The transportation pattern is completed by roads and railroads which supplement these waterways and also serve as feeders to them (Fig. 12). Of the three rivers, the Mag-dalena is by far the most important; for, despite the fact that navigation on it is slow and uncertain, it provides the principal means of reaching the interior and Bogotá, the capital of the country. Nowhere else in the New World is a national capital placed in a part of the country that is so difficult of access. Mexico City, La Paz, Caracas, and Quito are all reached by railways connecting directly with the seacoast. Undoubtedly,

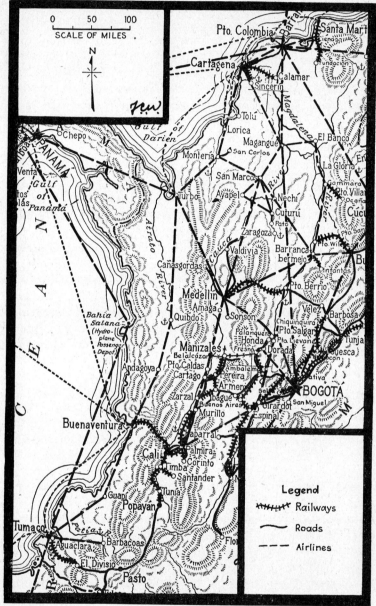

Fig. 12.—Principal transportation routes of Colombia. (*U.S. Dept. of Commerce.*)

the Magdalena has greatly assisted in carrying the elements of European civilization far into Colombia, and it keeps the remote interior in touch with the outside world. On the other hand, it is probable that this poor but usable means of communication has prevented the construction of a better one. The mouth of the Magdalena is a swampy delta with ever-shifting distributaries which only small native boats can navigate. The river port nearest the sea is Barranquilla, 10 miles up from the mouth.

Fig. 13.—Stern-wheel steamer on the Magdalena River, the chief transportation route of Colombia, but a poor one. (*Copyright Ewing Galloway, N. Y.*)

The mouth of the Magdalena has been deepened recently, and Barranquilla is now a seaport as well as a river port. Because of the shallowness of the lower Magdalena, it was necessary, before the channel was dredged, to transship all ocean-bound freight by railroad from Barranquilla to Puerto Colombia, 17 miles away.

The lower 70 miles of the Magdalena (above the delta) is a broad, strong river, 1 mile wide at high water, and navigable at all times of the year (Fig. 13). Farther up, the river shrinks to a shallow bar-clogged stream in the dry season (December to April). The large river steamers ascend 615 miles to a stretch of rapids around which a narrow-gauge railway transfers passengers and freight. Above this point, smaller steamers navigate the river to Girardot where the railway to Bogotá begins. For 100 miles farther upstream, navigation by small boats is carried on, giving a total navigable length of over 900 miles, about equal to the length of the Ohio River.

So accustomed are the people of the United States and Europe to rapid and convenient railroad transport that the kind of service obtainable by the Magdalena route may be of interest. So vital to the economic life of any country are its means of transportation that an understanding of these is one of the very best ways of appreciating the progress or backwardness of a country. When one understands the uncertainties, delays, and high cost of transportation on the chief commercial thoroughfare of Colombia, he sees one reason why the country is still in a backward state.

Let us assume that a consignment of hardware is shipped from New York to Bogotá. The goods are (1) unloaded from the ocean steamship at Puerto Colombia, and later are (2) loaded upon a freight car and taken 17 miles to the river dock in Barranquilla and there (3) unloaded.[1] In the course of time, the goods are (4) placed on board a river steamer; if this does not run aground on one of the many sand bars, it will eventually reach the lower end of the rapids at La Dorada. Here, the freight must again be (5) unloaded and (6) transferred to a railway which hauls it around the rapids, where it must be (7) taken from the train and (8) loaded upon a smaller river steamer. After a slow journey up the river, the freight is (9) unloaded from the river boat at Girardot and (10) loaded on the train that starts it toward Bogotá. About halfway to that city, the gauge of the railway changes, and all freight is again (11) unloaded and (12) reloaded upon another train which finally (13) delivers it in Bogotá. Thus, after the consignment reached the ocean port in Colombia, it had been six times loaded and seven times unloaded—thirteen times in all—in going a distance of 800 miles. If the goods are of average value, the cost is doubled, for the freight and handling charges are about equal to the invoice value of the goods, probably around $75 a ton, which is several times the cost of ocean transportation from New York. Goods may be 4 to 6 months in transit between Bogotá and the sea, although the trip may be made in 3 weeks. It costs $70 to send a ton of wheat from Bogotá to the coast and $60 to send a ton of coffee. This is ten times the all-rail rate on wheat from Chicago to New York, about the same

[1] As ocean trade shifts from Puerto Colombia to Barranquilla, owing to the deepening of the Magdalena channel, transshipment by rail will not be necessary.

distance. Under the very best conditions, passengers from the coast may reach Bogotá in 7½ days.

The Cauca River.—The Cauca, the principal tributary of the Magdalena, has two navigable sections. Shallow-draft steamers, drawing 3 feet or less, can ascend the Cauca 74 miles and its tributary, the Nechi, about the same distance, thus reaching one of the richest placer gold-mining regions of the country. In fact, these mines are well developed because they are reached by navigable water. The San Jorge, a tributary of the Magdalena along which placer mining is also active, is navigable for 112 miles at high water. Farther upstream, from Cali nearly to Cartago, the Cauca is navigable by small steamers half the year.

The Atrato River.—The Atrato, fed by the almost incessant rains of western Colombia, is a large river but is badly obstructed by sand bars. It heads in the principal region of the platinum mines and is regularly used for navigation.

Several other small rivers are somewhat used for navigation by shallow-draft steamers; for even these shallow, uncertain streams may be a cheaper means of moving products and goods than moving them on muleback. Colombia is in much the same condition with respect to river navigation as the eastern half of the United States between 1810 and 1830, before the railroad era began.

Roads and Trails.—Mules over mountain trails are the means of transportation most commonly employed in Colombia. Roads for wheeled vehicles are very few, are in detached stretches, and are exceedingly costly to build and maintain. There are some 5,000 miles of national highways partly built or actually completed; but much of this mileage is not modern, hard-surfaced road, for this costs too much for a country as poor in revenues as Colombia. Good roads are among the most pressing needs of the country; but the mountainous topography, the swollen rivers, and the tropical downpours all combine to retard their construction, and funds are always scanty. Upward of 50 national roads are authorized, but only part of them are long enough to be of much use (Fig. 12). Experience shows that in this rugged country it frequently costs as much to build a modern, hard-surfaced road as it does to build a narrow-gauge railroad and that it costs more to maintain it. Public funds are both wasted and misappropriated in the local road-building projects, which are usually mixed with questionable politics. Appropriations are made year after year, but there are meager results to show for them. For a long time to come, the construction of improved trails must be the principal reliance for overland transport in this large, thinly populated, mountainous country. The Department of Caldas, one of the most progressive departments, has somewhat more than 1,000 miles of public trails. The area of the department is about equal to that of Massachusetts which has 19,000 miles of public roads.

There are a few good automobile roads which connect several of the important cities. An automobile road has just been completed that crosses a considerable portion of Colombia and joins Quito, the capital of Ecuador, with Caracas, the capital of Venezuela, via Bogotá. Despite this main highway, only a small portion of the country is adequately served by automobile roads.

Railways.—In its small railway mileage, as in many other matters, Colombia is the victim of a tropical climate, difficult land surface, a long period of civil wars, and bad politics. The first railroad was not started until 1874, nearly a half century after the beginnings in North America. In the entire country, there are somewhat more than 1,800 miles of railway, divided among 22 lines; the longest one is about 350 miles in length. Three different gauges are used, but most of the lines have a gauge of either 3 feet or 1 meter (3.28 feet). Most of the lines have cost so much that there is little possibility of their paying a profit beyond cost of operation, maintenance, and interest. In nearly all cases, the government has assisted in financing the lines either by subsidies or by guaranteeing interest on the bonds. Many of the lines are badly located and poorly built and must be, in part, relocated and rebuilt before they can efficiently serve the regions that they traverse. There is no railway system; there are only short lines to the coast or to the Magdalena River. Most of the lines have never been completed; and two or three never ought to be, for they are unwisely placed. In Colombia, as in many other countries, local politicians and local organizations demand that "something be done for them," and thus ill-advised projects are undertaken and remain unfinished.

One vital need is that as much of the country as possible be freed from dependence upon the Magdalena River, whose sand bars, windings, fluctuations of depth from season to season, and general undependability make the commerce that uses it not only slow but almost nonexistent for months at a time. Yet both of the leading cities, Bogotá and Medellín, and the important departments in which they lie are dependent mainly upon this river for their connection with the outside world. Both these regions need direct rail connection with the Pacific coast, probably at Buenaventura. Railway connection between Bogotá and Buenaventura has been completed except for that portion crossing the Central range. This break is connected by an

Fig. 14.—View of auto road over Central Andes between Ibagué and Armenia.

automobile road between Ibagué and Armenia (Fig. 14). Of the $25,000,000 indemnity paid to Colombia by the United States in settlement of claims arising from the secession of Panama from Colombia, about $20,000,000 were set aside for railway construction.

As was stated above, it is largely on the basis of topography that the regional pattern is delimited. Thus four major regions are distinguishable: (1) the Highland Heart, (2) the Caribbean Coastal Margin, (3) the Pacific Coast and Atrato Valley, and (4) the Eastern Tropical Lowlands (Fig. 11).

THE REGIONS OF COLOMBIA

The Highland Heart.—A combination of factors makes this region, which occupies only about one-fourth of the country, the most important one of Colombia. It is the section of Colombia in which the European element predominates; it is the area in which a large portion of the eight million people of the country live; it is the region in which is located the center of government, of manufacturing, and of mining; it supplies a predominant proportion of the country's exports; it is the principal market for imported products.

Although the area is essentially highland country, it must not be thought that the Highland Heart is all at high elevations, for, included in this region, are many deep valleys. Altitudes range from 1,000 to 2,000 feet in the Upper Magdalena to peaks over 18,000 feet above sea level. Within its borders, from the tropical zone (below 3,500 feet) having a mean annual temperature of around 80°F. with little variation from month to month, to the cold, windy, perennially snow-capped peaks over 18,000 feet, almost every variation in temperature to be found on this earth is duplicated. Variation in temperature is matched by variation in precipitation and vegetation. Although the area as a whole is characterized by two rainy and two relatively dry seasons, there are marked differences in amount of precipitation due to elevation and exposure. In certain narrow and deep valleys, there is little rain and the flora is definitely xerophytic. On some of the exposed high slopes, precipitation may amount to as much as 140 inches per year.

From an economic standpoint, certain work patterns of the highlands are especially important. Of particular note are those of agriculture, mining, and manufacturing. Although mining and manufacturing are of considerable importance in Colombia, it is with agriculture that the economic welfare of the country is most closely associated. Not only does agriculture provide subsistence to most of the country's inhabitants, but it also provides coffee, the country's principal commercial crop and leading export.

Agriculture of the Highlands.—The most characteristic feature of the agricultural pattern is the marked zonation of crops— tropical and subtropical crops on the lower slopes and valley floors, and temperate-zone products on the higher slopes and plateau districts. In general, commercial crops are those of the tropical and subtropical areas, not all of which, however, are devoted to commercial production. Inaccessibility is too severe a handicap in many sections which might otherwise be suited. Throughout the highland district, certain crops stand out as commercially important. The principal ones are coffee, sugar, and tobacco. Of these, only coffee is outstanding; sugar enters primarily into local trade; tobacco is of minor significance as compared with coffee.

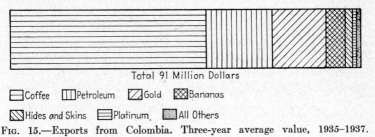

Total 91 Million Dollars

☐Coffee ⊞Petroleum ⧄Gold ⊠Bananas

⧄Hides and Skins ⊟Platinum ▦All Others

FIG. 15.—Exports from Colombia. Three-year average value, 1935–1937.

COFFEE.—Coffee is by far the chief commercial crop of the highlands, in fact of all Colombia. In most years, it accounts for some 60 per cent of the total value of all the exports (Fig. 15). Despite its great importance, it occupies only a small percentage of the cultivated land. The principal centers of production are on the highland slopes at between 2,500 and 7,000 feet elevation on both the eastern and western flanks of the Central Cordillera and on the western side of the Eastern Cordillera (Fig. 16). Although many exceptions can be found, the coffee plantations along the Eastern Cordillera are, in general, large and those in the Central Cordillera are small. Most of the coffee is high in quality, production being favored by good conditions of climate, soil, and drainage, as well as a good labor supply. A little coffee is produced in the southern part on the western side of the Western Cordillera. The isolated character of this area, however, is a severe handicap

FIG. 16.

to the extension of commercial agricultural production. Many portions of the Western Cordillera are accessible only by mule trail.

"Coffee is the economic salvation of this mountainous country. . . . Coffee grows on the steep slopes of the mountains at elevations varying from a few hundred feet to as high as 9,000 feet above sea level in nearly all parts of the country, on lands that could not be used for any other purpose. Few tools or equipment other than the universal machete are required, and there is no cultivation other than that of chopping out the larger weeds between the rows of trees. Very little labor is required other than that for picking the ripe berries, for which unskilled labor is employed. Women and children work as well as the men, the ripe coffee berries containing the beans being merely stripped from the branches of the low coffee trees and carried to the drying places. The machinery required for shelling and hulling the beans is not complicated or expensive, and large plants are not necessary."[1]

Coffee is essentially nonperishable if properly protected. It can, therefore, be stored without deterioration and is not necessarily injured by delays in transit, which are characteristic of Colombia. But when the crop is moving toward the sea for export, the transportation facilities are so inadequate that delays of 3 to 5 months are not infrequent. Consequently, injury often does come to this coffee because of exposure in transit. Bags of coffee are conveniently carried on muleback, and most of the crop is carried one or more times in this way before it reaches the seacoast. All things considered, coffee production in Colombia represents the most suitable commercial crop in this mountainous region.

As compared with Brazil, where plantations of several million trees exist, 25,000 to 40,000 trees make a large plantation in Colombia. In all, Colombia has over 450 million trees, each yielding *an average* of 1 pound of cleaned coffee a year. The exportation in 1910 was a little over 500,000 sacks (of 138 pounds each); but, in 1915, it passed 2 million and has lately attained nearly 3½ million. A large proportion of the coffee, as is the case with most of the country's exports (Fig. 17), goes to the United States. Because of its mild flavor, it brings a higher price than Brazilian coffee. Colombia is capable of much greater produc-

---

[1] Bell, P. L. Colombia: A Commercial and Industrial Handbook, *Special Agents Series* 206, U.S. Dept. of Commerce, Washington, D.C., 1921.

tion; and if the efforts of the Brazilian planters to maintain high prices had continued successful, Colombian planters would unquestionably have further increased their plantings.

SUGAR.—Much of the sugar of Highland Colombia, the major sugar-producing area, is raised in small patches in the valleys and ground in crude mills (Fig. 16). At one time, there were 4,700 of these mills in the single department of Antioquia. The

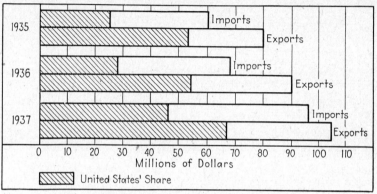

FIG. 17.—Import and export trade of Colombia.

sugar is made into small cakes of panela (unrefined brown sugar) and used locally. In the Cauca valley, cane achieves commercial importance and becomes an export product. Even in this center of production, though, there is only one modern sugar mill. Sugar is of some commercial importance in the Central Cordillera district below 6,000 feet elevation. In this region, it is grown, together with various subsistence crops (corn, beans, cassava, and bananas), on large haciendas. It is also raised on the coffee plantations of this area. Most of it is used as panela or reaches the consumer in the form of *aguardiente*, a low-priced alcoholic beverage. In the Eastern Cordillera, sugar also attains some importance. Low rainfall in this area results in frequent use of irrigation. In some parts of this district, sugar is known to have been raised in the same fields for 100 years without resorting to crop rotation or fertilization to maintain the soil's productivity. Owing to repeated cropping and the planting of poor varieties, yields are low, amounting to only 5 or 10 tons per acre.

TOBACCO.—Exports of tobacco add only about $250,000 to the income of Colombia. In the highlands, commercial production is confined primarily to the Upper Magdalena valley and the Eastern Cordillera. In the Upper Magdalena, a fairly high grade tobacco is produced in the area around Ambalema. Most of it is processed in local tobacco and cigar factories. Nearly all the tobacco is raised on small farms. More care is taken of the tobacco crop than of most crops in Colombia, but production could be increased considerably by greater care and more scientific management of the crop.

OTHER "LOW-ELEVATION" AGRICULTURAL PRODUCTS.—Crops on the lower slopes of the highlands, other than those already discussed, are principally those raised for subsistence purposes. Subsistence crops are produced on two kinds of farm: (1) on farms raising commercial crops, to provide food for the laborers; and (2) on strictly subsistence farms.

In the Western Cordillera, nearly all agricultural production is on farms of the second class. The rugged, humid, forested character of this isolated section leaves little opportunity for intensive cultivation. Population is sparse and, in the lower areas, is made up of indolent Negroes and mulattoes who live in crude huts and gain their livelihood with very little effort. Only on the western slope in the south is there commercial production. Here a little cacao and some coffee, as was mentioned, enter export markets. Largely lacking in minerals and in transportation facilities other than mule trails and not having a single important commercial center, this area can support little else than subsistence agriculture, and even this is not highly developed.

Much the same holds true for the lower areas of the rest of highland Colombia. Corn, cassava, beans, sugar, bananas, and occasionally a little cotton represent the principal crops raised in those sections out of contact with the mediocre thoroughfares that so inadequately serve the highlands.

Grazing is an activity of some importance throughout many of these less elevated regions. The Cauca valley, for example, is an area of vast *estancias* well supplied with a good grade of both natural and planted grasses. But isolation, high temperatures, disease, frequent drought, and insect pests are serious hindrances to expansion of the industry. Again, in the Upper Magdalena, grazing is the dominant agricultural activity. Cattle, goats, horses, and sheep attain some importance. But a careless labor supply, the low quality of the stock, and general lack of marketing facilities are handicaps that must be overcome before the activity can achieve more than local importance.

TEMPERATE-ZONE TYPES OF CROP.—At elevations above 6,000 or 7,000 feet, tropical agriculture gives way to subtropical and temperate-zone products. The temperate-zone crops are grown primarily for local consumption, many of them for subsistence purposes. The principal ones include corn, wheat, barley, and root crops. Production is confined primarily to the Central and the Eastern Cordillera, and attains maximum importance in the Eastern.

In the Western Cordillera, the thick tree cover and cloudy weather on the western side and the thorn forest and aridity on the eastern slopes are handicaps to temperate-zone agriculture. In a few scattered spots, temperate-zone subsistence agriculture is carried on, but nowhere is it important. In the Cauca and Magdalena valleys, elevations are, for the most part, below 7,000 feet; and, consequently, temperate-zone products are largely nonexistent. In the Central Cordillera, a relatively small part of the temperate belt is occupied by crops. It is, therefore, in the Eastern Cordillera that the temperate agricultural pattern is best defined. Corn is one of the principal crops. As was seen above, it fits into the crop combination of the lower elevations as a subsistence crop of the plantations and is a leading crop on the tiny subsistence farms. Corn is also important at the higher elevations. Largely owing to its low value in relation to bulk, its poor keeping qualities, and the general lack of adequate transportation facilities, corn does not enter trade, except on a very restricted basis.

Another valuable crop of the Eastern Cordillera is wheat. It is found principally on the high plateau around Bogotá, although production on steep slopes up to 10,000 feet elevation is also characteristic. Wheat raising, as is the case with nearly all Colombia's agricultural activities, suffers from inadequate transportation facilities. Production methods are crude; machinery is lacking; insect pests and plant diseases are prevalent; the farming class is illiterate; and there is little incentive to improve production methods or yields, even in those areas where improvements could be introduced, for the product cannot be economically moved to the market.

The wheat produced is of a fairly good grade but yields per acre average only about half those of the United States. Even though wheat is raised widely throughout the Eastern Cordillera, there is not enough produced to meet local demands, and Colombia must import both wheat and flour.

Although of little commercial importance, barley and root crops are important temperate-zone food crops, particularly at the higher elevations and on the poorer soils. These crops are found throughout all the highland region but are of relatively greater importance in the more densely peopled temperate portion of the Eastern Cordillera.

GRAZING IN THE TEMPERATE BELT.—The animal industry is well developed in the temperate zone of both the Central and the Eastern Cordillera. It is especially important in the northern departments of Antioquia, Caldas, and Tolima in the Central Cordillera. This district is the beef and dairy center of Colombia.

In addition to beef and dairy products, hides which are marketed in the near-by towns provide an important source of income. Sheep, hogs, and mules are also grazed in the area around Medellín. The hogs are a poor grade, receiving little or no corn and left largely to forage for themselves. The animals of the Eastern Cordillera are the same kind as those in the Central Cordillera. The best grazing area is in the high plateau around Bogotá; but here competition, with cattle raised on the great tropical lowlands to the east, must be met. Attempts have been made to improve the grade of the cattle by the introduction of pure-bred stock and by fencing the ranges, but only a start has been made in this direction. Backward conditions are particularly prevalent in the marketing of milk. All milk moves to market in unscalded cans by muleback or in two-wheeled carts drawn by oxen.

Although natural conditions are highly favorable to the expansion of the grazing industry, this is retarded by lack of transportation. Increased output would result only in a surplus which could find no market. Under such conditions, there is little reason to increase production or improve the quality of the product,

Mining.—One of the major economic activities of the highlands is mining, which provides an important source of income, not only to private enterprise, but to the Colombian government as well. Although many sections of the highlands give evidence of being highly mineralized, especially in the Central Cordillera, the inaccessible character of much of this area retards mining development and confines mining operations to a few areas and to a few minerals.

Four, or perhaps five, minerals deserve mention in this brief survey of Highland Colombia: (1) gold, (2) emeralds, (3) coal, (4) salt, and possibly (5) iron.

Gold is produced principally in the Western and the Central Cordillera and along the rivers that drain these areas (Fig. 16). Most of the output comes from placer mines, although quartz gold is obtained from lode mines in the departments of Antioquia, Cauca, and Caldas. Gold production in Colombia is valued at some $15,000,000 annually, and the bulk of the output comes from these regions. The increased value of gold in the United States has stimulated production somewhat and also, of course, added to the value of the gold produced. With the higher price for gold, it has been possible to handle lower grade ores. This condition is expressed in the increase in production from 143,000 ounces in 1928 to 298,000 in 1933 and to 442,000 in 1937.

Colombia is the chief source of the world's emeralds, although, owing to the great stock of gems on hand, little mining has been done in recent years. The chief area of production is in the so-called "Muzo mines" some 60 miles northwest of Bogotá in the Department of Boyacá (Fig. 16). The emerald mines, in large part, are controlled by the government and in some years have yielded as much as $1,000,000 to the public treasury. They represent an important potential resource to Colombia. One problem in the emerald-mining industry is the small value of the low-grade emeralds. Some attempts have been made to utilize them in the production of beryllium, but so far little has been accomplished.

A little coal is produced in the highland districts of Colombia, principally along the railroad line leading from Medellín to the Cauca valley and around Bogotá. It is a fair-grade bituminous, and most of it is used to supply local industry. Little is known concerning the coal reserves of the country, since careful geologic surveys have not been made.

Salt is an important mineral in Cundinamarca where it is obtained from underground mines. At Zipaquirá, there is a body of rock salt estimated to contain a billion tons. The salt industry is a government monopoly and provides much needed revenue to the government.

Iron is found in small, widely scattered areas, particularly in the Department of Cundinamarca. There is little or no production today, local iron ore being unable to meet the competition of imported iron and steel. Until more careful surveys are made, little can be said concerning the importance of Colombia's iron-ore deposits.

Manufacturing.—Manufacturing in Highland Colombia is confined primarily to the two leading departments of Antioquia and Cundinamarca and to the two leading cities of these departments—Medellín and the capital of Colombia, Bogotá (Fig. 12).

Medellín is by far the leading manufacturing center of Colombia. The general advanced condition of the population of this area and the favorable environment in which they live seem to be the principal reasons for this development.

With the exception of the political prestige attaching to the department that contains the capital city, Antioquia may be considered the leading department of Colombia. It lies in the heart of the mountainous district west of the Magdalena at an average elevation of nearly 5,000 feet, an altitude that provides a stimulating temperature. Whether or not the inhabitants of Antioquia are descended in part from Jewish ancestors, as they are reported to be, they do possess an energy, a business shrewdness, a desire for education and for financial advancement of an order that is unusual in tropical lands. Agriculturally, the department is of only average quality; but in its mineral wealth, especially in the output of gold, it leads the nation. It has between 30 and 40 cities of 10,000 people or more; and its principal city, Medellín, has an enterprising population of over 120,000. It has upward of 50 good-sized manufacturing establishments and easily leads all the departments in this particular. The products of its factories include: cotton and woolen textiles, ironware, shoes, ice, soap, candy, sugar, and many other manufactures. The majority of the factories are in Medellín and its suburbs. So large is the private wealth of the businessmen and so well are the finances of the department administered that the credit of Antioquia is as good as that of the nation. Illiteracy, which characterizes over 80 per cent of the Colombian population as a whole, is relatively low in Antioquia, and in Medellín more than

four-fifths of the factory workmen can read and write. Families
are large, and the increasing population is constantly overflowing
into neighboring regions, where they are none too cordially
received because of their pushing and money-making qualities.

Bogotá, the second largest manufacturing center of the country, is located in the Department of Cundinamarca on a high
tableland 8,650 feet above sea level (Fig. 18). Manufacturing in
Bogotá is centered in the processing of agricultural products,
particularly refining of sugar, brewing, and tobacco and cigar

Fig. 18.—Street scene in Bogotá. Montserrat in background.

making. In addition, there are some cement manufacturing and
the production of men's clothing, on a small scale, for local consumption. The city is semimodern, with electric lights, telephones,
streetcars, a few paved streets, a large distributing business, a
number of good-sized factories, and a large number of cultured
people, mainly of Spanish descent. Though lacking the business
aggressiveness of Medellín, it is the center of a fairly energetic
population. The Indians of the plateau are more numerous than
the whites and constitute the laboring class. Half the people are
literate; the National University is at Bogotá (founded in 1572),
and there are four provincial universities.

The Caribbean Coastal Margin.—This region of Colombia
occupies the area between the highlands and the Caribbean Sea

(Fig. 11). Although not characterized by the extreme variations found in the highlands, neither is there great uniformity in either the natural or the cultural patterns throughout the region. Temperature conditions are uniform, except within the more elevated portions, as, for example, where the Sierra Nevada de Santa Marta raises its lofty peaks 19,000 feet above the sea. In many respects, this mountainous region is similar to the Highland Heart, but its complete isolation from that area and its location within the low coastal plains fronting on the Caribbean seem to be sufficient justification for including it within the Caribbean coastal region.

Of the many economic activities in Caribbean Colombia, it is doubtful whether any is more significant than that of the commercial function carried on by the three ports: Barranquilla, Santa Marta, and Cartagena. The commercial function alone lends considerable importance to the region, for through these ports pass most of the country's imports and exports.

Although these three ports are close together and there exists a certain degree of rivalry among them, there has developed a certain amount of specialization, both in terms of products handled and in territory served.

Barranquilla, with its population of 75,000 people, is the largest city along the coast and the leading port of Colombia. Although Barranquilla is the leading port today, it was not always in first place. It is the newest of the ports and has achieved significance only in the last five or six decades. Before the dredging operations were completed that deepened the channel of the Magdalena, actual contact with the sea was via Puerto Colombia which lies 17 miles away by rail, as was mentioned above. Barranquilla owes its development in large measure to its location on the Magdalena River, the chief thoroughfare of the country, a position that no other port enjoys.

Cartagena, when Spain controlled much of the New World and when her ships plied the pirate-infested Spanish Main, was one of the great ports of South America. Founded in 1533, it was considered one of the most important and strategic cities of the Caribbean. Not only did it control the trade routes to the Pacific and the Interior, but from it were sent to Spain many valuable shiploads of cacao, forest products, hides, and tobacco. Later, it was connected to the Magdalena by a canal, the *Canal del*

Dique, and its future seemed assured. The canal, however, was allowed to fall into disrepair during Colombia's struggle for independence, and Cartagena lost to Barranquilla as the leading port of Colombia. Recently, the canal has been repaired, and steamers from upriver ports can now reach Cartagena. The city is also connected by rail to the Magdalena River at Calamar. It is likewise an important outlet for northwestern Colombia and is the terminus of a 325-mile-long pipe line which brings petroleum from the rich Magdalena-Santander oil field. All these developments have helped to revive Cartagena, but it has not returned to its former relative importance.

Somewhat to the east of the mouth of the Magdalena is the port of Santa Marta. Santa Marta owes its development primarily to the plantation agriculture of the adjacent Sierra Nevada de Santa Marta region. The port is joined to the Magdalena by rail, but this connection is of little commercial importance. Of far greater significance is the small railway net which links Santa Marta with the coffee and banana plantations and over which the principal export products move.

In addition to the commercial function, crop agriculture, grazing, gathering of forest products, and petroleum also add to the economic welfare of Caribbean Colombia. The full development of these activities, however, is severely handicapped by the heat and humidity characteristic of most of the area, as well as by poorly developed transportation facilities.

The Crop Agriculture Pattern.—Crop production in Caribbean Colombia is confined almost entirely to tropical products. The upper slopes of the highland districts are almost entirely unoccupied. Two major types of agricultural production are distinguishable: (1) commercial agriculture, and (2) subsistence agriculture. The principal commercial crops include: (1) bananas, (2) coffee, (3) sugar, and (4) cotton. Subsistence crops are similar to those of the lower elevations in the Highland Heart.

BANANAS.—On the piedmont plain surrounding the lower, western slopes of the towering Santa Marta mountains and below the coffee zone is the leading area of commercial banana production in all South America (Fig. 16). The constantly high temperatures of the lowlands (averaging around 80°F.) are almost ideal for banana culture. The district suffers somewhat from inadequate rainfall (averages vary between 35 and 65 inches), but this deficiency is overcome by irrigation with water obtained from the near-by well-watered Santa Marta slopes. Irrigation is not continuous but is practiced only in the two dry seasons which occur in July and August and between December and March. Neither severe winds nor plant diseases are so serious a menace here as in other parts of Caribbean America. Winds cause some damage, but the relatively protected location of the plantations reduces the danger of serious loss. Most of the laborers are Negroes and mestizos who suffer from malaria, anemia, hookworm, and the debilitating heat. Fortunately, though, once a plantation has been started, it requires relatively little care, except at the harvest, and the labor problem is not so serious as might at first be supposed. A banana plant yields for some 5 or 6 years without replanting.

Much of the banana country, both producing and potential, is in the hands of the United Fruit Company, to which, also, numerous private planters sell their crop. The United Fruit Company has the same excellent and well-organized marketing system that characterizes its other holdings throughout Caribbean America. There is considerable room for expansion of banana culture. The United Fruit Company, for example has only about one-third of its leased area under production.

COFFEE.—Along the northern and western slopes of the Sierra Nevada de Santa Marta, at elevations between 3,000 and 6,000 feet, is an important coffee-producing area (Fig. 16). This district is less important than the Highland Heart, but the section affords excellent conditions for the growth of coffee. The soil on the steep slopes is very fertile. The region receives about 60 inches of rain, so distributed that there are many sunshiny days and a long dry period for the harvest. Unlike so many sections of Colombia, this territory is well served by adequate transportation facilities to the port city of Santa Marta. The most serious problem is a general shortage of labor to carry forward the work on the plantations.

SUGAR.—Sugar is another crop that, in many ways, is favored by the environment of Caribbean Colombia. Most of it is raised in the Lower Magdalena district between Cartagena and the river (Fig. 16). Here sufficient rain combined with a sunny ripening period and fertile soil aids production. Occasionally, the area is subjected to damaging droughts. Various plant diseases and pests take their toll. But more serious than handicaps of the natural environment are the shortcomings of the human environment. The inefficient and inadequate labor supply as well as lack of modern methods is the greatest disadvantage to the extension of sugar production.

COTTON.—Although cotton is of only minor economic importance in Caribbean Colombia at the present time, it has considerable potential significance. Today, most of it is produced on a very small scale by careless mulattoes who give little attention to the crop, either during the growing period or at harvest time. The chief area of production is along both sides of the lower course of the Magdalena River. The district is favorable from the standpoint both of climate and of soil. The annual rainfall is around 30 to 40 inches. It comes during a long rainy season lasting from April to October. The rest of the year is dry and conducive to the ripening of the crop. Despite favorable natural conditions, however, production will not be significant until more scientific methods are followed by the natives.

Subsistence Agricultural Pattern.—As in the Highland Heart, subsistence crops are found both on tiny subsistence farms and on the commercial plantations.

In the lowland plains, on lands not devoted to plantations, the subsistence agricultural lands assume a spotty linear pattern along the rivers. Here, a relatively dense population of mulattoes and Indians carry on agriculture supplemented by fishing. Similar agricultural practices are followed by the Indian population who inhabit the isolated territory of the Sierra de Perijá.

Elsewhere, the pattern of subsistence agriculture corresponds closely to the distribution of the various plantations. On the coffee and banana plantations of the Santa Marta area, the native laborers engage, in a halfhearted fashion, in the production of corn, cassava, plantain, and beans for their own needs. Of these crops, plantain is one of the most important. It is closely related to the banana but is cooked before eating and is used more like a vegetable than a fruit. Subsistence crops receive practically no care. The little, scattered patches are not even plowed. A sharp-pointed stick is used to scratch the soil and prepare the land for planting. Occasionally, some of the weeds that smother the crops are cut away. Otherwise, crops are left unattended, except at the harvest.

The Grazing Industry.—Although cattle are raised in nearly all the farming districts of this region of Colombia, they attain their maximum importance in the savanna lands of the middle-plains district in southern Bolívar and south of the Santa Marta Mountains. In this region, cattle for meat, milk, butter, and cheese are raised on great *estancias.* The industry takes on a certain commercial importance in those sections served by river transportation. Cattle, hides, and cheese move to the interior-highland markets and to the outside. In most districts, though, the major commercial product is hides. The old bugbear of transportation, or rather lack of transportation, is the as yet unsolved problem throughout most of this area. The cattle receive little care and are harassed by many diseases and pests. So long as markets are remote, there is little incentive to improve conditions. On many of the *estancias,* subsistence crops are produced, but they achieve only minor significance as compared with the cattle industry.

Some grazing of goats is carried on by the sparse seminomadic Indian population of the backward, low-lying, desertlike region of the Goajira peninsula. These goats provide meat and milk for the half-savage, unassimilated Indians who raise them. Occasionally there is a surplus of goatskins for export.

Forest-products Industries.—The gathering of forest products is not particularly important in the tropical forested areas of Caribbean Colombia. The principal forested regions lie north of the central Andean chain and along the rivers. Products obtained from the forests include: coconuts, tagua nuts, balata, lirio (a substitute for chicle), and kapok obtained from the silk-cotton tree. The tropical forests also supply wood for the wood-burning steamers that ply in the river trade. In fact, an important occupation of many of the mulattoes who inhabit the territory along the rivers is cutting wood for the steamers.

Petroleum.—One final asset of Caribbean Colombia, though by no means the least important, is petroleum. Among all the mineral resources of Colombia, petroleum is the most important. It accounts for about 18 per cent of the country's total exports and after coffee is the leading export item (Fig. 15). Although geologic formations give evidence of oil in several regions, only one is as yet a significant producer. This region is composed of two fields (Infanta and La Cira) located in the Magdalena Valley in the vicinity of Barrancabermejo. Production in these two fields has been around 13 to 17 million barrels in recent years. A pipe line connects a refinery at Barrancabermejo with the coast at Cartagena. Operations are in the hands of the Tropical Oil Company, a subsidiary of Standard Oil of New Jersey. Although production did not begin until 1926, Colombia stands second to Venezuela as the leading South American producer. Although this is the only producing area along the Magdalena, geologic conditions are favorable to oil occurrence along the western slopes of the Eastern Cordillera from El Banco 500 miles south to Neiva.

In addition to this producing and potential area, there is evidence of oil in northeastern Colombia in the vicinity of the great Lake Maracaibo oil district of Venezuela. Conditions are also favorable along the Caribbean coast from the Santa Marta mountains westward to Panama. Some prospecting and even drilling has taken place in a few of these areas. In the case of the so-called Barco Concession, southeast of Lake Maracaibo in Colombia at the Venezuelan border, American companies have started operations and are building pipe lines across the mountains to the Caribbean coast (263 miles).

Pacific Margins and Atrato Valley.—The Pacific coastal region and the Atrato Valley are of considerable importance to the economic life of Colombia. The proximity of the area to the Panama Canal and the development of transportation facilities, which link this section with the highlands, have led to the development of the commercial function. In addition, the presence of minerals and tropical forests has helped stimulate mining and the gathering of forest products. Although attractive in these respects, the region is very unattractive from a physical point of view. It receives a heavier rainfall than any other section of South America. Temperatures are constantly high. Much of the lowland is low, swampy, and malarial. Soils in many sections are poor or even useless.

Agricultural Pattern.—Commercial agriculture is practically nonexistent in this division of Colombia. Climatic conditions are so severe and disease so prevalent that plantations find it almost impossible to obtain a satisfactory labor supply (Fig. 19). Moreover, it is so easy for the indolent Negro population to gain a livelihood by subsistence agriculture that routine labor, which plantation work entails, does not attract them. There are very few Indians in the area, most of them refusing to live in this hot, tropical country.

Subsistence agriculture is confined to the valleys and higher portions of the coastal margins. There is little agricultural utilization of the Atrato or its delta. Many of the soils here are practically useless because of poor drainage.

Mining.—One of the major economic activities of this area is the mining of gold and platinum (Fig. 16). These two minerals often occur together in placer deposits. Mining operations are, in general, on a small scale. The prevalence of disease and the extreme heat make it difficult to obtain an efficient and reliable labor supply. Negro and Indian laborers work sporadically, generally only a few days at a time in order to earn enough for a few days' leisure. Slave labor was once used in the gold placers. With the abolition of slavery, production in the area declined considerably. The fact that crude methods are followed and that many sections are not served by railroads also adds to the expense of exploitation and retards expansion.

FIG. 19.—Negro huts on western slope of the Andes.

Gold is found in most of the little rivers along the Pacific coast and in the so-called Chocó district at the upper end of the Atrato valley, inland from Bahia del Chocó. The Chocó district stands second in importance to the gold-mining district of Antioquia in the highlands. Along the coast, the principal producing district lies between Buenaventura and Tumaco in the vicinity of Timbiqui.

Colombia has been one of the world's leading producers of platinum. During the World War, when production was interrupted in Russia, Colombia was the world's leading producer. Since the war, several new areas have come into production.

Today (1938), Colombia ranks fifth with about 30,000 troy
ounces, being surpassed by Canada (290,000 ounces), U.S.S.R.,
South Africa, and Alaska. For a long time, platinum, which
occurred in the gold placers, was thrown away as useless. As soon
as the value of the mineral was realized, many old placers were
reworked. The principal mines are in the Intendencia de Chocó,
along the Atrato River and its tributaries. About two-thirds of
the mining is done with 2,000-horsepower electric dredges, and
about one-third is produced by natives working with pans. Most
of the platinum mined is shipped to the United States.

Forest Industries.—The dense tropical rain forests that
cover much of the area included within the Pacific Margins and
Atrato Valley yield a great variety of products. Anything ap-
proaching complete utilization of the forests, however, is handicapped by the meager transportation facilities, by competition
with the mining companies for a labor supply, and by the excessive and debilitating heat. Most of the forest products are obtained from the coastal districts and include about the same items
as are obtained from the forests of the Caribbean Coastal Margins: tropical hardwoods, tagua nuts, palms for the manufacture
of panama hats, kapok, and balata.

The Commercial Function and Ports.—The importance of the
commercial function along the Pacific coast is indicated by the
fact that Buenaventura is Colombia's second port on the basis of
value of exports and third from the standpoint of value of imports. Buenaventura, although it has a population of only 25,000
(90 per cent of whom are Negroes), is an important outlet for the
highlands. Railroads and roads tie the port with Cali and Bogotá.
The city is also well situated to collect the products of the Chocó
mining district, and the near-by forest regions. The harbor is
deep enough to accommodate boats drawing 27 feet. From
Buenaventura are exported gold and platinum of the Chocó
district, sugar, coffee, and hides from the Upper Cauca Valley,
and many of the products of the forests listed above.

Farther south and much less important than Buenaventura is
the port of Tumaco. The principal exports from this port are
three in number: coffee, cacao, and tagua nuts. The first two
products originate on the plantations of the western slopes of
the Western Cordillera, and the tagua nuts come from the near-by
tropical forests.

The commercial function of the west coast seems to be one that will continue and, if transportation facilities are improved, will increase in importance. Not only will improved transportation make the hinterland more accessible, but it should, at the same time, increase its production and add to the number of products moving to the coast for export.

The Eastern Plains.—The Eastern Plains of Colombia occupy nearly half of Colombia's 450,000 square miles but supply little of economic value to the country. The great disparity between the size of the region and its economic productivity is due, in large measure, to its remoteness. The Eastern Plains have little contact either with the highland district or with the outside world. As a result, the eastern half of Colombia is extremely backward.

Only one land-use pattern is of significance—that of the area devoted to cattle grazing. In the northern portion of the country is an open savanna grassland which supports some 300,000 cattle. The cattle raised are a very poor grade and receive little or no care. The absence of a market for the animal products that might be produced delays both the improvement of the herds and the expansion of the industry.

In the southern part of the Eastern Plains, there is little or no economic activity. The region is heavily forested but yields little except balata which is gathered by roving natives. There are few settled peoples in this sparsely populated area, most of the people of the Eastern Plains being concentrated in the northern cattle country.

Although disease, pests, and climate are handicaps to the development of the Eastern Plains, the future prosperity of the area is probably most closely tied up with the extension of transportation facilities. With better access to markets, there would be an incentive to improve herds, combat disease and pests, and improve conditions generally. So long as transportation is lacking, there is little to encourage improvements in the local economy.

Chapter III. Venezuela and the Guiana Colonies

A man and a mineral product, both developed within the last few decades of a turbulent history extending over some four centuries, have had a profound influence on the economic and political life of Venezuela.

The entry of General Juan Vicente Gómez[1] as a dictatorial ruler in 1910, introduced an era of internal peace, political quiescence, and economic stability. Whether Gómez be regarded as a ruthless tyrant or a kindly altruist, the changes he wrought in the political and economic life of the country cannot be denied. During his period in office, the national debt was nearly obliterated, the national budget was balanced, no new foreign loans were contracted, the credit of the country was restored, hundreds of miles of trails and highways were built, foreign capital was encouraged to enter the country, and foreign commerce made notable gains.

Gómez's activities were greatly aided, beginning about 1920, by the development of Venezuela's petroleum reserves. The stable political condition that Gómez had brought about with his iron rule helped to attract foreign capital to the oil fields of Maracaibo. The revenues from the oil fields were a great aid to Gómez in maintaining his power and in improving economic conditions. Oil has had a profound influence on the country's economic life. Although many of the profits of the industry have passed into the hands of foreign investors, Venezuela has had considerable income from oil royalties. In addition, benefits have accrued to the country from the sale of labor and supplies to the oil interests.

[1] General Gómez died in 1935.

63

In order to gain a clear perspective of the effect that General Gómez and the development of the petroleum industry have had on the country, it is necessary to look back over a few high lights of Venezuela's history. In view of the country's turbulent past, the change that has come about and the part that Gómez and petroleum have had in this change become more significant.

Venezuela's first contact with European civilization was at the hands of pirates and slave raiders. These pirates established a base of operations on a little island off the Venezuela coast in 1510 and profited by raiding the Indian villages of the interior for slaves. These slaves were sold to plantation owners of the Antilles.

A decade later, the first European settlement on the mainland of South America was established at Cumaná. The hope of finding gold attracted settlers, but their hopes were never fulfilled and the colony migrated farther west and established itself at Coro. Using Coro as a base, explorers worked back into the highlands and eastward to the present site of Valencia where they found some gold. In 1555, Valencia was founded. Twelve years later, Caracas, in a rich and easily protected valley, became the center of government. Within another 10 years, a port was developed at La Guaira, and conditions seemed favorable for the growth and expansion of the colony. The colony was well located for trade with Europe and for commercial contacts with the West Indies. Although in the heart of the tropics, the highlands afforded healthful conditions for white men and contained fertile agricultural valleys. The area lacked, though, an abundant supply of one important item—gold. Gold, in the eyes of Spain, was the one asset a worth-while colony should possess.

Owing to the absence of gold, the colony was largely neglected, and economy turned from mineral production to the development of agricultural and pastoral pursuits. Feelings between the colony and Spain grew more and more tense in the years that followed. Commercial restrictions of such nature were placed on the colony that agriculture, grazing, and trade were seriously handicapped. To avoid the penalties imposed on legitimate trade, smugglers came into existence, and smuggling developed as a profitable business. As a result, Spain enacted reprisals on the colony, and antagonism grew to hatred. Finally, in 1811, Venezuela declared her independence of Spanish rule.

It took Venezuela some 10 years of desperate fighting, however, to achieve actual independence. It was eventually accomplished under the leadership of that great South American patriot, Simon Bolivar, but at very great cost. The early gains in agriculture and grazing were practically wiped out and the population decimated. Up until this time, Venezuela had been united with Ecuador and Colombia under one government, but this union was dissolved in 1830. Despite a general increase in trade and the expansion of agriculture and grazing, internal strife continued. Each new president came into office by revolutionary activity and was deposed in the same fashion. A relatively quiet and prosperous period was enjoyed under the presidency of Guzmán Blanco, who held office for 20 years beginning in 1872.

In 1896, a new series of problems developed. A boundary dispute with Great Britain over the Venezuela-British Guiana boundary line caused trouble. About this time, too, the country was torn by a 2-year-long civil war. In 1903, Venezuela's ports were blockaded by England, Germany, and Italy, with the consent of the United States. The main reason for this was the treatment that Venezuela, under President Castro, was according foreign interests in the country. This unsettled condition continued until Gómez seized the reins of government in 1910. He became an absolute dictator, bringing civil peace and stability to the country. although, it must be admitted, it was an armed peace.

Many of Venezuela's economic problems, as was true in the case of Colombia, are problems that deal with the utilization of tropical lowlands and with the development of transportation facilities to link the country together into a workable economic unit. The degree to which Venezuela has solved these problems and thus been able to take advantage of her varied resources differs greatly from region to region. It is, therefore, only in the light of a more detailed analysis of the various regions which make up the country that even a partial evaluation of Venezuela's economic development can be made.

REGIONS OF VENEZUELA

Largely as a result of the distribution of highlands and lowlands, Venezuela is divided into four major regions, regions of contrasting economic activities, land-use patterns, and natural conditions. These variations are in part due to differences in elevation between highlands and lowlands but also result in part from location or the relative accessibility or isolation of the separate regions.

In the northwest section of the country, encircling an arm of the Caribbean known as Lake Maracaibo and surrounded on three sides by mountains, are the low hot plains known as the Mara-

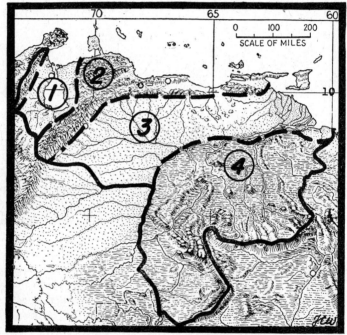

Fig. 20.—Major regions of Venezuela. 1, Maracaibo Basin; 2, Northern Highlands; 3, Llanos; 4, Guiana Highlands.

caibo Basin (Fig. 20). To the south and east, the plain gives way abruptly to mountains that are an extension of the great Andean system. These mountains, known in the south as the Cordillera de Merida and in the north as the Segovia Highlands, turn eastward along the Caribbean coast and continue as two chains. The northern, or outer, one is called the Coastal Range, and the southern one the Sierra del Interior; between them is an elevated basin. In the far east, the highlands continue as a single chain known as Sierra de Cumana or the Eastern Highlands.

These mountain chains and elevated basins of the northern and northwestern section of the country make up the region known as the Northern Highlands. South of these highlands, and almost completely cut off by them from oceanic contacts, is the most extensive plains district of Venezuela, the Llanos. The Llanos occupy a vast territory of some 130,000 square miles between the Northern Highlands and a southern mountain district, known as the Guiana Highlands, and extend from the Colombian border eastward to the delta of the Orinoco River. The fourth major region of Venezuela is occupied by the rugged, isolated, and little known section of the country, the Guiana Highlands.

These four natural regions (1) the Maracaibo Basin, (2) the Northern Highlands, (3) the Llanos, and (4) the Guiana Highlands cover some 394,000 square miles and have a total population of about 3,500,000 people (Fig. 20). Great variations in population density, economic

FIG. 21.—View of first gusher, Maracaibo basin, 1923. (*Courtesy of Winfield Givens.*)

activities, and natural conditions, however, necessitate a somewhat more detailed analysis of the separate regions.

The Maracaibo Basin.—Petroleum and the Maracaibo Basin are almost synonymous (Figs. 21 and 22). Not only is petroleum the outstanding mineral of this region, but it is also the country's most valuable export and major source of income. Although economic activity in the Maracaibo Basin centers in petroleum production, it must not be thought that oil is the only resource of the area. Agriculture, grazing industries, and the gathering of forest products also add to the economic welfare of the region.

Despite the great variety of resources, actual and potential, that the Maracaibo Basin possesses, the area has a relatively sparse population, varying in density from 10 to 30 per square mile. Moreover, the pattern of distribution gives evidence of only peripheral occupance. Most of the inhabitants are clustered

Fig. 22.—Exports from Maracaibo now are over $100,000,000.

around the northern shores of the lake, in the vicinity of the oil fields and of the city of Maracaibo, and along the rivers, particularly the Catatumbo and the Zulia. The population consists principally of a varied mixture of Negroes, Indians, and persons of Spanish extraction.

The peripheral character of the population pattern is to be accounted for in part by the relatively late development of the region. Economic utilization was long delayed, and is still handi-

capped, by the wild Motilones Indians of the Sierra de Perijá to
the west. These Indians frequently raided and destroyed early
settlements. Their menace, even today, is not entirely removed,
especially in the more isolated districts. In the economic penetration of this area, though, a far more serious problem than the
fierce Motilones is the terrific heat of these lowlands. Temperature averages in the basin reach 95°F. and give this area the
doubtful distinction of being one of the warmest in all South
America. Although the basin as a whole is characterized by a
modified savanna type of climate with two distinct wet and two
marked dry seasons, there is considerable variation in rainfall.
The low shores of the northern end of the basin, exposed to the
drying trade winds, receive practically no rain, but precipitation
increases toward the south. Maracaibo City receives about 21
inches per year and the southern end of the basin about 50 inches.
The rains, associated with the period of highest sun, come in two
seasons very close together, the first from May to July and the
second from September to November. Vegetation shows a
response to variation in rainfall, the northern belt possessing a
xerophytic type, the middle zone a savanna type, and the
southern end of the basin resembling the Tropical Rain Forest.

Agricultural Occupance.—The agricultural pattern exhibits
some striking associations with the climate and population
patterns. Although agriculture is widespread in the basin, only
a very small percentage of the land is under cultivation. Arid
conditions in the north and bad drainage in the south are retarding influences. Hostile Indians, insect pests, and disease are
additional handicaps to expansion. Moreover, away from the
lake, the rivers, and the three short rail lines that connect part
of the southern end of the basin with the northern slopes of the
Cordillera de Merida, transportation facilities are largely absent.
As a result, the agricultural pattern conforms closely to the
transportation pattern, the majority of the lands under cultivation being confined to areas served by the lake, the rivers, or the
three short rail lines of the south. Variations in products also
show associations with the climate pattern, but these will be
pointed out in more detail later.

Agriculture in the Maracaibo Basin is of two major types: (1)
commercial, and (2) subsistence. Most of the commercial crops
are raised on large plantations. Subsistence crops are grown on

plantations and on cattle *estancias* as food for the laborers, and in small patches in the forest clearings. Primitive forest agriculture is important in the basin. It provides practically the sole means of subsistence for many Indians, Negroes, and mulattoes of the region. A relatively small variety of fruits and vegetables is produced, and there is a notable emphasis on those of high starch content. The leading ones grown include: corn, beans, cassava, breadfruit, bananas, and mangoes. A few chickens and pigs complete the simple agricultural economy of the native. Crops receive practically no care; seeds are frequently sown among burned or girdled trees, and plants are almost never cultivated, though weeds may be removed once or twice a season. When soil fertility decreases, a new patch of the forest may be cleared and the old abandoned to the rapidly growing natural vegetation.

Although plantation agriculture is favored by many conditions, there are many difficulties to be overcome. One of the major handicaps to expansion is the labor problem. Aside from the matter of general inefficiency and poor quality of much of the labor, there is serious competition between the oil fields and the plantations for the altogether inadequate supply.

The leading crops of commercial importance on the plantations are sugar cane, cacao. and coconuts. In addition, a little cotton is produced.

SUGAR.—Large sugar-cane plantations reach maximum importance along the southern and eastern shore of the lake and along the Zulia River. This area is the major sugar-producing section of Venezuela. Sugar cane from these areas is treated in modern Centrals and enters into export trade to the extent of some 8,000,000 pounds annually. There is plenty of room for the extension of sugar production, but expansion seems unlikely. This district is badly drained; in fact, most plantations need drainage facilities, and the swamp lands are a breeding place for malarial mosquitoes. Moreover, a market of sufficient size to absorb the potential production of the area is lacking. Venezuelans depend for their local supplies on a coarse brown sugar (panela) which is refined from sugar cane grown in small patches and not on large plantations. In export markets, Venezuelan sugar must compete with Cuba and other areas where production costs are lower or where more favorable tariff arrangements create a differential unfavorable to Venezuela. Even though better markets were available, Venezuela would still face the problem of insufficient labor. Better production methods should also be introduced. The plantations get 40 to 50 tons of cane per acre, but the sugar content is very low. This deficiency could be remedied by more scientific agriculture; but, lacking a market, there is little incentive to improve production methods.

CACAO.—Nearly all cacao produced in the Maracaibo Basin is exported. The distribution of the cacao plantations corresponds closely to that of the sugar-producing districts, except that the cacao plantations tend to be somewhat nearer the highlands and, where possible, on somewhat higher and better drained lands. As in the case of sugar, though, poor drainage is one of the problems of cacao production. Although soil is good and the climate with its long rainy and short dry seasons favors production, there are many serious retarding influences. Most of the plantations are owned by absentee landlords. As a result, careful supervision is lacking, and the trees receive little care from the inadequate labor. In many cases, the tropical forest is not sufficiently cleared, and the plantations are too shady. This condition results in a fungus attacking the cacao trees and reduces production to a considerable degree. Other plant diseases, such as black pod rot, are also prevalent.

COCONUTS.—Coconuts represent a type of plantation product well suited to economic and natural conditions of the Maracaibo Plains. The crop requires little attention and hence a relatively small labor supply; the products obtained (coconut oil and copra) are relatively imperishable and give a good financial return to the growers; finally, the tree grows well in those parts of the basin having a porous well-drained soil. Coconuts are raised on both large and small plantations. Production is confined primarily to the north in the vicinity of the narrows that separate Lake Maracaibo from the Caribbean.

COTTON.—The only other crop of commercial significance in the Maracaibo Basin is cotton, and it is of only minor importance. The basin is not particularly well suited to cotton production. In the northern part, the plant suffers from lack of moisture; and, in the south, too much rain and too high humidity result in the production of an inferior boll. The product is short staple and is raised in small patches. Because of the handicaps outlined above and because of the inefficiency of the laborers, there seems little likelihood that cotton production will be increased significantly.

Lands Devoted to Grazing.—Grazing lands occur in three distinct portions of the Maracaibo Basin. In the north, conditions are too arid for normal agriculture, and the general lack of water precludes irrigation farming. As a consequence, the indigent population of mestizos and mulattoes depends almost entirely on goats for its livelihood.

West of the goat-raising region, xerophytic vegetation and perennially dry conditions give way to a savanna vegetation and a low-latitude climate characterized by wet and dry seasons. Here vast *estancias* occupy an important place in the land-occupance pattern. Cattle, sheep, horses, and mules are the chief animals of the area; dried beef and cheese are sent from here to towns and cities of the lake district, and hides are shipped to overseas markets. The animals, which are of poor quality, fare well in the rainy season but suffer from lack of nourishment during the dry periods when the pastures become parched. No good transportation facilities connect this area with its markets. Labor is supplied by a listless Indian population. Under these adverse circumstances, the grazing industry of this area will probably always find it difficult to meet the competition of more favored districts.

The third grazing area of the Maracaibo Lowlands is localized in the southern end of the basin where open grasslands occasionally break the continuity of the forest. Here, as in the northwest, large *estancias* are characteristic. Their pattern corresponds to the distribution of the rivers and railroads. Although, because of better transportation facilities, this section is more accessible to its markets, the cattle raised are of inferior quality. Pests and diseases, particularly Texas fever, are prevalent, and little or no attempt is made to improve the stock by careful breeding. As a result, the only exportable product is hides. Meat and other animal products are marketed in the towns around the lake, particularly in the oil-producing centers.

Forest Products.—The forests of the Maracaibo Basin yield a variety of products. Total production, however, is insignificant. The full utilization of the forests is handicapped to a large degree by lack of transportation. In the north the dry areas yield the valuable divi-divi, used in the manufacture of tannin extract.

The tropical forests of the south are exploited for cabinet woods, particularly mahogony, rosewood, and ebony. Productive utilization of these forests is confined to areas along the rivers and along the railroads.

Mineral Production.—Only one mineral product is of importance in the Maracaibo district, and that is petroleum (Fig. 22). It is the one product of Venezuela, though, that gives the country a degree of world importance. Without petroleum, which accounts for over three-fourths of the country's total exports, Venezuela would be a relatively insignificant country with an annual export trade valued at only some forty or fifty million dollars, instead of a country with an annual trade amounting to some two hundred millions.

The rise of oil production in Venezuela has been exceedingly rapid, and it has worked profound changes in the country. Production in 1920 amounted to only about $\frac{1}{2}$ million barrels. By 1936, production had exceeded 155 million barrels and had given to Venezuela third place among the world's petroleum producers. Although oil has made possible the elimination of external and greatly reduced internal debts in Venezuela and has made possible the development of transportation facilities, it has probably delayed the development of other resources in the country. As has been pointed out, the oil fields have drawn the scanty labor supply of the country away from other pursuits. The net result has been a general rise in living costs, particularly food costs, without a corresponding increase in income for most of the inhabitants.

Oil production is confined largely to the northern half of the basin on both sides of the lake, although the eastern side is by far the most important district. Development is handicapped in some measure by the sand bars that block the northern end of the lake. It is necessary to ship the oil in specially constructed shallow-draft tankers which ride over the sand bars at high tide. Formerly much of the oil was shipped to Curaçao for transfer to ocean steamers, but recently deep-water facilities have been developed on the Paraguaná Peninsula and on Aruba Island which reduce shipping costs somewhat.

Production is largely in the hands of some dozen foreign companies. American interests account for about half the total, and the British and Dutch control the other half.

Commercial Foci of the Lowlands.—Only one city of the
Maracaibo Lowlands warrants discussion in this short treatment
—Maracaibo. With its population of some 75,000 people, it is
the commercial capital of the lowlands and the leading port of
Venezuela. From Maracaibo go well over half of all the country's
exports, and into it are shipped about one-fourth of the country's
imports. The bulk of the outgoing trade is made up of petroleum,

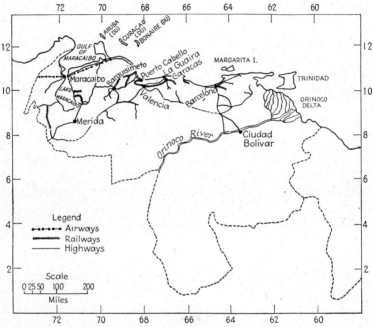

Fig. 23.—Transportation lines and principal cities of Venezuela.

coffee, and sugar. Coffee from the nearby Cúcuta section of
Colombia also finds its way into world markets via Maracaibo.

Maracaibo has a fair harbor which can be reached by boats
with 11-foot draft. The harbor is well protected, being a bay
20 miles inland from the open sea. The fact that the mouth of
Lake Maracaibo is blocked with sand bars is a handicap. It is
necessary to ship products from Maracaibo to Curaçao, Aruba
Island, or the Paraguaná Peninsula for transfer to ocean steamers.
As a result of the position of the Netherlands' West Indies off
the shallow entrance of Lake Maracaibo, these islands play an

important part in the foreign trade of Venezuela. Some 73 per cent of the export trade of the country is transshipped through the ports of the two islands of Aruba and Curaçao.

Urban development of the lowlands is retarded in large measure by the humid tropical heat and by a general lack of transportation facilities (Fig. 23). The lake serves as a highway of considerable importance in the movement of commodities from the lake-shore towns to Maracaibo and also aids in the development of the distribution function at that city. Contact with the highland, interior sections of Venezuela, though, is inadequate. Three short rail lines (Motatan to La Ceiba; El Vigia to San Carlos; and Táchira to Encontrados) contact the northern slopes of the eastern end of the highlands and are of some significance in getting highland products into world markets through Maracaibo. The undeveloped character of much of the territory, the small amount of commodities moving over the established transportation ways, and the general dependence of the Maracaibo Lowlands on the outside for most of its needs have all been instrumental in retarding the development of important commercial foci.

The Northern Highlands.—Although the Maracaibo Lowlands yield the single most important exportable product of Venezuela, the Northern Highlands, which extend for 600 miles in a general northeasterly direction from the Colombian border south of the Maracaibo Basin to the Paria Peninsula, are the economic heart of Venezuela (Fig. 20). Here, with the exception of Maracaibo, are located the largest cities; here is the greatest concentration of population; and, if petroleum is excluded, here are the country's leading industries. From the standpoint of commercial production, activity centers in two important commodities raised for export, coffee and cacao.

Because of the great variety in soil and climate that the highlands afford, a diversity in economic activity is possible. Full utilization of the region is retarded by lack of transportation facilities. Railroads can be constructed only at great expense over tortuous grades. Building is delayed also because of the cheaper services, though perhaps less satisfactory ones, provided by the slow moving pack trains. Transportation conditions are improving somewhat as a result of the development of motor roads. Of particular note is the great so-called Transandean highway which extends from San Cristóbal to Caracas and thus places much of the highland section in the hinterland of the port cities of Puerto Cabello and La Guaira (Fig. 23). In fact, since the building of this road, much trade formerly flowing through Maracaibo now reaches world markets via Puerto Cabello. It should be realized that, although motor roads do aid in the movement of commodities, highways also are a retarding influence in the development of rail facilities. Frequently less costly, owing in part to the steeper grades that automobiles can negotiate as compared with locomotives, roads possess a competitive advantage that railroads find difficult to meet. It seems altogether likely, therefore, that development of transportation facilities, at least in Highland Venezuela, will be in terms of new and improved highways rather than extensive rail lines.

The Economic Pattern of the Highlands.—Economic activity in the highlands focuses primarily on agriculture. Owing largely to variations in altitude, there is a marked zonation of crops. Variations in rainfall are also instrumental in bringing about differences in the agricultural pattern. Manufacturing industries achieve some local importance around Caracas and Valencia, though they yield little or nothing to the exportable surplus of the country. Mining, although it was gold that first attracted settlers into the highlands, is an occupation of extremely minor significance.

THE AGRICULTURAL PATTERN.—As was indicated earlier, a marked zonation of crops characterizes the agricultural pattern of the highlands. At lower elevations, bananas, corn, and cacao are the principal crops. Intermediate slopes are occupied by coffee, and higher elevations by temperate-zone grains. Above the region devoted to grains, there are some bleak grasslands given over to pastures on which livestock are grazed.

Commercial agriculture centers chiefly in the valleys and on intermediate slopes, and the more elevated sections are given over largely to the production of subsistence crops. Subsistence crops are also raised in lowland areas, but emphasis is on commercial agriculture. The outstanding cash crop of the highlands is coffee. Cacao stands in second place (Fig. 22). Other crops of commercial significance include cotton, sugar, and some tobacco. There is also some commercial livestock production, particularly the fattening of beef cattle from the Llanos, dairying, and the raising of goats for their meat, for skins, and for milk used in the manufacture of cheese.

Coffee.   Coffee is the outstanding commercial crop of the highlands, and, in fact, of all Venezuela. Production is widespread on the mountain slopes between 2,000 and 6,500 feet elevation. The bulk of the production is on large estates called *fincas*, although an important percentage is also raised on small-scale farms. Most of the coffee is high grade. Production is favored by deep, well-drained soils and by the alternate wet and dry seasons of the climate. The wet season, with a rainfall of over 40 inches, provides sufficient moisture. The dry season favors the ripening and harvesting of the crop. The chief center of production is in the western part of the highlands, just south of the Maracaibo Basin in the Sierra Nevada de Mérida. The second most important area is in the basin around Lake Valencia. Coffee is grown elsewhere throughout the highlands, but it is in these two districts (around Lake Valencia and in the Sierra Nevada de Mérida) that most of Venezuela's exportable surplus of coffee, amounting to some 100 million pounds annually, originates.

Cacao.   Cacao is more exacting in its climatic requirements than is coffee. Temperatures must be high at all times, and there must be a rainfall in excess of 40 inches, together with continuous high humidity, in order that the tree may produce well. Despite the need for considerable moisture and high humidity, the cacao tree must be grown on land that is well drained. Although local conditions of soil, drainage, exposure, precipitation, and other factors may modify the pattern somewhat in different parts of the highlands, nearly all the cacao is produced on slopes between 1,000 and 3,000 feet above sea level. It thus occupies the same general sections as coffee, but most of it is raised at somewhat lower elevations. One striking difference is noted. Whereas the principal coffee area is in the western portion of the highlands, most of the cacao is produced in the east. The western end produces a finer quality, but the total amount is less than in the east. The extreme eastern portion of the highlands alone accounts for about one-fourth of the 50 million pounds produced annually in the country.

Other commercial crops.   Most of the other commercial crops of Highland Venezuela find their market within the country. The more important ones in this group include sugar, cotton, and tobacco. None of these crops attains anything like the importance in the economic life of the highlands that is held by coffee and cacao, but they do form an important part of the agricultural complex and occupy a significant portion of the agricultural land.

Sugar, for the most part, is confined to elevations below 6,000 feet. The major centers of production are in the Sierra Nevada de Mérida, in the Coastal Ranges of the north, and in the basin around Lake Valencia. Most of this sugar, as in the Maracaibo Basin, is used locally in a coarse unrefined form (panela). Production could be extended considerably and yields in present areas of production increased were it not for the careless methods employed. Lack of capital for the installation of modern sugar Centrals and inadequate transportation facilities are also retarding influences.

Cotton is raised widely in the highlands for local consumption. Commercial production is localized near the city of Valencia where one-half of all the cotton grown in Venezuela is raised. Production in this area has been greatly stimulated by the development of the cotton-textile industry in Valencia. Were it not for the severe labor shortage, the area in cotton would doubtless be increased, for there is much room for expansion.

Tobacco attains only local importance. Most of it is consumed in the area of production. Several districts throughout the highlands are important; especially significant is the area in the vicinity of Valencia.

Other crops. Other crops in the highland districts occupy considerable area but are produced more for subsistence purposes than as cash crops. These crops display a zonation that is characteristic of the commercial products. Lower elevations are given over to the production of subsistence crops similar to those of the Maracaibo Basin; corn, beans, bananas, cassava, and breadfruit are among the most important. These products are found in little patches up to 6,000 feet elevation. Corn, in fact, is raised up to elevations of 9,000 feet. In elevations from 6,500 up to 10,000 feet, wheat is the loading crop. In the cold, barren areas above the limit of grain production, potatoes become the outstanding agricultural product, being grown at elevations up to 13,000 feet.

The livestock industry. Although grazing is an industry of some importance in many sections of the highlands and particularly on the high grasslands above the crop zone, two areas stand out as being particularly important. In one, the industry provides the principal source of income to the inhabitants; in the other, it is merely one item in the economic complex of the district. In the Segovia Highlands, a rough, rolling tableland east of the Maracaibo Basin, aridity imposes a severe handicap. Rainfall is generally less than 30 inches, and the evaporation rate is very high. This section has little in the way of agricultural production; there are few minerals; the xerophytic forests yield a little divi-divi; but most of the population depend on goats to provide them with a livelihood. A kind of *transhumance* characterizes the industry. During the wet season, the goats move into the more desert-like portions. In the dry season, they migrate to the moister districts surrounding the highlands. Although the animals lead a precarious existence, owing to the aridity, they do provide meat and cheese for the inhabitants of the area and some skins and manure for export. The other outstanding livestock area is in the Lake Valencia Basin. In this section, cattle, both beef and dairy, are important. Many of the beef cattle originate in the Llanos and are brought into this district near the market for fattening on natural and planted forage (Fig. 22). The dairying industry, which developed to supply the near-by urban centers, is important. Although in the past little attention has been paid to scientific methods of breeding, the industry is improving and shows signs of increasing importance. The development of the industry is largely due to the influence of President Gómez who was one of the wealthiest cattlemen of Venezuela.

MANUFACTURAL PATTERN.—Manufacturing in the Northern Highlands is chiefly in the cities of Caracas and Valencia. The development of industry in this section of the country is related to the concentration of population in this area, to the comparatively superior transportation facilities available, and to the fact that this district is the most productive agricultural region of the country and the best portion of the highlands. In addition to these advantages, the area also possesses other assets for the development of manufacturing. Coal is available from Coro to the west and Barcelona to the east. Oil is readily accessible from the great Maracaibo fields (Fig. 22). Water power from the steep Andean slopes can be utilized. Iron and copper are also available. Copper, although not very important today, has been mined for 300 years at Aroa in the Segovia Highlands. The iron is not used.

Were it not for the low purchasing power of the sparse population of Venezuela, manufacturing would probably be greatly increased. Until these handicaps are overcome, it seems unlikely that manufacturing will be significantly expanded.

The principal manufacturing industry of the highlands is the production of cotton textiles. At present, the country is able to produce about one-half of its needs for coarse cloth. The second

Fig. 24.—City of La Guaira, seaport for Caracas. A city of about 10,000 people. No natural harbor. (*Copyright Ewing Galloway, N. Y.*)

most important industry is the manufacture of cigarettes. Other manufactures include sugar refining,[1] leather tanning, shoe manufacturing, brewing, and making of straw hats, glass, rope, and chocolate. Recently 150,000 mulberry trees have been planted to stimulate silk production. In view of the labor situation, however, it would seem that this industry has little future. It should, perhaps, be noted that many of Venezuela's industries exist as a result of a high protective tariff. Without protection, it is doubtful whether many of them would be profitable enterprises.

[1] There are no modern sugar Centrals. All the refineries produce panela. Some of the sugar is also used in the production of rum.

HIGHLAND CITIES AND THEIR FUNCTIONS.—Highland Venezuela is by far the most urbanized section of the country (Fig. 23). The largest and most important city and the capital of the country is Caracas, a city with a population in excess of 200,000. Other cities of lesser importance include: Valencia (49,000), Barquisimeto (36,000), and San Cristóbal (22,000). Although not definitely in the highlands, the port cities of La Guaira (Fig. 24) and Puerto Cabello should probably also be listed as highland cities, for they function primarily as outlets for the economic heart of the country, and their existence is closely tied up with the highland cities.

Caracas. Caracas owes its importance to its political function, to its strategic location on routes to the coast, to the interior that has stimulated the development of commercial activity, and to its role as the principal manufacturing center of Venezuela. It is located at a break in the Coastal Ranges at some 3,000 feet above sea level (Fig. 25). Although the city is only about 9 miles distant, by air line, from the coast, the railroad that connects it with its port city of La Guaira twists and climbs for 23 miles to overcome the precipitous slope of the mountains. A railroad also connects Caracas with Valencia and with the Túy Valley, one of the major cacao-producing centers of the Highlands. Caracas lies on the Transandean highway, and a road also joins it with the Llanos. This focal position on the railroads and highways is one of the principal reasons for the importance of the commercial function in Caracas.

Valencia. Valencia, the second city of the Northern Highlands, is somewhat less favored than Caracas. Its elevation, about 1,500 feet, gives it a more tropical and less desirable climate than Caracas. The region tributary to the city possesses rich agricultural resources, and 33 miles away lies Puerto Cabello, the best harbor along the Venezuelan coast. The city's location on the Transandean highway has placed much of the highland area in the hinterland of Valencia and its port city. Puerto Cabello is drawing many of the products from the Sierra Nevada de Mérida which once moved out through Maracaibo. The fact that products can be loaded directly on ocean steamers and do not have to be transferred, as those do which are shipped from Maracaibo, gives Puerto Cabello a competitive advantage in this trade that helps to overcome the disadvantage of distance.

Fig. 25.—Caracas, chief city and capital of Venezuela, nine miles inland and over 3,000 feet above the sea. (*Copyright Ewing Galloway, N. Y.*)

San Cristóbal. San Cristóbal enjoys only local regional importance. It lies at the western terminal of the Transandean highway in the heart of a great coffee-producing area. The highway continues across the Colombian border to Cúcuta from where a rail line gives contact with Encontrados on the Catatumbo River in the Maracaibo Basin. The difficulties of access to the outside, by either Maracaibo or Puerto Cabello, delay the development of San Cristóbal. With better transportation facilities and more ready access to coastal towns, the region around San Cristóbal, and the city itself, would doubtless attain greater importance.

Barquisimeto. Barquisimeto, located in the Segovia Highlands, functions as an exchange center between the Sierra Nevada de Mérida and the eastern highlands and coastal cities. The city is connected by rail with the port city of Tucacas where motor launches give access to Puerto Cabello. It seems that it would have been more logical to construct a rail line directly from Barquisimeto to Puerto Cabello to serve this area. The line, though, was not built originally to give access from Barquisimeto to the sea but was constructed to serve the copper mines at Aroa and later extended to Barquisimeto.

The Llanos.—South of the Northern Highlands is a vast lowland district made up of the extensive savanna plains known as the Llanos and the delta plain of the great Orinoco River (Fig. 20). The delta covers some 9,000 square miles and is, for the most part, a vast jungle-clad area under water when the rivers are in flood and hot and humid at all times. No suitable harbor facilities are available along any of the mouths of the Orinoco, and boats serving upriver settlements operate from Port of Spain on the Island of Trinidad. The only inhabitants are a sparse population of Indians who maintain themselves by fishing, by gathering forest products, and by patch agriculture.

Upstream from the jungle district of the lower Orinoco the dense forest gives way to a great grassy savanna—a hot, level, alluvial plain whose maximum elevation is less than 1,000 feet and an area in which one industry is predominant. That industry is cattle grazing (Fig. 22).

The extensive character of these grassy plains, their nearness to the sea, the apparent ease with which transportation facilities can be built in this region and to adjacent sections, and the relative proximity of the area to the great cattle-consuming countries of Europe would seem to indicate that this region was endowed with valuable assets. Population, however, rarely exceeds 10 per square mile. In many places, the density falls to 2 per square mile; and, in sections, there are vast unpopulated areas.

Despite the assets that the Llanos possess, a combination of natural and man-made conditions has retarded the development of this great plain. Climate imposes a serious handicap on the region. There is a marked wet season lasting from April or May until October or November. During this season of the year, the Orinoco and its tributaries overflow their banks and cover thousands of square miles of low-lying territory. Cattle are forced to the higher interstream areas and to the margins of the foot-hills to escape the floodwaters. The rainy season gives way quickly to a marked dry season. The rivers recede rapidly, and soon the merciless sun turns the unprotected pastures into dry, burned grasses. The cattle are forced to wander over vast areas to obtain enough food and water to keep alive. The swamps left by the receding waters are breeding places for disease germs which further plague the cattle and the llaneros who tend them. Another serious handicap in the Llanos is the general lack of transportation facilities, There are no good highways and not a single railroad into the district (Fig. 23). Only two cart roads extend far inland. The Orinoco River is the chief highway. For a distance of some 1,500 miles, it can accommodate vessels drawing 12 feet. In the wet season, boats can proceed to the Colombian border. Away from this major highway, however, the only means of getting cattle out is by driving them northward to the high-lands, frequently from 100 to 400 miles. This practice causes the animals to lose flesh and necessitates fattening them in highland pastures before they can be sold. These pasture lands are expen-sive, and few cattlemen can afford them. Moreover, President Gómez and his friends controlled these lands and thus the cattle industry of the Llanos. In addition, the Llanos have suffered from a scarcity of labor ever since the population was decimated by the war for independence and the numerous civil wars that followed. Under these conditions, the development of the cattle industry of the Llanos faces many difficulties, not necessarily insurmountable, but probably ones that will not be solved in the immediate future. If wells were dug to supply drinking and irrigation water during the dry season, it would do much to alleviate the shortage of food and water during the long drought. Fenced pastures planted with nutritious grasses would also be a great aid, especially if these were placed along the routes by which cattle are driven to market. Improvement of transportation facilities and sanitary measures to better conditions for both animals and men are also badly needed. Until at least some of these improvements are made, it seems unlikely that there will be any marked growth of the cattle industry of the Llanos.

In view of the discussion above, it would seem that the Llanos were of little importance to Venezuela. Such, however, is not the case. The situation is merely that the country is not realizing anything like the potential resources of this area. In spite of the many difficulties that must be overcome, some of the richest men in Venezuela are cattlemen who made their fortunes on cattle ranches of the Llanos. They were the ones, though, who owned the more accessible portions, particularly the northwestern section, and who also had access to the pastures near the market areas.

Aside from cattle grazing, there is little of economic importance in the Llanos. A few subsistence crops of corn, beans, and cassava are produced; but the general lack of agricultural pursuits is indicated by the fact that the sparse population is dependent on imported foodstuffs. On some of the larger and better haciendas of the north and west, agriculture is more developed. Here cotton, rice, corn, beans, and cassava attain some importance.

The gathering of egret plumes was once an important occupation in the extreme western portion of this region. In gathering the plumes, the birds were killed and were almost annihilated. As a result, the government placed restrictions on the industry. Today, only plumes that are dropped by the birds in molting may be gathered. As a result, the industry has declined greatly and now yields only a few thousand dollars a year.

Urban Centers of the Llanos.—As might be expected, urban development is largely lacking in the Llanos. Ciudad Bolívar, with a population of about 25,000 and located 230 miles from the mouth of the Orinoco, is the metropolis of the Orinoco Basin (Fig. 23). Its site is a low hill above the general flood level. Being at the head of navigation for steamships that ply between the lower Orinoco River and Port of Spain, it has developed as a transshipment point and port for the Llanos and the Guiana Highlands to the south. Its principal exports include hides, some live cattle, and a few egret plumes from the Llanos and gold, balata, chicle, and tonka beans from the Guiana Highlands. All other towns of the Llanos are local commercial foci and seem destined to achieve little more than local significance. The next largest town after Ciudad Bolívar is Maturín with a population of around 15,000. Between Ciudad Bolívar in the south and Maturín in the north there has been some oil development. Although a pipe line is being constructed from the Areo Mercy field north of Ciudad Bolívar to Barcelona, these fields are largely in the development stage and their future is one of conjecture. Increased oil production would doubtless aid in the growth of Maturín. Unless some such economic development does take place, it seems unlikely that Maturín's population will increase greatly. San Fernando, far to the west of Ciudad Bolívar, is the center of an important grazing district and also the center of the now decadent egret-plume industry. It has a population of around 10,000 but seems unlikely to witness any great development in the immediate future.

The Guiana Highlands.—The Guiana Highlands of Venezuela is a region largely unknown and unexplored (Fig. 20). Isolated as it is from the heart of the country, it presents an economic enigma. Gold and diamonds have been found in some of the better known districts, and this has led some to believe that here is the land of El Dorado which the early Spanish were seeking. Large and rich deposits of iron ore are known but as yet are undeveloped. To some it might seem that this area would afford a highland refuge from the hot tropical lowlands, but this appears unlikely. Although some elevations exceed 8,000 feet, most of the area is less than 2,000 feet above sea level. This is hardly sufficient to give much relief in these latitudes. Moreover, the region is one of heavy rains (40 to 80 inches), is covered with a dense tropical forest, and has a very rugged surface. Under the combination of these unfavorable conditions, it seems unlikely that this section of the country will witness any marked development in the immediate future. Rather, the Guiana Highlands will probably continue as they are today: an area of exceedingly sparse population (probably not more than one person to each 4 square miles); a region of scattered, subsistence, patch agriculture; a section yielding a few forest products; and a gold-mining district of some importance.

The forests of the highlands possess many tropical woods, but these are entirely unexploited. The forests yield only three products of importance, all of which enter export trade. These are: (1) balata, used among other things for the manufacture of golf-ball covers, (2) tonka beans, used as a perfume base, and (3) chicle, used in the manufacture of chewing gum.

Gold mining, which yields an important item to Venezuela's export trade, is an old industry of the Guiana Highlands (Fig. 22). It is a product that, because of its high value in relation to its bulk, can stand shipment charges from remote areas, but lack of transportation facilities even in this industry is a handicap. Much of the gold is obtained by quartz mining, and getting machinery into the area is no simple matter. Obtaining and keeping labor in this hot malarial region is also a difficult problem. Most of the gold is produced in the vicinity of the Yuruari River in eastern Venezuela. The famous El Callao mine (Fig. 22), located in this area, was the richest gold mine in the world in 1885, yielding some $200,000 per month. It has long since ceased operations, but the region is still an important producer with nearly all operations in the hands of British companies.

TRANSPORTATION PATTERN

The developed transportation facilities of a country are frequently a good index of its degree of economic maturity. This principle applied to Venezuela indicates a country in a very youthful stage of economic development. Except for a few short rail lines between the cities of the northern highlands and the port towns and some short lines between the highland cities of the east, rail lines are almost entirely lacking (Fig. 23). In fact, there are only about 600 miles of railroads of varying-size gauge in all Venezuela, and none of these lines taps the interior regions of the country. Highways, although affording more mileage and thereby giving access to greater territory than the railroads, are extremely inadequate. There are some 5,500 miles of roads in the country, but only 2,000 of these miles are surfaced. By far the most important road is the Transandean Route across the Northern Highlands (Fig. 23). In many cases, as has been pointed out previously, highways parallel and compete with established rail lines, frequently to the disadvantage of the latter. Away from roads and railroads, transportation depends entirely on pack animals.

The development of an adequate transportation system has been delayed by many conditions. Railroads in particular have been slow in expanding because of the tremendous expense involved in their construction. The little railroad (but the

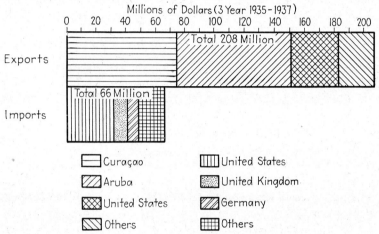

FIG. 26.—Import and export trade of Venezuela, by countries.

principal one of the country) between Caracas and Valencia (114 miles) has 219 bridges and viaducts and cost $135,000 a mile to build. The small amount of goods to be moved, the sparsity of the population, the low purchasing power of the people, and the difficulties of an unfavorable climate in many sections have been further retarding influences.

FOREIGN TRADE

The foreign trade of Venezuela is a significant item in the country's economic structure. Largely owing to the increasing importance of oil, trade averages around $250,000,000 per year, of which about one-fourth is made up of imports and three-fourths are exports. Venezuela thus has a striking export balance. The United States provides nearly half of all Venezuela's imports and takes about one-sixth of her direct exports (Fig. 26). The United Kingdom and Netherlands also have important trade relations with the area.

Practically all of Venezuela's exports are raw materials (Fig. 27); petroleum and its products makes up 80 to 85 per cent of the total; coffee accounts for 5 to 10 per cent; and cacao and gold, each, account for about 1 to 2 per cent. Imports are extremely diversified but are, in general, foodstuffs and manufactured goods. The only item that accounts for as much as 5 per cent of the total

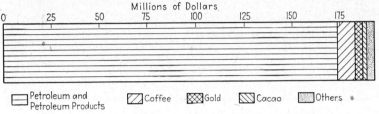

Millions of Dollars

☐ Petroleum and Petroleum Products   ☐ Coffee   ☒ Gold   ☒ Cacao   ☒ Others

FIG. 27.—Principal products exported from Venezuela.

is cotton fabrics. This product usually accounts for 6 to 9 per cent of all imported goods.

The Guiana Colonies

Throughout a large part of the colonial period in America, British, French, and Dutch ships preyed upon Spanish vessels that were engaged in trade with the Spanish colonies, and fleets belonging to these powers repeatedly attacked Spanish and Portuguese colonies. In that period, Spain and Portugal controlled virtually all of South America. The British and French controlled nothing on the mainland. The Dutch, however, gained a foothold in Guiana. But as the outcome of three centuries of struggle, Spain and Portugal now hold no possessions in South America, and their old enemies—Great Britain, Netherlands, and France—have three small tropical colonies—British Guiana, Dutch Guiana, and French Guiana. These are the only European possessions in all continental South America. They first attained importance as suppliers of tobacco. Later, sugar plantations were established utilizing slave labor. In fact, descendants of some of these early slaves make up a significant part of the present population of Dutch Guiana. They have settled in remote interior sections, outside of Dutch governmental control, and follow a way of life much like that of their African ancestors. These so-called Bush Negroes gain a livelihood by carrying on migratory cropping supplemented with products from forest and stream.

They remain completely apart from the rest of the population of the colony and show little evidence of ever becoming assimilated.

The Guianas, aside from a low coastal strip some 25 or 30 miles wide and except for a few minerals, are of little economic importance. The land along the coast, if properly drained and freshened, is fertile and well suited to a variety of tropical plantation crops. Interior regions, primarily because of transportation difficulties, are largely unexplored. Although rivers tap this area, falls and bars interfere seriously with navigation. Climate also delays development of both the coastal margins and the interior. Heat and humidity combine to produce particularly enervating conditions. Although trade winds provide some relief along the seacoast, temperatures are always high, and rainfall everywhere exceeds 60 inches per year.

BRITISH GUIANA

The Colony.—Portions of the Guiana colonies passed back and forth from British to Dutch and Dutch to British several times during the colonizing period. The present colony of British Guiana was ceded to the British by the Netherlands in 1803. In point of size, the colony is actually larger than England and Scotland combined, but it has fewer people than the little island of Jamaica. It is the most sparsely populated of all the British colonies in America. The capital, Georgetown, has a population of 66,000.

Of the 320,000 people in the colony, about 95 per cent are Negroes and Asiatics, and persons of mixed races. There are a considerable group of Portuguese and about 4,000 other persons of European stock. The Indian aborigines are declining in numbers; only a few thousand remain in the interior. The Negroes are descended from African slaves who were brought to the New World to supply labor for the tropical plantations and who were freed in British Guiana in 1834. The Asiatics are in part descendants of Chinese laborers who were imported prior to 1867; but most of them are East Indians or Hindus who were brought in as indentured laborers. In the hot and sultry climate, they are inefficient and lacking in physical stamina. Tropical maladies are common, for there is widespread apathy in regard to sanitary conditions.

Half the colony is lowland, partly forest-covered and partly savanna or grassland. Only a narrow strip, 5 or 6 miles wide along the coast and river banks, is under cultivation. This does not total over 200,000 acres, or about three-tenths of 1 per cent of the land of the colony. An Englishman, writing of the cultivable land of British Guiana, says:

"It was they (the Dutch) who rendered it possible for us (the British) to utilize these amazingly fertile lowlands which form the sugar-producing portions of the colony. 'Every acre has been the scene of a struggle with the sea in front and the floods behind'; and the whole system of embankments, canals, and sluices to which we owe the safety from inundation, and the possibility of cultivating our coast and riverside lands is due to Dutch skill, industry, and perseverance."[1]

Between 1917 and 1922, the colony expended $4,500,000 on the maintenance of the works necessary to protect the low agricultural lands from inundation. In the interior are rugged mountains belonging to the Guiana Highland already referred to in connection with Venezuela. There are dense forests containing many species of trees of commercial value; but, like all the tropical forests of South America, they are yielding only a few commercial products, the chief of which is balata, gathered only under government license. More than 3,000 laborers are at times engaged in collecting this substance.

It is the lament of the English that the colony is unable to attract the capital and labor essential to its development, and the colony makes little progress. It is an interesting fact that the Island of Trinidad, a British colony not far from Guiana, having only one-fiftieth as much land, actually has a greater production. There are a few short narrow-gauge railroads with a total length of about 100 miles, also 300 miles of fair or good roads, and nearly 500 miles of inland navigable waters.

Commercial Products.—Great Britain has always encouraged the raising of sugar cane in her tropical colonies. Sugar is the chief crop of British Guiana, occupying one-third of the land under cultivation. It yields nearly 200,000 tons of sugar a year, which is more than Venezuela produces. Next in importance is rice, whose cultivation greatly increased after the East Indian laborers were brought in; for they use rice as the chief item in

[1] Chalmers, Sir David. British Guiana, *Scot. Geog. Mag.*, vol. 12, p. 126, 1896.

their diet. The sugar estates, of which there are about fifty, are scarcely able to produce sugar at the low prices which the great modern plantations in Cuba and Puerto Rico find reasonably profitable (Fig. 28).

At one time, gold mining was an industry of some importance; later, when diamonds were discovered, many gold miners turned diamond hunters and met with considerable success. For a time, the diamond export was valued at some $2,000,000 or $3,000,000 annually and constituted British Guiana's second most valuable export. High prices for gold in recent years have stimulated its

Fig. 28.—Sugar cane in the low coastal plain of British Guiana. (*Courtesy of Otis P. Starkey.*)

production again. In 1937, about $1,000,000 worth was exported as compared with only about $500,000 worth of diamonds. Another mineral of increasing importance is bauxite, the principal ore of aluminum. Production, which in 1937 amounted to over 300,000 metric tons, is in the hands of the Aluminum Company of America and the British Aluminum Company. The ore is exceptionally high grade, and extensive deposits are available. Two areas, one along the Demerara River and the other along the Berbice River, are the principal producing centers.

Trade of the colony is very insignificant, amounting to a total of only some $10,000,000 or $12,000,000. Per capita trade of $33, though, is much higher than in most South American countries.

Three-fourths of the exports go to the British Isles and Canada, and only a small part to the United States.

On the whole, British Guiana, with its monotonously hot climate, its colored population, and its inability to attract immigrants or to maintain a sufficient supply of labor, is making slow progress, and its future does not seem encouraging.

DUTCH GUIANA (SURINAM)

This colony, of which much was once expected, has proved to have no attraction for colonists and is nearly at a standstill in economic development. In the settlement of one of the many wars of the seventeenth century, the Netherlands gave up New Amsterdam (New York) to the English in exchange for the colony of Dutch Guiana. At that date (1667), tropical colonies were more highly valued than those in colder climates, and South America was considered more promising than North America. New York is now the metropolis of the New World, and Dutch Guiana, or Surinam, is an almost forgotten spot somewhere on the coast of South America. Its area (58,000 square miles) would make four countries the size of Netherlands. Its 166,000 people are mainly Negroes, Asiatics, and half-castes; there are less than 2,000 whites. A few tribes of uncivilized Indians occupy the interior. The capital Paramaribo has a population of 50,000 people.

Cultivation is confined to reclaimed lands and other lowlands lying near the sea and a short distance up the rivers. In all, only 50,000 or 60,000 acres are devoted to crops, no one of which is produced in any quantity. Sugar leads the list, followed by cacao and coffee. The forests, like those of other tropical lowlands in South America, supply balata, and a few mines are still worked for small quantities of gold. Bauxite is also of some importance. Production in 1937 amounted to 392,000 metric tons, an increase of some 64 per cent over the preceding year. The principal deposits are located in the Paramaribo region in an area 15 to 100 miles from the coast. All of them are worked or controlled by the Aluminum Company of America.

Netherlands has a group of three small but commercially important islands off the coast of Venezuela. Of these, Curaçao is the most important. It is a leading port of call and one of the principal transshipping points in the Caribbean.

FRENCH GUIANA

French Guiana is the least important of the three Guiana colonies. Of its 35,000 square miles of land, only 12 or 14 square miles are under cultivation. The capital Cayenne has a mixed population of 14,000. A part of the colony is used as a penal settlement for habitual criminals sent from France. Its products are similar to those of the other two colonies, but French Guiana provides little for export, having an exportable surplus valued at only about $1,000,000.

Chapter IV. Ecuador

Ecuador, a country with considerable potentiality, is in a low stage of economic development. The present status is linked closely with the rise and fall of a one-crop agricultural industry. Once in first place in cacao production, contributing one-third of the world's total, Ecuador has declined to seventh place and supplies less than 3 per cent of the world's cacao. Although cacao is still the country's leading export, the relative importance and absolute value of the crop have changed greatly in the last quarter century. From an average peak of around 100 million pounds annually before 1921, production declined rapidly to 24 million pounds in 1933, from which point it rose to 45 million pounds in 1937 (Fig. 29). The bankrupt, disunited, and undeveloped character of the country today is not due entirely to the decline in the importance of cacao; the facts that production decreased so rapidly, especially in the face of increasing world demands for the commodity, and that no crop or industry has taken its place, are indicative of the economic backwardness of the nation.

That the country is backward cannot be denied. With an area of 60,000 square miles west of the Andean crest and another 120,000 square miles east of the mountains (although control of this eastern territory is disputed with Peru), Ecuador is by no means the smallest country of South America (Fig. 30). From the standpoint of productivity, though, Ecuador ranks low and its per capita trade is the smallest of all the states of the continent.

Many conditions, of both human and natural origin, handicap Ecuador, but the land is not without advantages. Along the west coast is one of the potentially richest districts of tropical South America. Soil, sun, and rain combine in many parts of the 30,000

95

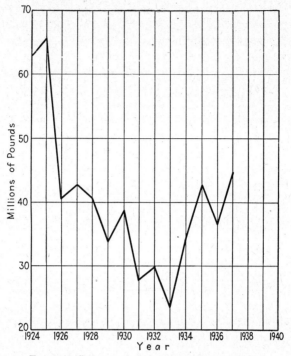

Fig. 29.—Cacao production, Ecuador, 1924–1937.

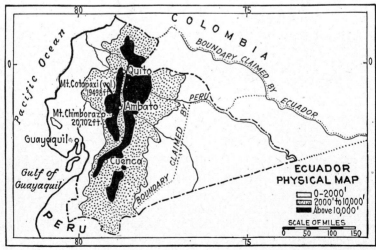

Fig. 30.—Map showing the highlands and lowlands of Ecuador. (*Altitudes according to Goode.*)

square miles of the coastal plain to favor the production of a great variety of tropical crops. Many are grown, but the land is far from being effectively utilized. Cacao, coffee, cotton, and banana acreage could be enormously increased and yields greatly improved. In the highland valleys, total agricultural production could also be much greater, if less primitive methods were used in preparing the fields, planting, and harvesting. The eastern part of the country, beyond the Andean crest, seems to afford little opportunity for economic development. Its inaccessibility from the rest of Ecuador is a tremendous handicap. Until the other regions of the country are more fully utilized, the Amazon-basin area would seem to be of only small value to the country.

Unfortunately for Ecuador, disadvantages far outweigh advantages at the present time. The answer to the why of the nation's retarded economic development is not a simple one, but there is no denying that many of the difficulties are of human origin. Failure to maintain cacao production at its once high level, when market demands justified it and when natural conditions favored expansion, inability to foresee the result of an excessive tax levy on the crop, neglect of plantations by absentee landholders, lack of initiative or interest in developing some other crop or industry to replace cacao, and inattention to the building of an adequate transportation system—all these can be charged in large measure against the Ecuadoreans and not against their environment. From this, the impression must not be gained that the country is one without natural environmental handicaps. There are many and serious problems of a natural character to be solved, but for the most part they are not insoluble.

THE PROBLEM OF DISUNITY

One of the major problems to be solved in Ecuador is that of disunity. The various productive regions are neither coordinated nor connected to a degree sufficient either to give economic solidarity or to permit efficient utilization of the country's resources. Disunity, in part, goes back to the separation of Ecuador from Spanish rule and later from the republic of Colombia. In the Spanish colonial period, the region now occupied by Ecuador was the Presidencia of Quito, somewhat larger in extent than the present republic. After a long struggle, extending from 1809 to 1820, Quito obtained its independence from Spain and joined

New Granada and Venezuela in forming the first republic of Colombia. But Ecuador (like Venezuela) withdrew from the union in 1830 and formed the republic of the Equator, which is the significance of the word Ecuador. Wars with both Peru and Colombia followed, and Ecuador yielded some of the territory that it had claimed. Boundary disputes with all its neighbors arose. The dispute with Colombia has been adjusted in so far as it concerns these two countries, but a large area in the unsettled and scarcely explored eastern section is still in dispute among the three countries.

The neutral observer cannot escape the feeling that the secession of Ecuador from Colombia and her decision to attempt a separate national existence were based upon sentiment more than upon reason. There was a historical, but not a geographical basis for this action; for there had been a separate Presidencia of Quito during the colonial period, and this gave a basis for the nationalistic aspirations of its people. The nation has been formed and now has a right to continue, though small, poor, and struggling. Once having been a nation, its people could not persuade themselves to be anything less. But this "sovereign nation" has to exist on revenues that would scarcely maintain a medium-sized American city. Since the country became independent, it has shared the experiences of most of its sister republics, namely, frequent revolutions or attempted revolutions, considerable bloodshed, very little immigration, little money for education or for public improvements, difficulties with its creditors, and retarded progress; yet there has been progress.

Unification is made more difficult by the physical structure of the country. There are three major physical provinces quite different from each other in economic development, in productive capacity, and in kinds of product grown. Along the coast is a hot, sultry plain (Fig. 31). This plain is well drained along the seaward slope of the Andes, but wet and poorly drained in the west. Climate varies from a desert type in the south to tropical rain forest conditions with heavy rainfall (60 to 80 inches) in the north. The fertile soils of this area aid in the production of a great variety of tropical and subtropical crops, many of which enter export trade. East of the Western Lowlands is Highland Ecuador, a region composed of two great Andean ranges between which is a basin divided by mountain spurs into separate valleys.

The climate of the highlands is modified greatly by elevation. Although athwart the equator, temperatures in the high valleys average about 55°F. the year around, and annual rainfall amounts to some 40 or 50 inches. This area is quite different in its economic development from the lowlands. It is a region essentially of cereal production and subsistence agriculture. East of the Andean mountains is the Transandean Lands (Oriente) section of Ecuador. The Transandean Lands is an area almost completely separated

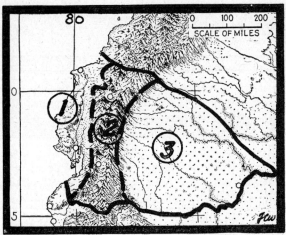

FIG. 31.—Regional map of Ecuador. 1, Western Lowlands; 2, Highland Ecuador; 3, Transandean Lands. (*Base map, courtesy of Guy-Harold Smith.*)

from the other regions by the massive, lofty, and steep Eastern Cordillera. These isolated equatorial lowlands are in a primitive stage of economic development.

These three regions (Western Lowlands, Highland Ecuador, and Transandean Lands) are not connected by adequate transportation facilities. The cordillera is so difficult to cross that it constitutes a formidable barrier between the coastlands of the west and the montaña of the east, and relatively few of the people of Ecuador have seen both sides. The Andes are very high in Ecuador and have no less than 22 great volcanic peaks, partly active and partly quiescent, attaining heights exceeding 3 miles. No highway or railroad crosses both ranges, and there is little intercourse between the eastern and western parts of the country.

Throughout the whole 2,500 miles of the tropical Andes, there are only occasional stretches of roads suitable for wheeled vehicles. For the most part, travel and transportation are carried on by mules or llamas over trails that have existed for hundreds of years and that connect towns and settlements, as main highways do in the United States. The trails are merely narrow paths that wind and zigzag along a valley or up the face of a slope, working their difficult way up one valley to a pass in the range, and then similarly down into the next valley, soon to begin another ascent. In the wet season, the trails are slippery and dangerous and are likely to become a sort of earth ladder of humps and hollows, as the feet of the mules wear deep holes in the muddy path. Often the trail follows a narrow shelf worn in the sheer face of the mountain, with a yawning chasm below and a frowning wall above. From time to time, a mule loses his footing and plunges down the precipice, carrying his load with him.

The carrying of goods and passengers is a regular occupation of a class known as *arrieros*, usually mestizos or Indians who have more or less standardized prices over the established trails. They compete actively with the railroad where one exists, and a mule train may be seen carrying bags and bundles along a trail parallel to the railway, and doing so at the same rate as the railway charges. In fact, in Ecuador, the *arrieros* insist upon using the railroad as a trail and drive their mule trains along the right of way. In parts of the more mountainous sections where population is very sparse and only small quantities of products seek an outside market, the mule train is the most economical means of transport, better fitted to the environment than either vehicles or railroads. But when the tonnage of goods to be moved rises to any considerable quantity, the mule train is, of course, inadequate. Assuming the average mule load to be 200 pounds and the distance covered to be 25 miles a day, the mule's achievement is $2\frac{1}{2}$ ton-miles a day. A light freight train of 15 cars, carrying an average of 8 tons to the car, will cover, even in the mountainous sections, an average of 70 miles, or 8,400 ton-miles a day, equivalent to the work of 3,300 mules.

Ecuador has about 700 miles of railroads, a mileage small even for South American countries (Fig. 32). Of this, 280 miles are included in the line completed in 1908, extending from Durán, across the river from Guayaquil, to Quito. This principal railway of the country was a long time in building and was finally carried to completion by an energetic American engineer. Financially, the road has been a failure, and its first mortgage bonds have sold as low as 30 cents on the dollar. Traffic is very light, and earnings are correspondingly small. Passenger trains do not run during the night and require 2 days to make the 280-mile trip between Durán and Quito. The road, however, is a genuine benefit to Ecuador and has helped to quicken the economic life of the country.

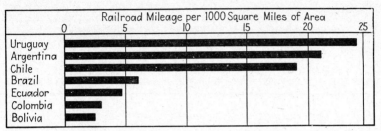

Fig. 32.—Railroad mileage per 1000 square miles of area, 1929.

The engineering difficulties involved in constructing this railroad may be judged from the following account:

"About 58 miles from Guayaquil, the climb into the sierra begins, and the trains from this point are shorter and are handled by heavier locomotives. The railway after a short climb enters the Chan-Chan Valley, which is followed along a route laid out under great engineering difficulties. The curves on this section are extremely wide and numerous, and the grade reaches $4\frac{1}{2}$ per cent. The railway, in a general way, is laid out along the route of a torrential river, which is crossed and recrossed at various points. At an approximate altitude of 4,000 feet, the city of Huigra is reached; from this point, a rugged, broken country is entered, and wonderful engineering feats had to be performed in making the climb up the Andine slopes. Along this section of the railway is located the Devil's Nose, where the line enters a deep gorge. In this gorge, the line comes to an abrupt end, and the trains have to be backed up over a switch along a ledge blasted out of the face of the precipice. By this means. a higher ledge is reached and forward progress is again possible. The Alausi Loop, at an altitude of 8,553 feet, is another splendid engineering feat. The road then climbs to the Palmira Pass, 10,600 feet above the sea. Then there is a slight descent to Riobamba, one of the largest towns in Ecuador, located at an altitude of 9,020 feet. There is another heavy climb from that place to the Chimborazo Pass, the altitude of 11,841 feet being the highest point reached on the entire line. The railway then drops to Ambato, 8,435 feet, located in the center of a well-cultivated district, reclimbs to the base of Mount Cotopaxi, 11,653 feet, and enters the Machachi Valley, reaching Quito at 9,375 feet elevation."[1]

In addition to the line from Durán to Quito, there are several short railroads which are being slowly extended as funds are available. Their total length is approximately 400 miles.

The following illustration of the enthusiasm with which a temperamental people are likely to begin a great public undertaking and the slow progress which it may make afterward is found in the history of the Ambato to Curaray Railway, a government project. In 1904, the president of the republic authorized the railroad to be built at once and secured from the United States nine experienced engineers, who came to Ecuador to make the surveys and select the route. In 1906, construction was begun but was soon discontinued. In 1912, 8 years after the authorization of the railroad, the actual inauguration of the work took place. In 1924, 20 years after its official authorization, 25 of the 72 miles between Ambato and the Curaray River had been completed, an average progress of about 2 miles a year.

With all these difficulties, the unification of Ecuador would seem to be attainable only in the distant future. Until roads and railroads are constructed that effectively connect the diverse regions of the country and until the great natural barriers have been conquered, only a partial realization of Ecuador's resources is possible. Capital for the extension of transportation facilities must come in large measure from agricultural products. Mineral resources are scant, and manufacturing is little developed. In fact, lacking minerals, capital, and transportation lines, manufacturing can assume little more than local significance.

Unlike its neighbors on the north and south, Ecuador is not an important producer of minerals. Some interest has developed in the oil fields of western Ecuador, but the output of oil is not large, scarcely one-tenth as great as that of the oil fields of Peru across the boundary. It is a unique fact that a part of the oil is obtained by digging open pits or wells to a depth as great as 100 feet. Into these wells, small quantities of oil seep and are dipped out from time to time. Such wells may yield a few gallons to

[1] Halsey, F. M. Investments in Latin America and the British West Indies, *Special Agents Series* 169, pp. 285–286, U.S. Dept. of Commerce, Washington, D.C., 1918.

several barrels a day. There is one gold-mining region, Zaruma, that produces rather steadily a half-million dollars' worth of gold yearly. It lies in the southern part of the country, back in the mountains away from any railroad, and the ore must be carried 40 miles by mules. This region has produced gold since early Spanish days. Beds of low-grade coal have been located in several places, but no actual mining on a commercial scale is in progress. The inferior quality of the coal, the great cost of mining it in out-of-the-way mountain valleys, and the absence of suitable transportation—all combine to discourage mining operations. Very little is known of the possible resources of coal or other minerals, and mineral production is less than in any other Andean country.

Ecuador lacks most of the essentials for the development of manufacturing. The small importance of manufacturing is indicated by the industrial census. At present, the leading manufactured products include cotton and wool textiles (19),[1] shoes (3), cement (1), flour (28), cigars and cigarettes (17), sugar (23), rum and other alcoholic beverages, "Panama" hats,[2] soap (22), candles (12), furniture, leathers (8), rope, matches, and petroleum refining (4). This seems to be a formidable array, but of these articles only the Panama hats represent an item of export significance. Most of the factories are small-scale and supply only local markets.

Ecuador's export trade is essentially in agricultural products which account for at least 60 per cent of all exports. Since other resources are largely lacking, it would seem that the country's development turns on a fuller utilization of her agricultural lands. The problems that involve the expansion of agriculture, though, are better understood on a regional basis; for they differ in the various sections of the country, and it is only in terms of a more detailed analysis of the regional pattern that they can be fully comprehended.

ECUADOR—THE REGIONAL PATTERN

As was mentioned previously, there are three major physical regions in Ecuador—(1) the Western Lowlands, (2) Highland

[1] Figures in parentheses indicate the number of factories in each case where information is available.

[2] The production of Panama hats is entirely a household industry.

Ecuador, and (3) the Transandean Lands (Fig. 31). These three areas, partly owing to marked contrasts in the character of the natural and the human environment or perhaps owing to a different combination of the elements in the environments, present various problems of development.

The Western Lowlands.—The principal resource of the coastal plain along the Pacific is the region's capacity to produce a variety of tropical crops. Although there are some subsistence farming and a grazing industry of minor importance in the Western Lowlands, emphasis is on commercial farming. Economic activity centers in the production of cacao and coffee and in the export of these commodities into world markets. Cotton, bananas, rice, and sugar attain minor commercial importance. The heavily forested slopes of the Andes supply three forest products of some significance: (1) the tagua palm yields ivory nuts; (2) the toquilla palm supplies the fiber used in the manufacture of Panama hats, and (3) rubber. The prosperity of the region depends in large measure on its success in the production of these various commodities. Among all, cacao is by far the most important.

Cacao Production.—As analysis of the rise and fall of cacao production reveals much of the economic history of Ecuador. Cacao cultivation was (and is) favored by: (1) a climate in which temperatures are always high (70 to 93°F.) and in which there is an average of 70 inches of rain during the year so distributed that there is a short dry season which favors ripening; (2) large areas with fertile clay loam soils; (3) easy and cheap river transportation by canoes, rafts, launches, and shallow-draft steamboats which bring the beans to Guayaquil for export; and (4) cheap labor.

Despite these favorable conditions, decrease in the importance of cacao has been rapid, and the industry has been in a depressed state for many years (Fig. 29). Disease attacked the cacao trees and perhaps to some extent hastened the decline; but there were many human factors that seem more important, and many of these difficulties might have been avoided.

The size of the landholdings and the attitude of the landlords toward their holdings helped bring economic disaster to Ecuador. One-twelfth of the population owns the land. Many of these people do not live in Ecuador but entrust the operation of their plantations to overseers. This has resulted in careless methods of

Fig. 33.—Modern equipment for drying cacao beans in Ecuador. The low, flat cars may be run under sheds at night or during a shower. Most plantations use more primitive methods. (*Copyright Ewing Galloway, N. Y.*)

production. Where once Ecuador had the reputation of producing only high-grade cacao, this reputation has been endangered by careless methods of harvesting (Fig. 33). Ripe and green beans are mixed together with a resulting decline in quality. Partly owing to neglect of the owners, too, new planting did not keep pace with increasing world demands.

In the face of rising prices and the quasi monopoly the country enjoyed, Ecuador made the fatal mistake of placing an excessive export duty on cacao. This, combined with rather unstable political conditions and the apparently disinterested attitude of the country toward expansion of cacao acreage, resulted in new capital going to other areas. Thus, not only was the country deprived of new cacao lands and additional capital, but other producing regions were developed which in time competed with Ecuador in world markets and eventually surpassed her. The industry, once having gained a foothold elsewhere, now threatens Ecuador's economic life. The Guinea coast of Africa, for example, is highly suited to cacao, and production costs are low. It seems unlikely that Ecuador will ever be able to regain her former position. It would seem that economic prosperity for Ecuador lies in the substitution of some other crop for cacao or, at least, in a greater diversification of agriculture. That the country has failed as yet to change her economy to meet the new conditions indicates its backward state, for there are many tropical products that might be grown more extensively in the area. Of these, coffee seems to offer the greatest promise.

Coffee.—Coffee is second in importance to cacao as an export commodity. Its value to the export trade is around $2,250,000 or about one-half that of cacao. Plantations are confined primarily to the western flank of the Andes at elevations somewhat higher than those devoted to cacao. Planting is increasing, and there is much room for expansion; but unfortunately much of the coffee is of poor quality owing to careless production methods.

Other Commercial Crops.—Along the upper Guayas River, there is some cotton raised. Production has attained only minor significance owing largely to primitive and careless farming methods. Sugar is also raised in the region. Much of it reaches the market in the form of rum. Banana plantations are being developed, and bananas now are exported to the amount of some 3,000 to 4,000 bunches annually. A little rice also enters export trade.

Forest Products.—Three forest products add to the material wealth of the Western Lowlands, but none of these seems to promise increased importance in the future.

The tagua palm provides "vegetable ivory" from the hard white kernel of its seed. The chief use of the ivory is in the manufacture of buttons. The tagua palm grows in the tropical forest, and the seeds are gathered by natives. Unless the tagua palm should become a plantation crop, there is little likelihood that production will expand in any significant way.

There is one manufactured article for which Ecuador is justly famous, and that is the so-called Panama hat, given that name because most of the hats are shipped to Panama on their way to the United States and Europe. They have been made for centuries by the Indians, especially by natives of the region just north of the Gulf of Guayaquil, the finest hats coming from the towns of Jipijapa and Monte Cristi. The material comes from the broad leaves of the toquilla palm. Sometimes the fiber that is used is as fine as thread. Some of these hats have sold for $150 each. Even the coarser hats usually sell in the United States for $10 to $25 each, although the patient Indian who laboriously weaves them may have received not more than a dollar or two. It is said that the better hats are woven only when the atmosphere is damp. Exportation of Panama hats from Ecuador has exceeded 40,000 dozen a year, but the quantity has fallen off recently.

The only other forest product of any significance is rubber. It enters export trade in only a minor way ($368,000[1] in 1937), and there seems little likelihood that its importance will increase. All of it is obtained from wild trees, and plantation production in competition with other areas seems a remote possibility.

Commercial Activity and Commercial Foci of the Western Low-lands.—The export trade of Ecuador is confined almost entirely to products of the Western Lowlands; 90 per cent of the imports and 60 to 70 per cent of the exports pass through the port of Guayaquil (Fig. 34). Guayaquil (estimated population 140,000 in 1937) is the largest city and most important commercial cen-

---

[1] This figure is the total export of rubber from Ecuador. Since most of that exported from the Transandean Lands goes down the Amazon River, this figure represents essentially the rubber of the coastal area.

ter of the country. It is located at the head of ocean navigation on the Guayas River in the most productive and most densely populated district of the thinly populated Western Lowlands. Probably less than 700,000 people live in the whole region, and nearly all of these live in the river valleys tributary to the Guayas and within 75 miles of Guayaquil. To speak of commercial foci in the Western Lowlands is to employ somewhat of a misnomer, since Guayaquil is the only such center of significance.

Export trade of the country, which has averaged about $13,000,000 per year between 1934 and 1937, has been going

Fig. 34.—Launches racing to meet boat anchored in deeper part of the Guayas river, Guayaquil.

primarily to three countries—the United States (40 per cent), Germany (13 per cent), and France (12 per cent). Imports, which have averaged $10,000,000 per year for the same period, come chiefly from the United States (33 per cent), Germany (18 per cent), and Great Britain (11 per cent). A country that produces only a little more than the needs of its own people can have little to export and hence is able to import little. In a mountain-ribbed country like Ecuador, a majority of whose people are living on a low economic plane, it is quite out of the question to keep abreast of the progressive commercial nations. If Ecuador's participation in world trade is proportionately smaller now than 50 years ago, it means that the little country is progressing more slowly than the world as a whole.

Highland Ecuador.—Highland Ecuador is much less important than the Western Lowlands from a commercial standpoint, but far more significant in its ability to support a relatively dense population. At least three-fourths of the country's population of 2,800,000 live in the valleys between the two great ranges of the Andes (Fig. 35). Isolated as various sections of the highlands are from each other and from the rest of the country, emphasis is on subsistence agriculture. Wheat, corn, barley, beans, and potatoes are the leading crops. On the upper highlands, grazing attains local importance.

FIG. 35.—View of plateau in Ecuador. Mt. Chimborazo is in the background. (*Courtesy of Philadelphia Commercial Museum.*)

Unless the primitive farming methods of the plateau can be improved, there seems little likelihood of bettering economic conditions in the highlands, since production has about reached the maximum development under primitive methods (Fig. 36). Aside from agriculture, there are few activities within the region. There is no mining and little manufacturing of consequence. Neither are there present the potentialities for any significant development of nonagricultural enterprises.

Owing in large measure to the general subsistence character of the highlands, commercial centers are of minor importance, and their functioning is for the most part confined to small areas.

The only city of the highlands of more than local significance is the capital of the country, Quito (estimated population in 1937, 118,000). Although the political function of Quito gives the city an interregional importance, the isolation of the capital from other portions of the country weakens rather than strengthens the unity of Ecuador. Quito is connected by rail with Guayaquil (at Durán), but service is available only on alternate days.

Fig. 36.—An Indian farmer and his wife plowing with the wooden plow common in the tropical Andes. Modern farming implements are wholly unknown to most of the mountain Indians. (*Copyright Ewing Galloway, N. Y.*)

The Transandean Lands.—The lowlands of the east, isolated as they are from the rest of Ecuador and their ownership disputed with Peru, are almost entirely undeveloped. This area is connected with the highlands by only a few trails which become muddy and treacherous during the rainy season. The eastern slope of the Andes is so steep that road and trail building is exceedingly difficult. Inhabitants of the area probably number not more than 75,000, most of whom are Indians. The only commercial product from the area is rubber, most of which is shipped eastward down the Amazon and not through Ecuador. The Transandean Lands is one of the most isolated and undeveloped sections of all South America.

Chapter V. Peru

Peru is one of the most interesting and complex of the South American countries. In the deserts of the coastal plain and on the plateau of Peru and neighboring countries, some of the earliest civilizations of the Americas developed. In the highlands

FIG. 37.—Ruins of an Inca structure at Ollantai tambo, Peru. The massive stones were quarried, shaped, and fitted by a people who knew nothing of iron or steel.

of this country, with the capital at Cuzco, the Incas built their famous empire at least three centuries before the coming of Columbus. The Incas and their predecessors, who once possessed these lands, built marvelous stone structures (Fig. 37), paved roads, terraced mountain sides (Fig. 38), and developed irrigation works. A tribute to their masterful work, there remain throughout the country numerous ruins that are wonders of the

111

ancient American world. The greatest architects have marveled at the buildings of Machu Picchu, the Temple of the Sun at Cuzco, and the great fortress of Sacsahuaman (Fig. 39).

FIG. 38.—Terraces of early Indian civilization, Pisac. (*Courtesy of Mattie Sue Walker.*)

FIG. 39.—Ruins of the old fortress of Sacsahuaman.

In 1531–1532, Francisco Pizarro with a few hundred soldiers overthrew the Incas. He and his successors reduced the native peoples to the pitiable condition in which their descendants now are. Peru became the most thoroughly Castilian of the colonies. It was the first viceroyalty established by Spain in the South American continent, and Lima was created as the capital. Products from the southern and southeastern parts of the continent were routed through Peru, and this further enhanced the importance of the viceroyalty. The desirable lands passed into the possession of influential families and are still held largely by the descendants of those families; and Spanish ideas regarding caste, manual labor, the church, education, and business became stamped upon Peru.

In 1821, the country declared its independence from Spain and, a few years later, began a stormy career of self-government. Like many of her sister republics, Peru has passed through a long series of political disorders, revolutions, and attempted revolutions. It also suffered a disastrous defeat at the hands of Chile in the War of the Pacific (1879–1883) and, along with her ally Bolivia, lost the immensely valuable strip of coastland that contains the nitrate of soda deposits and now belongs to Chile.

Considering the highly developed stage of the early civilization and the exalted position given Peru by Spain in the colonial period, it would seem that this country should be one of the leaders in wealth and in influence among the South American republics. But although Peru is a fairly large country, with about 500,000 square miles,[1] it has but 6,000,000 people and its total wealth is relatively small. Few people visit it, and its total annual foreign trade for recent years is less than $150,000,000. This is only about one-fourth that of Brazil and less than one-sixth that of Argentina. It is rich in certain natural resources; but they are poorly developed, and industrial activity is exceedingly small. It has a favorable balance of trade, but much of the profits go to foreign investors. A greater amount of internal development in Peru by its own people would make it a more prosperous and progressive nation.

Peru has the three major physiographic provinces characteristic of the west-coast countries of South America within the tropics: (1) a narrow coastal plain, with tributary mountain

---

[1] It is impossible to give the exact area of Peru because of unsettled boundary disputes between Peru and Ecuador. Exclusive of a disputed area of 120,000 square miles lying to the east of the Andes and north of the Amazon River, the country's area is about 430,000 square miles.

valleys; (2) a massive cordillera, 200 to 250 miles in width; and
(3) an Oriente (montaña), or eastern region of dense tropical
forest, which includes more than half of the land of the country
(Fig. 40). In Colombia and in most of Ecuador, the coastlands
lie in the belt of tropical rains and are heavily forested. But in
Peru, conditions are quite the reverse, for the country lies in the
belt of the southeast trade winds, which precipitate their moisture

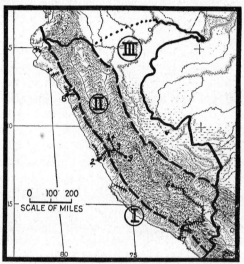

FIG. 40.—Regions, cities, and railroad lines of Peru. Regions: I, Coastal Region;
II, Cordillera; III, Eastern Peru. Cities: 1, Lima; 2, Callao; 3, Oroya; 4, Cerro de
Pasco; 5, Arequipa; 6, Cuzco; 7, Mollendo; 8, Trujillo; 9, Huancayo. (*Base map,
courtesy of Guy-Harold Smith.*)

on the eastern slopes and on the high portions of the Andes
(Fig. 41). In so far as these winds pass the mountains and descend
the western slopes to the coastal plain, they are dry winds.

Along the Peruvian coast, the winds are directed mainly by
local conditions and usually blow from the south and southwest.
Blowing thus from the cool Humboldt Current to the warm land,
they increase in temperature and are drying winds. The result
is that the coast of Peru is a desert; no crops can be grown except
by artificial irrigation, and the amount of water that can be
diverted from the 50 or more short mountain streams is the
determining factor in agriculture on this coast; and agriculture
is the dominating industry of coastal Peru.

The huge mountain wall of the Peruvian Andes has no low passes. The two railways that cross the main range do so at elevations of 14,688 and 15,665 feet, respectively. No attempt has yet been made to build a railroad across the eastern range in Peru. In the geography of this country, two factors are of primary importance: (1) the exceedingly mountainous surface

Fig. 41.—View of dissected western slope of Andes. Note the general absence of vegetation. (*Courtesy of Fortune Magazine.*)

and (2) the lack of sufficient rainfall on the Pacific slope. To these geographic handicaps, the life of the nation must be adjusted.

THE COASTAL REGION

Influence of the Humboldt Current.—Often currents are due mainly to prevailing winds which blow more or less constantly over parts of the sea. On the coast of Chile and southern Peru, these winds from the west and southwest impel the surface waters of the ocean partly against the edge of the continent and partly parallel with it from south to north. Thus, a strong north-flowing current of cold water, known as the Humboldt Current, is propelled northward along the coast of Peru and makes the temperature of the air above it many degrees cooler than the usual temperature for those latitudes. It is said that the temperature of the ocean waters off the port of Callao (latitude 12°S.) is comparable to that off New York (41°N.) and Monterey, Calif. (36°N.).[1] In the more northerly parts of Peru, the cooling influence of the current is increased by the upwelling of cold waters from the depths to replace the surface waters that the trade winds cause to drift westward across the Pacific as the Equatorial Current. At least one investigator believes that this is the main cause of the low temperature along the Peruvian coast.[2] Since the ocean is cooler than the coastlands of Peru and since the winds blow from the sea across the littoral, they are warmed rather than cooled, as previously explained, and precipitate little moisture although mists and fogs are conspicuous in the winter. Thus, the lofty Andes cut off the coast of Peru from rainfall that might come from the east, and the Humboldt Current prevents the local winds from the Pacific from delivering rainfall to the coast, and so this coast gets scarcely a shower from year end to year end.[3] In the exceptional year of 1925, frequent and very heavy rains fell for 2 months, and enormous damage was done. Twenty or more miles inland, where the land is more elevated, there is some precipitation.

Another important influence of the cool ocean current is its effect upon marine life in the waters along the Peruvian coast. "No waters in the ocean teem with life as do those on the west coast of South America."[4] The result of this upon the economic history of Peru has been far-reaching. The superabundance of the lower forms of marine life provides food for a superabundance of fish with which these waters teem. The fish, in turn, provide food for the countless thousands of sea birds that haunt these waters and breed on the islands along the coast. The excrement

[1] Coker, R. E. Ocean Temperatures off the Coast of Peru, *Geog. Rev.*, vol. 5, pp. 127–134, 1918.

[2] Murphy, Robert C. *Geog. Rev.*, vol. 13, pp. 64–85, 1923.

[3] See Bowman, Isaiah, "The Andes of Southern Peru," chap. 9, discusses the climatology of the Peruvian Andes.

[4] Buchanan, J. Y. *Proc. Royal Geog. Soc.*, vol. 8, p. 766, 1886.

of the birds and the fish waste that they leave form the valuable fertilizer known as guano, great quantities of which are found in this region. The Chincha Islands alone have yielded hundreds of millions of dollars' worth of this fertilizer.

The Guano Deposits and Their Economic Significance.—Along the coast of Peru are 38 small islands or groups of islands upon which the guano birds congregate in enormous numbers. A computation by a scientific investigator placed the number of birds on one island at nearly a million.[1] The surface of the sea and the air are literally alive with them, and steamers almost plow their way through the endless flocks of birds flying close to the water. No less than 24 species of birds frequent the islands, and 12 or more nest upon them. However, a few, particularly the cormorants, pelicans, and gannets, deposit most of the guano. It has been estimated that, at current prices, each pair of cormorants deposits guano to the value of $1.50 a year. The great naturalist Humboldt directed attention to these deposits in 1804, but shipment of guano to Europe did not begin until 1840. In later years, the shipments reached hundreds of thousands of tons a year, and a steady stream of wealth flowed into Peru. Government revenues thus easily obtained were spent lavishly and wastefully. Contracts for railways, harbor improvements, and other public works involving great sums of money were let on the strength of the future revenue from guano.

It was not long, however, before the unpleasant truth dawned that the deposits were being rapidly exhausted. The disastrous war with Chile came in 1879–1883, and Peru emerged from it virtually bankrupt, with staggering debts and her nitrate lands lost to Chile. In a settlement with foreign creditors, the guano deposits were turned over to the Peruvian Corporation (British) to the extent of 2 million tons. Removal by this corporation under laws that protect the birds had proceeded to the extent of 1½ million tons, when a disagreement arose. The Peruvian government now seeks to stop further shipment of guano abroad because the fertilizer is needed by the planters of Peru for their own land.

As a point of geographical interest, it is worth noting that not only is the Humbolt Current responsible for the abundant marine

---

[1] Coker, Robert E. The Fisheries and Guano Industry of Peru, *Bull. U.S. Bureau of Fisheries*, vol. 28, pp. 335–365, 1908.

and bird life of this coast, and hence for the vast accumulations of guano, but it is also mainly responsible for the arid climate which has preserved the deposits from being removed by rain, for the most valuable constituents would be dissolved and carried away in a humid climate. The output of guano is now between 50,000 and 75,000 tons a year, most of which is used in Peru. The guano chapter in the history of Peru may be regarded as practically closed, but the financial burdens under which Peru will long struggle are a reminder of the orgy of spending which took place during that period of her history.

The Agricultural Pattern of the Coastal Lands.—Everywhere along the west coast of South America, the mountains are close

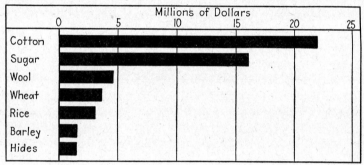

Fig. 42.—Approximate annual value of Peru's agricultural products.

to the sea, sometimes rising sharply from the water's edge and sometimes bordered by a belt of lowland. In Peru, the coastal strip has a width varying from almost nothing up to 100 miles; but the average width does not exceed 30 or 40 miles, and this is not all level land. Low mountains or foothills appear everywhere, but among these are level lowlands and terraces of considerable extent, and there are alluvial valleys reaching well back into the mountains. The coastal region has resulted from the comparatively recent uplift of a narrow border of continental shelf. The soil in the many valleys is alluvial. It is porous and, under irrigation and fertilization, produces splendid crops of cotton, sugar cane, and rice, although rice is not a major crop (Fig. 42). On the western ranges of the Andes, in which the coastal rivers head, enough rain falls to give rise to some 55 short rivers that flow toward the Pacific and are partly or wholly diverted into irrigation canals. In the rainy season (December to April), these streams carry a large volume of water; but, in the dry season, they shrink to mere rivulets, and about half of them do not reach the sea at all. These mountain streams are the life-givers of the coastlands; for, without them, the coast would be an absolute desert. Rain seldom falls on this coast. On rare occasions, heavy downpours have occurred as they did in 1925; but such occasions are very far apart, and the amount of water that falls in an average 5-year period is insignificant. One of the most lasting pictures that the traveler carries away from Peru is the utter bareness of the hills and mountains that skirt the coast and reach far inland. Most of the year, not a green thing can be seen except along the streams where irrigation is practiced; the Sahara is not more bare.

Small as is the productive area of this coastal zone, it is agriculturally and culturally the most important part of Peru. It contains the great sugar and cotton estates which supply most of the agricultural exports of the country. It includes, of course, all the seaports, and there are not less than 20 of these which carry on overseas commerce. It includes Lima, the capital and educational, social, and financial center of the republic. It is in the coastal zone that the wealthy and influential families have their homes. Moreover, this coastal strip contains the most important oil field in western South America. The rest of Peru supplies little to the outside world except minerals and wool. Nearly one-third of the value of Peru's exports consists in cotton and sugar produced on less than 1 per cent of the land of the coastal strip.

Extent and Importance of Irrigation.—The rainfall is 30 to 40 inches a year in the high Andes; and, during January, February, and March, the mountain streams are at flood. They plunge downward several thousand feet in flowing a distance of 150 miles or less and become heavily laden with silt and gravel eroded from the upper valleys. As they flow out upon the coastal plain, their velocity is checked, and they deposit their load in the form of alluvial fans and flood plains of considerable size. These flood plains and fans are the only agricultural lands of the coast of Peru. The Incas, and probably the pre-Incas, built irrigation works for controlling the floodwaters and utilized them for the growing of crops. The Spaniards took possession of these canals

FIG. 43.—Buildings of the Cartavio Sugar Estate, Peru. The long row of low buildings in the foreground contains the homes of the workmen. (*Courtesy of F. A. Smith.*)

and lands and assigned them to friends of the king or viceroy. Many of the irrigation works built by the Indians are still in use. A competent authority[1] believes that more land was irrigated by the Incas than is now under irrigation in Peru. In all, about 1,000 square miles, 640,000 acres, are wholly or partly under irrigation along these streams; and it is believed that nearly as much more land is capable of irrigation by the expenditure of large sums of money for new and improved works. There are only a few storage reservoirs of large size, and nearly all of the irrigation improvements are privately owned. The Peruvian Government, however, is interested in the extension of irrigation. This area of a few hundred square miles of irrigated land in a country of more than 500,000 square miles is the salvation of the nation, so far as agricultural exports are concerned. One of the large sugar estates (Fig. 43), with its sugar Central and ·

[1] Charles W. Sutton, former irrigation expert for the Peruvian Government.

other structures and its livestock is worth from $4,000,000 to $6,000,000. One large group of estates having its own railroad and port is valued at $20,000,000.

Fifty-four per cent of the agricultural capital of Peru is invested in irrigated farms, and 59 per cent of the agricultural income is derived from them. It is estimated that one-half the total national income from all sources is derived from activities dependent upon irrigation. Aside from the increase of national wealth from mining operations, about the only important means of augmenting the country's income is through an increased use of irrigation and improved methods of cultivation. But the planters are making money by present methods, and so it is difficult to persuade some of them that there is any serious need for change. A profit of $100,000 from a sugar hacienda in a good year is not unusual.

The Sugar Estates.—In value, sugar is the second crop of Peru. More money is invested in the sugar industry than in any other (about $150,000,000), and yet the area of land devoted to sugar cane is slightly over 100,000 acres, about one-third the area of a fair-sized county in the United States. The yield of cane per acre on the best estates is large (40 to 60 tons), and the cane has a large sugar content (10 to 12 per cent) resulting in a high yield of sugar per acre. The average cost of production on the better haciendas is about 2 cents a pound. If the raw sugar sells for the moderate price of $2\frac{1}{2}$ cents a pound, the owner of the hacienda receives a profit of $50 per acre, or about $100,000 on an estate containing 2,000 acres of sugar cane. Most of the sugar haciendas are in the northern valleys of the coastal plain (Fig. 44). Here in seven or eight valleys are about 30 large sugar estates. There are also many smaller ones, making a total of more than 100. The production is 500 million to 800 million pounds a year, most of which is exported. All of the more important irrigated valleys are connected by short lines of railway to ports from which the sugar is shipped. The largest of these valleys is Chicama, at whose seaward end is the chief city of northern Peru, Trujillo, and its shipping port Salaverry. In the Chicama valley are six large estates, one of which contains 17,000 acres, though not all of this is planted to cane. The Rimac valley, in which Lima is situated, contains two large sugar estates, and a small quantity of cane is grown still farther south; but most of it is grown north of Lima.

To produce well, sugar cane requires rich land, and the Peruvian planters use guano and Chilean nitrate generously. In planting a new field of cane, the land is plowed and harrowed, and a series of shallow parallel trenches a few feet apart is made. In

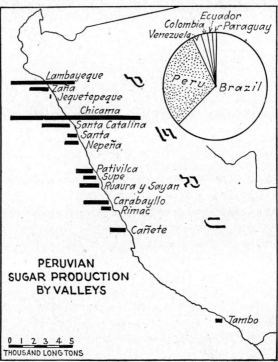

Fɪɢ. 44.—Most of the sugar of Peru is produced in irrigated valleys north of Lima. The circular graph indicates the relative production of sugar in six South American countries.

these, pieces of sugar cane, containing at least one joint, are laid and covered with soil. Soon, the new plants spring up, growing from the joints. While the growing cane is still small, the ground is cultivated to keep down the weeds, and irrigation water is supplied from canals or wells, for many wells are used to supplement the river water. Within 18 or 20 months from the time of planting, the cane is ready for cutting and, thereafter, may be cut every 18 months for several years, usually 6 to 10 years. Cutting may take place at any time in the year and is not controlled by the season as it is in Louisiana or even in Cuba. The large mills grind cane practically throughout the year.

On the large estates are workmen's villages of small huts in which the Indian laborers live. The greater part of the labor is done by Indians who live in the mountains and come to the sugar estates to work when they are not needed on their little farms. Schools are provided by the owner of the estates; and the children of the workers may learn to read, write, and compute. Common laborers earn 50 cents to $1 a day, and there is usually a shortage of labor. Heavy drinking of intoxicants is common, and coca chewing is almost universal among the Indians.[1] On the whole, the social and living conditions are far from satisfactory, but those employers who seek to improve conditions get scant cooperation from the ignorant laborers who are accustomed to this plane of living. Labor agitators, however, are common, and labor troubles are frequent.

THE CHICLIN SUGAR ESTATE.—The Chiclin sugar estate is the one that is doing the most for its workmen and their families. On the estate are six school buildings in which 400 or 500 children of the workers are given excellent educational opportunities. There is a night school for workmen themselves and a domestic training school for girls. A park, playground, theater, and church are maintained. There are electric lights, running water, and modern sanitary improvements. About 2,500 people live on the estate of 5,000 acres, mainly devoted to sugar cane; and about 3,000 cattle are kept for draft animals and for beef. Only a small part of the water needed for irrigation comes from the river; the larger part is obtained from six very large wells which are constantly pumped by means of engines. Notwithstanding the expenditures for social betterment made by the owners, this estate is a highly profitable one.

THE CASA GRANDE GROUP OF ESTATES.—The Casa Grande group of estates is noteworthy for the magnitude of the properties and their operations, for nearly one-fourth of the sugar produced in Peru comes from them. There are 10 estates in the group, and three other groups in Chicama valley have 18 estates, or a total of 28, comprising over 1½ million acres. In addition, the company

[1] Leaves of the coca plant contain the important nerve stimulant found in cocaine.

owns 425,000 acres in the foothills of the Andes. Thousands of cattle, sheep, and hogs are kept, mainly to provide for the needs of the people who live in this little sugar principality. Rice, cereals, fruit, dairy products, and other foodstuffs are produced. The company has a modern sugar mill capable of grinding 4,500 tons of cane daily. It owns and operates 125 miles of railway, in addition to a much larger mileage of portable field railways; and it owns its own docks at the port. The total property is said to be worth upward of $20,000,000. It belongs to a company that was originally German but is now regarded as Peruvian. Many a feudal holding in Europe was far smaller and less wealthy than this.

The Cultivation of Cotton.—The leading crop of Peru in value is cotton, of which a number of varieties are grown. Practically all the cotton is produced on about 140,000 acres in 30 irrigated valleys near the coast. The most important of these cotton-growing districts are in the neighborhood of Chincha and Pisco, south of Lima (Fig. 45). The Rimac valley, in which Lima is located, is another important cotton-growing district. Another leading district is the region near Piura in the extreme north. A little cotton is also raised in the montaña, in the region of Iquitos on the headwaters of the Amazon. The variety most largely grown in Peru is known as *Tangüis*. It is a disease-resistant variety developed by Señor Tangüis, a scientific cotton planter of Pisco. This is proving to be the salvation of cotton growing in Peru, for the industry was threatened with ruin by a disease known as the *wilt*. The dreaded boll weevil has not invaded Peru. Not only is the *Tangüis* resistant to wilt, but it has a long staple ($1\frac{1}{4}$ inches) and yields 25 to 30 per cent more cotton to the acre than any other variety. In recent years, it has supplied about two-thirds of the Peruvian crop.

A variety known as the *full rough* has been grown in the north of Peru since the days of the Incas. Its peculiarity is the crinkly nature of the fiber which leads to its being mixed with wool in making certain types of textile. Most of the Peruvian cottons have a long fiber, which adds to their value. Under the ideal climate and water control, the cotton fields of Peru produce on an average twice as much cotton per acre as those of the United States. The crop is not planted every year, as it is in the United States; but the plant bears for several years, and some species grow to a height of 10 to 15 feet. Picking goes on every month of the year in one field or another. The best success is achieved on large plantations whose owners have the necessary capital to finance their operations, to employ up-to-date methods, and to own their own ginneries. There is a tendency for the small plantations to be absorbed into the larger ones.

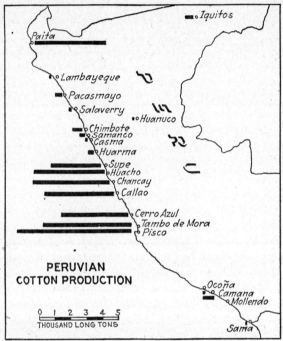

Fig. 45.—The cotton is grown in irrigated valleys and shipped from ports at the mouths of the valleys.

When prices are high, cotton growing is very profitable, occasionally yielding 50 per cent profit. About nine-tenths of the crop is exported; 1,500 bales a year are used in the 11 textile mills of the country, 8 of which are in or near Lima. The average annual production of cotton approximates 180 million pounds.

National Significance of the Sugar and Cotton Crops.—Both sugar growing and cotton growing are excellent adjustments to the peculiar geographical conditions of the Peruvian coast. Both crops readily adapt themselves to perennial growth; both are staple products in steady demand in a world-wide market; both are well suited to transportation long distances and are not perishable. They can be stored without deterioration and yield a good return to the planter.

The annual crop of sugar and cotton is steadily increasing, and in 1928 it was more than double what it was prior to 1915. As an illustration of the importance of the intensive agriculture that is carried on in the irrigated valleys of the Peruvian coast, it may be pointed out (1) that the value of the sugar exported each year from less than 150 square miles of this land nearly equals the value of all the agricultural products exported from the country of Venezuela and (2) that the cotton annually exported from 220 square miles of Peru equals in value all the exports from Ecuador. The cotton and sugar of Peru are produced almost within sight of the seaports from which they are shipped, whereas the coffee of Colombia and Venezuela is grown back in the mountains, necessitating an expensive journey to the port of shipment.

The Cultivation of Rice.—Rice is the most important food of tropical peoples. In the coast provinces of Peru and in many other parts of South America, rice and beans form the staple and preferred food of the working class. Of all the cereal starch foods, rice is the most convenient to use. It is as easily threshed and cleaned as other cereals and does not require the grinding and bread-making processes that wheat, barley, or rye requires. A handful of rice thrown into a basin of water and boiled a half hour over a little fire is ready to eat. It is nourishing and satisfying and, combined with the nitrogenous food supplied by beans, makes a substantial meal.

The production of rice in Peru is practically confined to a narrow strip of coast in the extreme northwestern part of the country, where it is raised under irrigation and yields two crops a year. Much of the rice is of inferior quality and may be bought at a low price, which is welcomed by the poorly paid peons. Some rice of superior quality is raised and is largely exported, and less expensive Asiatic rice is imported. The chief movement of this product is in the form of imports. The production of rice in Peru is increasing, having risen from 65 million pounds in 1910, to approximately three times that quantity 30 years later.

Petroleum Production.—Peru was long the chief producer of petroleum in South America but has been surpassed by Venezuela

FIG. 46.—Oil fields of Talara, Peru.

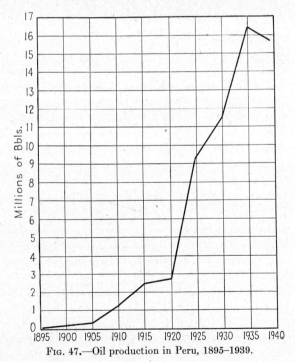

FIG. 47.—Oil production in Peru, 1895–1939.

and Colombia. The oil fields are close to the sea; in fact, most of the wells are on the shore, thus greatly cheapening the cost of marketing the oil (Fig. 46). There are three recognized oil fields, all in the extreme northwestern part of the country, not far from the boundary of Ecuador. Drilling operations in this region date from 1870, but production did not reach a million barrels until 1908; it rose steadily to about 16 million barrels in 1935 (Fig. 47).[1] Production since 1936 has amounted to about 16 million barrels annually. None of the three fields has ever been a spectacular producer, and the average daily production is 10 to 15 barrels per well; but individual wells have yielded upward of 1,000 barrels a day in the first days of their production. The oil is of excellent quality, containing a high portion of kerosene and gasoline. A large refinery is located at the port of Talara. The leading company in the field is a subsidiary of the Standard Oil Company.

The Cordillera

The Andes of Peru form a lofty mountain belt 200 to 250 miles in width and occupy nearly 40 per cent of the area of the country (Fig. 40). Between the narrow coastal plain and the towering western range is a belt of low mountains averaging 50 miles in width and constituting the western foothills of the mighty cordillera. The western range contains peaks 18,000 to 20,000 feet high and forms the water parting between the small rivers of the Pacific slope and the headwaters of the Amazon. The latter reach within about 100 miles of the Pacific and have cut their zigzag way eastward across almost the entire width of the cordillera. The western range is practically continuous from end to end of Peru, and the two railways that have surmounted it do so at elevations of 14,688 and 15,665 feet, respectively. Nowhere else do standard-gauge railways reach such altitudes.

Between the western range and the Oriente are other ranges, roughly parallel, less towering, and cut through by river valleys, and thus travel through them is less difficult. Between the ranges are high intermontane valleys such as the beautiful valley traversed by the Southern Railway between Lake Titicaca and Cuzco or the broad valley that includes Cerro de Pasco, Oroya, Huancayo, and the connecting railway. In these mountains, the

[1] The world's production in 1935 was over 1½ billion barrels.

rainfall is sufficient for crops, and many of the valleys have a dense population of Indians. The Sunday market held at Huancayo is famous throughout Peru and is attended by hundreds or even thousands of Indians (Fig. 48). The valley floors and gentler slopes are everywhere cultivated by the Indians, and their mud huts and small villages dot the treeless landscape. Until the eastern range is reached, there are practically no forests. Cattle,

FIG. 48.—Types of people seen in the Andes. The famous Sunday market at Huancayo, Peru. (*Copyright Ewing Galloway, N. Y.*)

sheep, alpacas, and llamas are raised; but the only well-developed grazing industry is in the province of Puno, which is adjacent to Bolivia.

The Inca ruins that are found in the cordillera amaze the visitor. The mountains are rich in mineral veins, and thousands of mines were worked by the forced labor of the Indians in the days of Spanish control. Now, most of the mining is done by corporations in a few localities where especially valuable mineral deposits occur.

Crops of the Cordillera.—Owing to the different altitudes in Peru, crops of the middle latitudes as well as of the tropics are raised, but none of them in large quantities, for there is only a limited area of land suited to agriculture. Deserts, mountains, and jungles make up most of the country. Under irrigation, small parts of the coast desert are supplying practically all the surplus agricultural products. In the mountain valleys and on the tablelands, the Indians raise nearly sufficient food for the needs of those who live in the mountains and a small surplus for the coast cities. If sugar be omitted, however, Peru imports much more food than it exports, a condition that ought not to exist.

FIG. 49.—Irrigated fields near Cuzco, Peru. (*Courtesy of Mary Gwen Shaw.*)

In the long valleys between the main ranges, almost all the land that is fairly level and receives enough rainfall for crops is cultivated, for the Indians are mostly farmers if left to their choice of an occupation. Frequently, irrigation is practiced to supplement the scanty rainfall (Fig. 49). Wheat, corn, barley, rye, potatoes, beans, cassava, and many kinds of vegetable are regularly grown. So far as quantity is concerned, the leading food crops are bananas, corn, and potatoes. Wheat and wheat flour constitute one of the larger imports of the country. Peru produces very little coffee or cacao but considerable coca, the plant from which cocaine is made. This is a plantation crop grown mainly on the eastern slopes of the Andes. Coca is more fully discussed on page 141. A semiofficial investigation of the agricultural resources and products of 12 important zones, or regions, of Peru was conducted in 1918. These 12 zones include the principal agricultural sections. The results showed that approximately 1 million acres were devoted to food crops (not counting sugar) in these zones. The percentage of land devoted to six of the leading crops was: corn, 23 per cent; wheat, $21\frac{1}{2}$ per cent; barley, $12\frac{1}{2}$ per cent; rice, $10\frac{1}{2}$ per cent; potatoes, $10\frac{1}{4}$ per cent; beans, $8\frac{1}{2}$ per cent.

The investigation showed that from sea level to 6,000 feet elevation rice, bananas, and cassava were leading crops; from 6,000 to 11,000 feet, corn and wheat were the most important; and potatoes at the higher altitudes.

Livestock.—Livestock are significant in the economic life of the cordillera. Cattle, sheep, llamas, alpacas, and vicuñas are the principal animals, and of these sheep are by far the most important.

Cattle.—In the mountainous parts of Peru, there are numerous cattle haciendas, or ranches, covering tens of thousands of acres each. Most of them belong to men or families who live in Lima or in other cities. There is little or no tax on this land, and Indian or Cholo labor is cheap. Most of the cattle are of an inferior type, and little attention has been given to improving the stock. On the irrigated estates near the coast, cattle are kept both for beef and for use as draft animals. On some of the estates, blooded stock of high quality is raised. Most of the beef finds its market in Peru, whereas the hides are exported. It is estimated that there are $1\frac{1}{2}$ million beef cattle in the country, a small number for so large an area.

Sheep and Wool.—The raising of sheep for wool is the outstanding industry of the plateau of southern Peru, especially of the Department of Puno, already mentioned (Fig. 50). In these lofty pastures, 10,000 to 13,000 feet in altitude, sheep are raised with notable success. There are upward of 8 million of them in this region and 12 million in the entire country. The government has established an experimental sheep farm in the great valley traversed by the Cuzco division of the Southern Railway and has placed it in charge of a sheep expert from Scotland, assisted by a group of Scottish shepherds. In 1928, there were 18,000 sheep on this farm, partly natives and partly crosses between native sheep and high-grade imported stock. The sheep of this region are being slowly improved through these efforts, and the fleeces of the improved breeds weigh two or three times as much as those of the native sheep. The high Peruvian pastures are free from burr-bearing plants; and the wool is, therefore, especially clean. The sheep are healthy in the dry, cool climate; and the government expert considers this region one of the best for the production of wool, and the industry capable of great expansion.

Sheep have been raised in a desultory fashion in Peru since the early Spanish days. In a general way, the people of the Andes recognized that the region was suited to sheep raising; but they were isolated from the outer world, knew little of the progress in sheep breeding that was going on elsewhere, and remained content with inferior sheep. They found profit in the industry even under those conditions and were not concerned over improve-

Fig. 50.—Halfbreed Hampshire Down sheep on Peruvian Government Experimental ranch. (*Photo by courtesy Col. R. J. Stordy.*)

ments. But, eventually, someone in Peru caught the spirit of scientific animal husbandry applied to sheep raising; the experimental farm was established, and Peru seems to be on the way to the important sheep industry to which its Southern Cordillera is exceptionally well adapted. Under the old regime, man was making a half-intelligent economic adjustment to the environment of the high pastures of Peru. Now he is learning that a much better adjustment can be made. But people of the tropical countries are slow to make changes. The whole economic history of any country is a series of new adjustments to environment to the end that the country shall support more people and do it better.

The west coast of South America is making those new adjustments but is doing it with characteristic deliberateness.

The city of Arequipa (Fig. 51), between Puno and the sea, is the great wool market of Peru; and the greater part of the country's clip passes through this city, where the wool is sorted, cleaned, graded, and baled.

Fig. 51.—Main plaza of Arequipa, Peru. Similar plazas occupy the center of most cities in Spanish America.

The Llama, Alpaca, and Vicuña.—The llama, sometimes called the "camel of the Andes," is an American member of the camel family (Fig. 52). The Indians had domesticated the llama long before the Spaniards arrived, and they still regard it as the most valuable of animals. Its gentleness, sure-footedness, and ability to go long distances without water and to live on surprisingly little food make the llama peculiarly suited to the lofty and rocky Andes where it lives. These animals will carry about 100 pounds; but, if overloaded, they lie down and decline to move until their burden is lightened. They travel slowly, grazing as they go, and will not be hurried. The plateau Indian's wealth is often measured by the number of llamas he owns. The animals are locally valued at the equivalent of about $5 each. Their long wool is used for spinning by the industrious Indian women who spin as they walk, tend the sheep, or sit in the market. It is estimated that there are 700,000 llamas in Peru, and twice that number of alpacas, kept for their long heavy wool. The value of alpaca wool exported from Peru has usually exceeded the value of sheep's wool. The vicuña, a member of the same general family as the alpaca and the llama, lives wild at very high altitudes and is hunted for its skin which bears a fine, silky wool, like beautiful fur. These animals were threatened with extermination by the hunters; the government has enacted a law for their protection, but the law cannot be well enforced.

Fig. 52.—Flock of llamas near Arequipa, Peru. Mt. Misti in the background.

Indians in the Economic Life of the Cordillera.—The full-blooded Indian clings to the mountains and plateaus (Fig. 53). He prefers isolation or residence in his own village among his own people to residence among the whites or mestizos of whom he is suspicious. Of all occupations, he loves best to cultivate a piece of ground that has belonged to his ancestors and now belongs to him. He may accumulate a little wealth by rearing and caring for llamas, alpacas, or sheep. He is content with a mud hut, particularly if it is the one in which he was born. The white man's luxuries make little appeal to him, and money is desirable only because it will purchase coca, liquor, and a few other items that he cannot produce on his little mountain farm. These are the "free Indians," some of whom are induced to work in the mines or on the sugar and cotton estates at times when they can leave their own crops. But when the time comes for harvesting these meager crops, the Indian is wont to leave the white man's employ and his

money wages and to return to the mountains. The accumulation
of money has little attraction for him. He is happiest when left
entirely alone; but, under that condition, he is scarcely a factor
in the economic life of
the nation, for he pro-
duces only enough to
maintain his poor ex-
istence.

In the interior, there
are considerable num-
bers of "community
Indians" who have al-
ways held their land in
common but who are
otherwise like the other
free Indians. Another
large class owns no
land but lives on the
haciendas; these peons
are bound to give their
patrons a certain
amount of labor each
year and are more or
less legally attached to
the estates. They may
live on the same estate,
generation after gener-
ation, and often regard
themselves as attached
to it. Some seek to
escape and may be

Fig. 53.—Lampa Indians near Puno, Peru.

forced unwillingly to remain until their "debt" is paid. Since
the overseers keep the accounts, the debt may be very slow in
liquidation. The Indian is, by nature, docile, stupid, sullenly
obedient, silent, slow, and quite lacking in loyalty to his employer
or patron.

Inefficient and irresponsible as the Indian is, he nevertheless
does most of the manual labor of Peru and the other Andean
countries within the tropics (Fig. 54). By such labor as the white
man can obtain from the Indian, the larger industries of the

country are carried on. These are chiefly mining, ranching, and plantation agriculture. Economic progress under such labor conditions is slow, the growth of the national wealth is slight, and the purchasing power of the nation is small. There is no comparison between the economic advance that can be made under the labor

FIG. 54.—Street scene in Pisac showing Indian porters. (*Courtesy of Mary Gwen Shaw.*)

system of Peru or Bolivia and that of the self-respecting, intelligent, free labor of Canada and the United States.

Mining Industries of the Cordillera.—A great deal of mineralization has taken place in the rocks of the Andes in past geologic ages. During the Spanish colonial period, Peru was a synonym for gold, and great quantities of gold and silver were mined by means of forced Indian labor which cost almost nothing. Transportation from the high Andes to the coast was expensive in time, but time was a small element of cost in the reckoning of those days. Hundreds of deposits of gold and silver

were worked then that could not at present be mined at a profit. After the revolution that separated Peru from Spain, mining operations fell off, and, one by one, most of the mines were abandoned. More recently, a few of the richest deposits have passed into the ownership of foreign corporations, are being mined on a large scale by modern methods, and are proving profitable, in some cases very profitable. As already pointed out, the ranges of the Andes place great difficulties in the way of transportation. It is probable that many rich mineral bodies exist among these mountains; but most of them could not be worked at a profit if they were found, because of the cost of transportation to the nearest railway or to the coast, which might be 100 miles away. Very slowly, railways are reaching a few of the chief mineral regions. The importance of railways may be seen from the fact that, aside from the petroleum fields near the coast, about 90 per cent of the value of all metallic minerals now being mined in Peru comes from the region along the Central Railway and its extension to Cerro de Pasco.

Railroads are essential to the development of the mineral resources; and, conversely, the development of mines is essential to the success of the railroads. The two must grow together. Both require foreign capital, and foreign capital requires a safe and friendly attitude on the part of the government. Tens of millions of dollars must be risked in the larger enterprises, and years may elapse before there is any return. Having taken the risks and awaited the returns, the investor has a right to expect considerate treatment from the government. On the other hand, the foreign corporation has a duty to maintain a just attitude toward the country in which it is operating. It is only logical that South American countries should look, at least in part, to North American capital for their development and that North American capital and skill should increasingly go into South America. But this can be achieved only on a basis of fair treatment on both sides.

Gold and Silver.—Peru yields gold to the extent of about $3,000,000 a year, mainly obtained from the copper workings. Silver is produced also in connection with copper, and in a smaller way with lead, in values exceeding $5,000,000 a year. The Cerro de Pasco Copper Corporation is the largest single producer in Peru of both gold and silver. Another strong and experienced American corporation is developing proved deposits in northern Peru and is likely to increase notably the copper, silver, and gold output of the country in the future. Peru ranks third or fourth among silver-producing countries, the others being the United States, Mexico, and Canada. The Cerro de Pasco mines were worked for their silver for more than 250 years and produced over a half-billion dollars' worth during that time.

Copper.—The mines of the Cerro de Pasco Corporation (underground workings) are east of the western Andes, at an altitude of about 15,000 feet. The company's $15,000,000 smelter is located at Oroya, on the Central Railroad of Peru, and is connected by railway to several mines in the region (Fig. 55). Over $30,000,000 have been invested, and 25,000 people are almost wholly dependent upon the operations of this company. The workmen are

Indians, who can endure hard work in the extremely high altitudes; a staff of about 200 white men direct the operations and
supply the technical ability. The annual output is above 100
million pounds of copper, with the large silver content already
mentioned. The company mines its own coal and from the best of
it makes part of the coke that it requires. Additional coke is
imported. There are a number of small copper mines operating,
but the mines at and near Cerro de Pasco produce more than 90

Fig. 55.—General view of Oroya, site of the Cerro de Pasco copper-smelting plant.
(*Courtesy of Philadelphia Commercial Museum.*)

per cent of the copper mined in Peru. The freight traffic developed
by these mining operations constitutes the main support of the
mountain portion of the Central Railroad, which passes through
Lima and has its ocean terminal at Callao.

Coal.—No country in South America produces much coal;
but, among those that produce any, Peru ranks second, following
Chile. Coal of medium quality occurs in many places in Peru, but
it is mined only in connection with the working of the Cerro de
Pasco mines, railways, and smelter. Coke made from Peruvian
coal would be unsatisfactory for iron production though it can be
used for the smelting of copper. Some of the coal beds have a
thickness of 6 to 12 feet, but usually they are thinner. The total

output is from 90,000 to 100,000 tons a year. No coal is exported, and only a little is imported. Houses are not heated in Peru, and coal is seldom used for cooking. The increasing use of fuel oil, particularly by railways and industrial plants, is causing a decline in coal requirements.

As Peru's need for power increases, there is available a large amount of potential water power. Potential horsepower is estimated at 6,400,000 of which only 100,000 has been developed.

Other Mineral Products.—Small quantities of lead, bismuth, borax, and tungsten are produced, but they are of relatively little consequence. Nearly all the world's supply of vanadium—not a large amount—comes from mines near Cerro de Pasco, owned by an American corporation. When alloyed with steel, vanadium makes the latter exceptionally strong and tough. This alloy steel is used extensively in making parts of automobiles where great strength and lightness are demanded. The annual output of vanadium ore in Peru rarely exceeds 1,000 tons a year. The famous *quicksilver* mines of Huancavelica which were important in the Spanish days were shut down after the War of Independence; and although several subsequent attempts were made to reopen them, the efforts were unsuccessful. The total annual value of the mineral products in Peru reaches $90,000,000, the chief minerals being petroleum, copper, and silver. These three together greatly exceed in value the combined output of sugar and cotton. Among the South American countries, Peru ranks third in the value of mineral products, following Chile and Venezuela, and leading Bolivia.

EASTERN PERU

The Montaña, or Oriente.—Since Peru has a boundary dispute with Ecuador, its area can be given only tentatively at 500,000[1] square miles. More than half of this lies east of the cordillera. Here, the rainfall is heavy, reaching 100 inches a year and more, and falling most heavily from December to April. The so-called dry season is far from dry. Most of this region is lowland, a part of the great Amazon jungle already described, and known both as the *montaña* and as the *Oriente*. The intense tropical heat of the lowlands, the excessive rainfall, the poor drainage in the wet season, and the resultant dense tangle of trees, vines, and

[1] See footnote, p. 113.

undergrowth make this a region to which white settlers are little attracted. At some future date, the pressure of population in the attractive parts of the world may bring about the settlement of the higher and cooler lands of the montaña.

There are lands of a few thousand feet altitude on the eastern slopes of the Andes and in the mountain valleys that are exceedingly fertile, reasonably healthy, and capable of agricultural development, and they are occupied here and there by farms and

Fig. 56.—A suspension bridge (puente Rio Colorado) in the Montaña of Peru. A bridge is a rare thing in this jungle.

haciendas. At some one of the various altitudes, almost any crop of the tropics and subtropics can be grown in soil enriched by ages of plant decay. If agricultural settlers should attempt the conquest of these lands, as they are already doing in a small way, crops of coffee, cacao, cotton, tobacco, corn, and fruit can be produced. But when they are produced, what shall be done with them? Any surplus beyond the needs of the near-by population must seek markets considerably removed or far removed; and the cost of sending these products by rail over the many ranges of the Andes to the Pacific coast or by the rivers to the Atlantic coast 2,500 miles away will be very high—so high that the farmer of the montaña will get little for his labor, if in fact the products will even pay the cost of transportation (Fig. 56). It is one thing to raise crops in such a remote region and another to market them at a profit. Whatever may in truth be said of the fertility and low price of land in the montaña of Peru, the fact remains that its geographical location in one of the most inaccessible parts of the continent will cause a long delay in its development.

Rubber.—Eastern Peru is part of the basin of the Amazon, which for many years was the chief source of the world's rubber. The city of Iquitos, on the upper Amazon, was the chief rubber-collecting port for Peru, whose production amounted to millions of dollars a year in the decade from 1900 to 1910. Rubber gathering was then one of the leading industries of Peru, but it declined to a fraction of its former volume because of the cheapness with which plantation rubber is produced in the Far East. In 1923–1924, the United States Government sent a commission of specialists into the Amazon valley to study plantation rubber possibilities, with a view to the liberation of American rubber users from the control of the rubber supply by far-eastern producers. It is doubtful whether the Amazon valley with its limited supply of competent labor can develop a plantation rubber industry in competition with the Far East. With the decline in the price of rubber, some of the rubber-gathering companies turned their attention to the collecting of balata which is fairly abundant in the Amazon forests and which is in demand in European and North American markets. In 1925, raw rubber increased in price and reached a figure that temporarily stimulated production, but the price and production soon returned to a low level.

Coca.—On the eastern slopes of the Andes, the coca shrub is grown. This plant has no connection with either the cacao or the coconut tree. The coca shrub grows wild in the forests of the montaña, but most of the coca leaves come from plantations. From the leaves of this shrub, the important drug cocaine is made. The Indians of the cordillera chew the leaves almost constantly and derive from them powers of endurance and resistance to hunger that are remarkable, but the general effect upon the user is stupefying. Nearly all the Andean Indians from Colombia to northern Chile are addicts to this habit and will make almost any sacrifice to secure the leaves. It is believed that the mental dullness of the Indians is partly due to the use of coca.

generation after generation. Coca is one of the chief products of the middle slopes of the montaña of Peru and Bolivia, and the *cocales* are the most profitable industries of the region.

INDUSTRIAL AND COMMERCIAL ACTIVITIES OF PERU AS A WHOLE

Waterways of the Oriente.—Several large tributaries of the Amazon flow through eastern Peru and provide water routes that are used by canoes, launches, and steamboats. Ocean-going steamers reach Iquitos in northern Peru, 2,300 miles from the Atlantic. When rubber was a large export from the Oriente, these rivers were in constant and active use and formed almost the only routes of travel in this densely forested region. Since the decline of the rubber-gathering industry, the rivers are much less used. An illustration of the extent to which shippers will go in order to escape the difficulty of transporting goods overland from the eastern and western parts of Peru is seen in the journey in 1922 of a Peruvian ship from Callao through the Panama Canal, around the northern part of South America, and up the Amazon to Iquitos, a trip of 6,500 miles. Yet Callao and Iquitos are only 700 miles apart in a direct line.

Trails.—Throughout Peru, much of the freight is carried by pack train composed of mules or llamas. The former carry 200 to 300 pounds and the latter 75 to 100 pounds. Railways are so far apart that a large proportion of the products that are shipped by railroad are carried scores of miles by mules or llamas to or from the railway. Coffee, cacao, and coca raised in the edge of the montaña can reach a market only by long journeys on mule-back. Wool and hides may be carried thus 100 miles to reach a railway or market. Even ores are carried scores of miles from mines by mules or llamas. Under such conditions of transportation, no country can make rapid economic progress. Yet, in such a mountainous country, the cost of motor roads and railroads is nearly prohibitive; and when a railroad is built, it is sometimes possible for a pack train to carry products at as low a cost as the railway and in direct competition with it.

Roads for Vehicles.—The building of modern roads in much of Peru is very difficult. Particularly is this true when attempts are made to construct east-west highways that would cross the three major physiographic provinces. Added to the topographic drawbacks of construction are areas of sparse population and extensive areas of economic poverty. A few years ago, Peru conceived a definite plan for road construction which has, in part, been achieved. There are some 12,000 miles of road of which about 1,200 miles are surfaced—60 concrete and the rest macadam. Over 3,000 miles are of graded earth, and the remainder (considerably more than half of the 12,000 miles) are vehicle trails. Obviously, many of these roads are almost impassable in the rainy season.

Among the important highways are: (1) from Lima across the Sierras to La Merced, with branch roads from Oroya to Cerro de Pasco and Ayacucho; (2) along the coast from the northwestern part to Lomas in the south; (3) in the plateau from Quittabamba through Cuzco and Puno. Many of the roads are purely local and practically terminate in dead ends. As a result, highway transportation is expensive and often must be supplemented by trails, waterways, and railways.

Air Service.—Air services are well developed for passengers, express, and light expensive freight. North-south flights over the coastal area are frequent, and other air services connect Lima with interior cities, even with faraway Iquitos in the upper Amazon valley.

Railways.—Peru has some 30 different railway lines, with a length of about 2,500 miles; more than half of the mileage is controlled by the Peruvian Corporation (British). Of these 30 separate lines, four exceed 100 miles in length: the Central (250 miles), the Southern (550 miles), the Northwestern (130 miles), and the Cerro de Pasco (135 miles). Most of the others are short lines extending from a port to irrigated plantations of sugar and cotton. There is no railway system in Peru, but rather a number of detached lines of different gauges. A few of the short lines and the Central Railroad earn a small profit; but as a whole, the railways of Peru are unprofitable, and the bonds and stocks of the Peruvian Corporation are quoted much below par.

The Cerro de Pasco Railway belongs to the Cerro de Pasco Copper Corporation and is used mainly, though not wholly, for the operations of that company. The Peruvian Government has constructed and operates several short lines. Other lines are being extended by the government, but progress is slow because of high costs and lack of funds.

The Central Railway of Peru is one of the most daring feats of railway construction in the world. Without employing cograil, the line ascends the Andes to a height of 15,665 feet, following the valley and cañon of the Rimac River. It runs from the port of Callao through Lima to the summit tunnel near the crest of the mountains, thence to the smelting city of Oroya, and thence by a more recently built extension southward to Huancayo. There are 65 tunnels, 67 bridges, and 16 switchbacks on the line. For miles, the track is built on a narrow shelf of rock cut into the precipitous wall of the cañon. It does not seem possible that any engineer would have undertaken to construct a railway to such an altitude and by such a route, but it was done. Passenger trains go "up the hill" one day and back the next, and accidents are practically unknown. By reason of the traffic supplied by operations of the mines, this railway is paying a profit on its present capitalization, but not on its original cost. The road was laid out and largely built by the intrepid American engineer Henry Meiggs, who died before the work was completed. It was undertaken during the years when Peru was deriving very large revenues from guano and was expending money lavishly. It is estimated that the 136 miles of road from Callao to Oroya cost an average of $200,000 a mile and a total of not less than 7,500 lives. It was the expenditures on railways that hastened the financial collapse of the Peruvian Government and led to the subsequent transfer of its railways to the Peruvian Corporation by which they are now controlled.

The Southern Railway of Peru was also the product of the genius of Henry Meiggs, but it was completed by another American engineer, Henry Thorndyke. Its ocean terminal is at Mollendo. The road winds and loops among the mountains, climbing gradually to 7,550 feet at the city of Arequipa and thence on to an altitude of 12,535 feet at Lake Titicaca. The lake is navigated by modern steamships belonging to the railway company; from the Bolivian end of the lake, the railway continues to La Paz. A northern extension of the railroad from the junction at Juliaca crosses the divide at an elevation of 14,688 feet and reaches Cuzco (Fig. 57), the old capital of the Inca Empire. The Southern Railway, like the Central, is standard gauge ($56\frac{1}{2}$ inches), and its entire length is about 550 miles. It is planned to connect the two main railways of the country by a line that is

now slowly extending through the valley between the Andean
ranges. The Southern Railway has no great mining centers along
its route as the Central has. Its largest item of freight is wool, and
that is far from sufficient to afford a profitable business. The
Bolivian portion of the line can scarcely meet the competition of
the shorter route to the coast at Arica. The poor financial return
of this railroad illustrates a fact of wide application in the mountainous parts of South America, namely, that the majority of
railways do not pay. Governments must bear a considerable part

FIG. 57.—Cuzco, ancient capital of the Incas.

of the deficit until such time as the increasing development of
the region shall supply the necessary traffic to meet the expenses
of the railway, and this period may be a long one. Unfortunately,
the tropical Andean countries are poor in revenues, and their
borrowings are always about up to the limit of their credit.

Owing to the large part that the Peruvian Corporation plays in
the economic life of Peru, a brief account of the origin and
activities of this company seems desirable. In 1869, 1870, and
1872, the Peruvian Government obtained large loans in London
and with the proceeds embarked upon a course of heavy expenditures. A few years later, Peru entered a disastrous war with Chile
and emerged in a condition of almost complete bankruptcy. The
British bondholders formed a protective organization; and, as the
result of prolonged negotiations, it was finally agreed between

the bondholders and the Peruvian Government that the former should take over the entire Peruvian debt represented by the loans of 1869, 1870, and 1872. In return, the government granted to the bondholders for 66 years all the state-owned railways, the free use of harbor works at the principal ports, and the right to the navigation of Lake Titicaca. The bondholders were to be allowed to remove 3 million tons of guano (afterward reduced to 2 million tons) and to have the exclusive right to export Peruvian guano; they were also to be paid £80,000 annually for 30 years. In 1890, the Peruvian Corporation was formed to represent the bondholders, to operate the railways, and to carry out the terms of the agreement. The bondholders have lost very heavily, for the preference stock and ordinary stock that they received is worth but a fraction of its face value and is paying little or nothing in dividends.

Manufacturing.—Nearly all the manufacturing that is done in Peru consists in working certain of its agricultural or mineral products into marketable form. The largest manufacturing establishment is the great copper smelter at Oroya which smelts the ores of the three copper-silver mining regions controlled by the Cerro de Pasco Corporation. There are a few other small smelters in the country.

In the oil fields of the north are refineries which refine the major part of the petroleum products used in Peru. Many of the large sugar estates have their own sugar mills in which raw sugar is made. Cotton ginneries, cottonseed oil mills, and cotton-spinning and -weaving mills form a group of manufacturing industries of growing importance. There are several small woolen mills which make coarse woolen goods for the home market. The textile industry occupies a high rank from the standpoint of the number of persons engaged.

A number of flour mills, tanneries, rice-polishing mills, and small factories for making cocaine, tobacco products, alcoholic liquors, soap, shoes, clothing, leather, furniture, and several other products are in operation.

Both coal and electric power are used in the Cerro de Pasco operations. Fuel oil is used to an increasing extent. The sugar mills use the refuse cane (bagasse) for fuel, and there are the beginnings of the development of hydroelectric power in the country. Since 1931, there has been a relatively rapid expanse in manufacturing, but individual development has only begun. Under a high protective tariff on imported manufactures and with a better developed home market, progress may be expected; but Peru has not yet reached the industrial stage of development.

Foreign Commerce.—In proportion to its area and resources, the foreign trade of Peru is small. This condition is due mainly to two causes: (1) the high proportion of Indians and mestizos in the population, and (2) the difficulties of transportation within the country. The Indians buy few imported goods and produce little that enters foreign trade, except as they work on the sugar and cotton estates and in the mines. Their wages are low and their buying power small. Most of the mestizo population also has small purchasing power, though it is probably double that of the Indian, man for man. Indians and mestizos make up fully 90 per cent of the population of Peru.

Of the country's annual exports of approximately $100,000,000, four items constitute about 80 per cent of the total: (1) sugar, (2) petroleum and its derivatives, (3) copper and its included gold and silver, (4) cotton and its products. Great Britain and the United States take almost one-half the exports of Peru. Germany, Canada, and Chile are other large buyers of Peruvian products.

The imports always total less than the exports in value, and often not over half so much. These are mainly manufactured goods which come most largely from the United States, Germany, and Great Britain. Since the opening of the Panama Canal, the trade of the United States with the west coast of South America has increased notably.

Ports and Other Cities of Peru.—Callao, the port of the Lima-Callao marketing area, is the most important in Peru and receives more of the imports of the country than all other ports combined. Callao accounts for almost 70 per cent of the country's total imports and about 30 per cent of its exports. Wheat, general merchandise, lumber, and automobiles make up a large part of the import tonnage. The principal exports through Callao are copper bars, ores and minerals, cotton, wool, and smaller amounts of a large number of miscellaneous products.

There are a great number of small ports along the coast of Peru. The large number is due mainly to the poor transportation on land and the fact that nearly every irrigated valley has its own port. Talara is a major port, shipping large quantities of oil.

Mollendo is the port for Arequipa and southern Peru and the chief wool-exporting point of the country.

With the exception of Lima, there are but two cities with a population of 50,000 or more in Peru. Arequipa, situated in the highland area on the western slope of the Occidental Range, has a delightful climate. It is located on the Southern Railway, and here is sorted and washed much of the wool that comes from the plateau of southern Peru. There are several small industries here, including textile and leather manufacturing. Cuzco, with a population of 30,000 people, is one of the most interesting of Peruvian

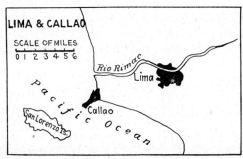

Fig. 58.—Lima and its port, Callao.

cities. It was the capital of the ancient Inca Empire, and in its environs are found many of the remarkable stone structures built by the Incas, or their predecessors, for which Peru is noted.

Iquitos is a small city of 15,000 but is of interest as it is the only commerical center of importance in the tropical montaña. It is a river port on the upper Amazon, 2,300 miles from the river's mouth and some 1,268 miles by land routes from Lima.

Lima, the capital city of the Republic, has a population of almost 300,000. It is the outstanding city of Peru in numbers and political and economic importance. The Lima-Callao marketing area is the most populous and highly developed section of the country (Fig. 58). This area is the most important manufacturing district, and in Lima there are offices that handle a great deal of trade in all parts of the country. Lima's industries include cotton, woolen, and knitting mills; cottonseed oil factories; lumber and flour mills; and scores of others, particularly those which make products for the people of a large city.

THE TRADING COMPANIES

W. R. Grace & Co.—No account of the commerce of the west coast of South America can omit reference to the great and varied activities of W. R. Grace & Co., or Casa Grace, as it is commonly known in scores of west-coast places. The founding of this company dates from 1851, when James Grace of Queenstown, Ireland, established an unsuccessful agricultural colony in Perų. His son William R. Grace, afterward mayor of New York, became interested in selling ships' supplies in Peru, and from this small beginning has grown the enormous business now conducted by the House of Grace. It operates various lines of ships between United States, Caribbean, and South American ports. It has banking houses or agencies in 45 cities in Peru and Chile and many more in other Latin American centers. It owns one of the large sugar estates of Peru, a nitrate property in Chile, cotton mills, and other mills in Peru, and a chain of retail stores in Chile. In practically every port of any importance from Panama to Concepción, the Grace interests have a fleet of launches, lighters, and other harbor craft for the handling of ocean commerce. On the east coast, Grace is one of the largest coffee dealers in Santos and Rio de Janeiro. Through its steamship lines, banks, mercantile establishments, and ramifying trading interests, it is the outstanding commercial company of the west coast of South America.

Other Large Trading Companies.—In the west-coast ports, one sees again and again the names of these American and British trading companies—Gibbs & Co., Wessel Duval & Co., Williamson & Co., Duncan Fox & Co., Graham Rowe & Co.— and less frequently, those of the German firms of Gildemeister & Co. and Huth & Co. All these companies have been long engaged in importing, exporting, and mercantile enterprises and are widely known. Each company is the exclusive local selling agent for a long list of European or United States manufacturers. A very important part of the mercantile business of the west coast is handled by these trading companies.

Chapter VI. Bolivia

A war with Chile (1879–1883) deprived Bolivia of its Pacific Coastal Margins and left the country the only nation in South America, except Paraguay, without an ocean frontage. Today, as during the past four centuries, the chief economic activity of the country is mining; minerals, on the average, constitute 90 per

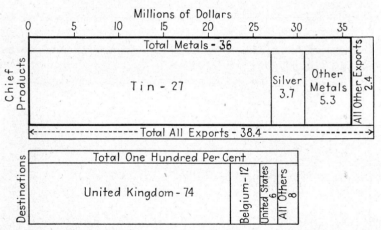

Fig. 59.—Bolivian exports and their destinations. Average 1935–1937.

cent of Bolivia's exports, and tin alone accounts for two-thirds of the total. Rubber, coca leaves, and hides make up the balance of the export commodities, but agricultural and forest products seem destined to play a minor role in Bolivia's economy for some time to come (Fig. 59). Since it lies as it does athwart the broadest and highest portion of the Andean chain and lacks ready access to the sea, the isolated position of the country and the difficulties encountered in developing cheap and adequate transportation

150

facilities are serious handicaps in the way of Bolivia's economic expansion. The relatively high unit value of the country's chief minerals, as compared with her agricultural products, would seem to give mining precedence over agriculture as the chief

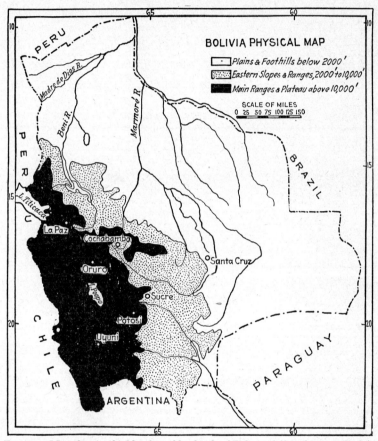

Fig. 60.—Map showing highlands and lowlands of Bolivia. (*Altitudes after Goode.*)

economic activity of Bolivia so long as the minerals last and a market for them continues.

Although mining is the leading industry of the country and despite the fact that most of the economic life of the nation is localized in the highlands, Bolivia must not be thought of as entirely a mountainous country. In the 420,000 square miles which make up Bolivia, there are two major physical regions, each of which has distinct subdivisions. About two-fifths of the country is made up of the lofty ranges of the Andes and the plateaus that lie between them; and about three-fifths consists of tropical plains that may be reached from either ocean only with large expenditure of time (Fig. 60). Between the ranges of the cordillera lies the great tableland of Bolivia, an intermontane

FIG. 61.—View in the La Paz Gorge. (*Courtesy of Philadelphia Commercial Museum.*)

plateau, formerly a huge valley but now filled up to a level of over 12,000 feet with gravels and lavas which have accumulated throughout long geological ages. In the peculiar gorge at La Paz (Fig. 61), these gravels are exposed for a depth of more than 1,500 feet. The peaks of the Bolivian Andes attain heights of 20,000 to 24,000 feet and are perpetually snow-capped although they are within the tropics; the lowest passes are 12,000 to 14,000 feet above sea level. Nowhere else does a nation with cities, railways, and modern industries exist at such an altitude. The plateau of Tibet is larger and is equally lofty, but it is the home of one of the most secluded and least known of peoples, scarcely touched by European civilization.

East of the Andes lie the great tropical plains which make up 60 per cent of the total area of the country (Fig. 60). In part, these are densely forested; but, toward the southeast, the forests give place to the scrub and grasslands of the Bolivian Chaco. Through these eastern plains flow large and partly navigable rivers that reach the Amazon and the Paraguay. A large part of the contact of eastern Bolivia with the outer world is by way of these rivers which flow to the distant Atlantic. If the people of Bolivia succeed in maintaining a progressive nation in a region like this, they deserve the respect of the world.

THE BOLIVIAN PLATEAU

Upon the lofty Bolivian tableland live three-fourths of the entire population of the country. Here are the capital, the mining centers, the chief cities and towns, most of the railways, and nearly all the industrial activities of the nation of 3 million people (Fig. 62). The surface of the plateau is strikingly level and has an area of about 40,000 square miles. At the northern end, extending across the boundary into Peru is Lake Titicaca, the shrunken remnant of a vastly larger lake that once occupied this intermontane valley. Lake Titicaca is 138 miles in length and 69 miles in width, has a maximum depth of 900 feet, and lies at an altitude of over 12,000 feet. It is a fresh-water body, draining southward into the shallow Lake Poopó, which has no outlet and whose waters evidently disappear by evaporation and by seepage into the great depth of underlying gravels. As previously stated, two steamers of 600 and 1,000 tons, respectively, navigate Lake Titicaca. All parts for these steamers were made in Great Britain, taken to South America, carried over the Andes, and put together on the margin of the lake. The materials for the first steamer had to be transported overland on muleback, for no railway then reached the lake.

The striking localization of population and of economic activity is due largely to the fact that the mining industry is in this region (Fig. 63). It is in the rocks of the highlands that the rich deposits of tin and lesser deposits of copper and silver are found. Agriculture is not particularly favored. The northern half of the plateau receives sufficient rainfall for agriculture, but the southern half is virtually a desert. The altitude offsets the tropical heat, so that the plateau is cold and bleak in winter and cool in the shade in summer. Driving storms sweep over the plateau and leave it white with snow, while flowers are blooming in the gardens of La Paz in its cañon 1,500 feet below. There are great

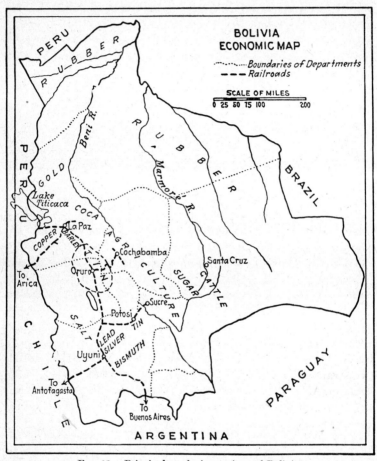

Fig. 62.—Principal producing regions of Bolivia.

extremes of temperature from day to night and from sun to shade. One may find the air in the sun warm and delightful but, in the houses or in the shade, entirely too cold for comfort. After visiting the Bolivian plateau, James Bryce wrote that he understood why the Incas were sun worshippers.[1] At times, the winds sweep across the bleak plateau, driving sand before them like a sand

[1] "South America: Observations and Impressions," p. 172, 1912.

blast. It is not a pleasant climate, and that is why the Spaniards
built the city of La Paz in its sheltered cañon and why the people

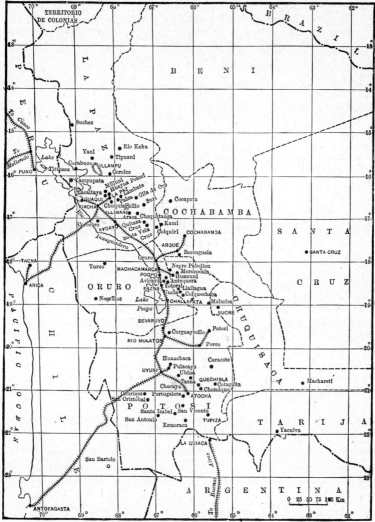

FIG. 63.—Map of Bolivia showing location of mining districts. (Not including
extreme northern and eastern unmineralized parts.) Mining localities with
initial capitals, other localities all capitals. (*Miller and Singewald*.)

of Bolivia insist upon making it their seat of government, though
Sucre is the legal capital.

The Mining Industry.—Mining is the basis of economic life in Bolivia to a far greater degree than in any other South American country. The major producing centers are in the departments of Potosí and Oruro (Fig. 63). Until about the end of the nineteenth century, silver was the chief mineral produced; but, since that time, tin has become the all-important product. In addition to tin and silver, there is some production of copper, lead,

Fig. 64.—Region of Potosí, once the foremost silver-producing region of the world. Now a leading tin-mining center. (*Copyright Ewing Galloway, N. Y.*)

antimony, and other lesser minerals; but the fact that tin alone accounts for about three-fourths of all mineral production indicates the important place it holds in the economy of the country.

Tin.—Bolivia now ranks second only to the Straits Settlements in southeastern Asia as a producer of tin. For more than 300 years, the famous silver mines of Potosí (Fig. 64) were among the wonders of the mining world; but their silver lodes had been so thoroughly worked out by 1895 that it became necessary to consider what should be done. The Antofagasta and Bolivia Railroad reached the center of the plateau in 1892 and made it possible to ship out ores of lower value than those of silver or gold. Moreover, the rapid advance in the use of tin created an expanding market for that metal. It had long been known that tin ores existed in the Potosí region; and, about 1895, the mining of these ores began in a serious way. By 1900, the region was producing 16,000 tons of tin bars and concentrates a year; and, in 1929, the exports exceeded 70,000 tons of concentrates, containing 43,000 tons of pure tin. In 1938, exports of concentrates amounted to 56,657 metric tons containing 25,893 tons of metal. Bolivia is producing over a quarter of the world's annual supply of new tin; and not only does this single item exceed all other Bolivian mineral products, but it is three times as important as all other minerals combined. Tin mining has become the dominating economic interest of the Republic. One of the wealthiest men in all South America is Simon Patiño, the "tin king" of Bolivia, who rose from poverty to great wealth through the fabulous profits of his tin mines originally obtained at a trifling cost. In 1924, an interest in his great properties was bought by an American corporation.

The tin ores of Bolivia are intimately associated with other minerals, notably those bearing silver and pyrite and others bearing copper, lead, tungsten, and bismuth. The tin deposits are confined to the eastern range of the Andes, known as the Cordillera Real. Strangely enough, the rich tin ores extend practically to the Peruvian boundary on the north and to the Argentine boundary on the south; but, up to date, few valuable tin deposits have been located beyond the boundaries of Bolivia. During a geologically recent epoch, intrusions of igneous rock forced their way upward into the overlying rocks and brought about the concentration of tin-bearing ores both in the older rocks into which they intrude and also in the igneous rocks themselves (Fig. 65). The tin is found in mineral veins that branch and penetrate the surrounding rocks in all directions and often form a complex network of large and small veins, some of which attain a width of 5 feet or more. The famous Cerro de Potosí has become honeycombed with galleries from which the silver ores were removed at an earlier date and from which tin ores are now being taken. At one time, this mountain had 742 mine entrances leading into the maze of galleries.[1]

The richer ores carry 6 or 8 per cent tin and even more, but the average is nearer 3 per cent. They lie near the surface but

[1] See Miller and Singewald, "Mineral Deposits of South America," p. 122.

also extend to an unknown depth below. The deepest working extends downward less than 1,000 feet. There are upward of 25 districts that are producing tin, but most of the ore comes from a few properties. The most valuable of these are in a mountain (Cerro de Llallagua) south of Oruro. These two groups of work-

FIG. 65.—Mining camp of the Caracoles Tin Company. (*Courtesy of Caracoles Tin Company.*)

ings have produced upward of half the tin mined in Bolivia. Another large and excellently equipped property belonging to an American company is at Caracoles, about midway between La Paz and Cochabamba. At times, the tin ores have been smelted largely at Perth Amboy, N.J.; but, owing to lower smelting costs in Great Britain, most of the ore goes there. Very little smelting of tin is done in Bolivia, mainly because of the high cost of fuel;

before shipping, the ores are concentrated so that they consist of about 45 to 55 per cent pure tin.

Several years ago, the average cost of producing and marketing a ton of tin concentrates as reported by two typical mines in Bolivia was as follows:[1]

	Per Ton	
Mining and conveying to concentrating mills..........	$4.78	
Sorting and handling..............................	0.48	
Milling and assaying..............................	1.51	
General expenses.................................	0.36	
Cost of production............................		$7.13
Railroad freight to Guaqui on Lake Titicaca.....·......	35.88	
Railroad freight from Guaqui to the port of Mollendo..	10.14	
Ocean freight from Mollendo to Europe...............	7.80	
Cost of transportation to smelter.................		53.82
Export duties...................................		15.60
Commissions, insurance, etc.....................		10.92
Total cost laid down at smelter in Europe.......		$87.47

In the above table, three facts stand out prominently: (1) the extremely *low* cost of production of tin concentrates, $7.13; (2) the very *high* cost of transportation to the coast, $46.02; and (3) the relatively low cost of ocean transportation, $7.80. Fifty-three per cent of the total cost at the smelter is due to the relatively short haul by railway to the coast.

Silver.—The silver mines of Potosí, Bolivia, have yielded more than $1,000,000,000 of silver since they were discovered nearly 400 years ago (1545).[2] This enormous output places the Potosí group of mines in the position of the greatest silver producer in the world. These mines were one of the largest sources of wealth in all the Spanish colonies. They were worked in the colonial days by forced Indian labor, and the ores were taken some 300 miles to the Pacific on the backs of men and mules. Some were also taken 800 miles overland by mule or oxcart to the Paraná or the Paraguay river and shipped thence to Spain.

---

[1] Wilson, Otto. South America as an Export Field, *Special Agents Series* 81, p. 59, U.S. Dept. of Commerce, Washington, D.C., 1914.

[2] *Special Agents Series* 81, p. 58, U.S. Dept. of Commerce, Washington, D.C., 1914.

Other mines in Bolivia yielded upward of $500,000,000 in silver, making a total for the country of nearly $2,000,000,000. So rich in silver were these surface ores that, even with the crude methods of mining then in use, they yielded fabulous profits. Tin was constantly encountered in the silver-mining operations; but it had no value at that time and in that place, and the tin ores were thrown upon the dumps as worthless.

Bolivia is no longer an important source of silver. In recent years, it has yielded only about 2 per cent ($2,500,000) of the world's putput as compared with about 40 per cent produced by Mexico and 20 per cent by the United States. The Americas yield 80 to 85 per cent of all the silver mined in the world.

Copper.—At various places in the Andes, bodies of copper ore exist. The Cerro de Pasco region of Peru has already been referred to; and in Chile are found three very large copper-ore bodies, Chuquicamata, Potrerillos, and El Teniente. Thus far, however, no copper-ore body of such magnitude has been found in Bolivia, but many smaller ones are known. The most important producer is at Corocoro, on a branch of the Arica-La Paz Railway (Fig. 62). This deposit yields native or pure copper. Most of Bolivia's output comes from this region, but the total production averages only about $1,000,000 or $2,000,000 a year, a small fraction of the value of Bolivian tin. Since the World War, the copper mines of the world have been able to produce more copper than has been needed, and some mines in the United States have been unable to produce at a profit at the prices that have prevailed. There has been little incentive, therefore, to develop new copper mines in Bolivia.

Miscellaneous Minerals.—Lead, zinc, gold, antimony, tungsten, and a number of other minerals are mined in Bolivia (Fig. 62); but the lack of cheap transportation, the scarcity of labor, and the high cost of fuel and supplies—all tend to retard the mining of any but very rich ores, or less rich ores at times of high prices. Most of the world's supply of the metal bismuth comes from Bolivia where it is nearly all produced by a single company. Bismuth is valuable chiefly because of the easily fusible alloys that it forms with lead and tin. These alloys melt at such low temperatures that they are employed in making safety fuses in electrical apparatus, safety plugs for boilers, and automatic fire-extinguishing sprinklers. The metal is also of value in medicine.

Agriculture on the Plateau.—A leading Bolivian authority[1] estimates that there are in all Highland Bolivia about 10 million acres suited to agriculture, about half of which is actually under cultivation. This means that less land is cultivated in all Bolivia than in a quarter of a state like Ohio. In the northern half of the plateau, the rainfall is about 24 inches a year, falling chiefly from October to March. This is barely enough to support agriculture, and the crops are light (Fig. 66). All the agriculture is

Fig. 66.—Agricultural lands on the Bolivian plateau near Tupiza.

carried on by the Indians either for themselves or as tenants on the large estates. The Indians refuse to change their traditional ways of farming, which are worse than medieval in their crudeness. Modern implements, except the plow, are practically unknown and wholly undesired. The Indian loves his little piece of land and loves to cultivate the land beyond any other occupation, provided that he can do it in his own way.

An American[2] who lived many years in Bolivia thus describes the Indian's attachment to his ancestral lands:

"It is no surprise to find that to the Bolivian aborigine, 'land is the very breath of life.' If he holds it as free property, it is his 'pearl of

[1] Señor Louis Crispo, quoted by George M. McBride, The Agrarian Indian Communities of Highland Bolivia, *Am. Geog. Soc. Research Series* 5, p. 3, 1921.

[2] McBride, George M. The Agrarian Indian Communities of Highland Bolivia, *Am. Geog. Soc. Research Series* 5, p. 3, 1921.

greatest price.' So dear is it to him that, in time of famine, he will sell his child rather than part with his diminutive parcel of ground. He fences it with a wall of stones or mud. He carefully guards the boulders that mark its bounds. He looks upon every traveler with a suspicious eye for fear the stranger may covet his tiny holdings. If, as is usually the case, the land belongs not to an individual, but to a group of persons who hold it collectively, it is no less dear. Every member of the body is *per se* a defender of its holdings. No greater perfidy can be committed than to violate or fail to support the ancient custom of guarding the common holdings.

"The Indians not only love their land; they cling to it generation after generation. Most of the families have lived on their present holdings from time immemorial. Nothing will induce them to move. There is far more fertile soil in the valleys east of the cordillera. A milder climate may be found in the valleys which the Indian traders visit from time to time. But these facts do not entice them to abandon the lands upon which their fathers lived. Even the inducement of good wages in the cities, at the mines, or upon the railroads can seldom uproot these devoted farmers from their little plots of ground. Even if, as often happens, the land be absorbed by an adjoining hacienda, and passed repeatedly from one owner to another, the Indian remains on it, being transferred with the soil. Only by the use of violence and by the demolition of his humble cottage, the destruction of his sheep corral, and the appropriation of his fields, can he be driven from the place. Centuries of occupation have fixed him fast to the soil."

Barley and potatoes, with occasional fields of wheat and oats, are the chief crops of the plateau. Not only are the level lands cultivated, but the mountain slopes also, although terracing is less common than in Peru. So small is the yield that the plateau region does not produce enough food for the population, and supplies are brought up from the eastern slopes and valleys and are imported from abroad. Bolivia, as a whole, is far from self-sufficient in food production, although it might be if better farming methods were used. Only recently has the government given attention to the improvement of agriculture, and little has yet been done. The Indians and the rural *cholos* cannot read and, hence, could not be reached by agricultural instruction in printed form if it were attempted. They constitute an inert, unresponsive mass, unwilling to be instructed, and employing only primitive methods, they are incapable of producing enough food for the nation. The situation presents a strange anomaly: agriculture wholly dependent upon the Indians' labor, yet these same Indians constituting a stone wall against any improvement, and the nation faced with a food-production problem that the efforts of the next hundred years will not solve. However, the large exportation of minerals provides the means for purchasing such foodstuffs as must be imported.

Cattle and sheep of inferior quality are raised in various parts of Bolivia, but even the approximate number is not known. The sheep are raised on the plateau and the bordering highlands. Fleeces, when washed, weigh only about 2 pounds instead of the usual 4 or 5 pounds. The sheep are sheared once in 2 or 3 years, and this may be done with a piece of broken glass. So stubbornly do the Indians resist any innovation that they not infrequently refuse to use sheep shears when offered them.

Alpacas are fairly numerous, and llamas are believed to number at least 500,000. The llamas of the high Andes are the cheapest carriers known. They live on next to nothing, and their owners can underbid the railways in carrying products. Thousands of them may be seen carrying bags of ore from mines to mills or to railways. Their wool is much used by the Indians.

Problems in the Economic Development of the Plateau.—Mention has already been made of some of the problems that must be solved before Bolivia's future economic development is assured. Since the plateau is the heart of the country and will probably continue to be so for some time, these problems are confined largely, though not exclusively, to the plateau. An adequate labor supply, low-cost fuel, better and cheaper transportation facilities, and sufficient capital for development are a few of the most pressing problems that must be met.

The Labor Problem.—Bolivia has a small population of only about 3 million. Of these, about one-half are pure-blood Indians, about 1 million are *mestizos* or *cholos*, and the rest whites. There is scarcely any Negro blood in the country.

In the high altitudes of the plateau, the air is thin and man's physiological and nervous system must become adjusted to life conditions wholly unlike those of the lowlands. Only the Indians, accustomed throughout many generations to these altitudes, can do heavy manual work. Future mining development depends in large measure on this factor of Indian labor. Only by a wiser attitude with regard to the conservation and uplift of the Indian population and a wiser use of mechanical appliances can a future labor supply be assured.

The following account[1] of two Indian groups of Bolivia, the Aymarás and Quechuas, gives an insight into the character of a large part of the population and its place in the economic life of the country.

The Aymarás (ĭ-mä-rás)

"The normal environment in which the Aymará lives, and which accounts for his peculiar temperament, is highly unfavorable to human life, when unaided by the resources of modern civilization, which are beyond the reach of the Indian. The Aymará's existence has been a continuous struggle against the environment of the bleak and inhospitable plateau—against cold and hunger and the lack of oxygen. The hard conditions of life have left little place in him for affection or any other of the finer feelings. One of his strongest sentiments is his ineradicable attachment to the 'ayllu,' the community in which he was born and in which his ancestors lived. So strong is this attachment to his traditional home that he refuses to migrate to the warmer valleys beyond the Andes where the conditions of life are much more favorable. His music is in accord with the dreary circumstances of his life and consists of the melancholy and monotonous minor notes of the 'quina' or reed flute. His few songs are mournful chants that are seldom heard.

"The country-dwelling Aymará lives in a hut made of mud or stones, where he sleeps on a sheep pelt on the bare floor or on the floor itself. His clothing consists of a peaked woolen cap with long 'ear flaps' that hang down over the side of his face; a homespun woolen poncho, generally of great age; rough trousers split part way up the back of the leg; and crude sandals, which he wears over the rocky roads of the mountain country or the sharp cobblestones of La Paz, but which are generally discarded. His sparse diet is made up of potatoes, usually in the desiccated form known as 'chuno,' a stew made of vegetables and barley, or 'quinua,' and parched corn. He eats little meat or bread, though he may kill a sheep to celebrate a fiesta.

"The Aymará is the agricultural laborer of the 'altiplano,' though seldom a proprietor, save where the ancient communal tenure has been permitted to survive in some distant localities. He also does the rough work of the city and can always be seen carrying burdens about the streets of La Paz. He cares for the herds and flocks of the plateau and drives the pack trains of mules, burros, or llamas from place to place. He is often the owner of small flocks of sheep or droves of pack animals,

[1] Schurz, N. L. Bolivia: A Commercial and Industrial Handbook, *Special Agents Series* 208, U.S. Dept. of Commerce, Washington, D.C., 1921.

whose life he shares in a strange intimacy. Most of the workers in the mines are also drawn from his class. He has no place in the political life of the nation, and sharp barriers of caste separate him from those who own and rule the country. Even the majority of the 'cholos,' who have sprung from a mixture of his race with the Spaniard, look down on him and refuse to speak his language."

Much more numerous are the Quechuas, the most important racial group of the Inca Empire, now forming the chief element in the highland population from Ecuador to northern Argentina.

The Quechuas (kĕch'-wȧs)

"The Quechua is smaller in stature than the Aymará, less robust and of finer features, some of the men of the Sucre district being of quite handsome appearance. However, the Aymará 'cholos,' particularly the 'cholos' of La Paz, are generally superior, as regards stamina and appearance, to the majority of the Quechua mixed breeds.

"There is a vast difference in the character of the two races. The Aymará, at the time of the Spanish conquest, had lived under the Incaic dominion only a comparatively short time and still lived in a semi-barbarous state. The Quechua, on the other hand, had long been subjected to the peculiar civilizing régime of the Incas, which had given him certain fundamental elements of culture and a settled order of society, even though it had deprived him of all personal initiative. The Incaic institutions have disappeared, save in the survival of a few customs, but the Quechua still preserves in his temper much of the heritage of pre-Spanish days. He is eminently docile and passive, whereas the submissiveness of the Aymará can never be taken for granted. He, also, is taciturn and uncommunicative but never defiantly or sullenly so. His temper is, in general, much gentler and kindlier than that of the Aymará. However, he has the same propensity for drink, which he shares with the other Indian races of South America. Except in the high mountain districts of Oruro and Potosi, he prefers the milder 'chicha' to the strong liquors that serve the Aymará. This is particularly true in the valleys of Cochabamba and Chuquisaca, where large areas of corn are devoted to the making of 'chicha.' In the city of Cochabamba, there are 1,400 'chicherias,' or shops where 'chicha' is dispensed. This is at the rate of about 1 to 25 persons in the population.

"The Quechua's manner of life varies considerably in different districts. In the valleys of Cochabamba and Sucre, which are the favorite habitats of the race, it is much superior to the conditions in the more unfavorable environment of the Oruro and Potosi highlands. In the former, he is an agriculturist, working in a good soil and a temperate climate. There he has enough to eat of corn and vegetables and often of meat, and the climate makes few demands in the way of clothing and housing. In Potosi and Oruro, he is a worker in the mines or farms the barren and rocky soil of the mountains. Here his conditions of life are much like those of the Aymará of the La Paz 'altiplano.'

"Like the Aymará, he lives apart from the political life of the republic but is less esteemed as a soldier. Yet with the Aymará, he forms the very basis of the whole economic life of the country."

The Problem of Fuel on the Plateau.—The tableland and high mountains of Bolivia are treeless, and so are the western slopes of the Andes all the way to the sea. Practically no wood for fuel is available, nor is workable coal known to exist in Bolivia or in the parts of any neighboring country readily accessible to Bolivia. Petroleum seepages are common in places, and the evidences of oil were sufficient to lead the Standard Oil Company to expend millions of dollars in exploration and drilling, without satisfactory results, however, up to 1930. In March, 1937, all the concessions to foreign companies were taken over by the government, and today private concessions are not granted. Partnerships with foreign companies are permitted, but no such agreements have been reached up to the present. Production of petroleum during the past 6 years (1933–1938) has ranged between 119,000 and 182,000 barrels per year.

On the plateau itself and on the Pacific slope, there are relatively few streams and little available water power. But, on the eastern slope of the Cordillera Real, there are heavy rainfall and enormous potential water power which can be converted into electrical energy and transmitted to the mining camps. Potential water power is estimated at 3,600,000 horsepower of which only 16,000 horsepower has been developed. Electric smelting of ores has not yet proved economical. Clearly, the plateau is seriously deficient in fuel. Even *taquia*, the dried dung of the llamas, is widely used for domestic fuel, for steam boilers, and even for small smelters. For example, the Corocoro Copper Company has used 10,000 tons of *taquia* a year, paying the Indians $4 a ton for it.

The second local source of fuel is the *yareta*, a woody, resinous mass of fibers resembling enormous fungi; this grows on the rocks and is gathered, dried, and sold by the Indians. Large heaps of it may be seen piled along the railways at the stations on the plateau. Imported coal costs $30 to $40 a ton at the mines in Bolivia.

The absence of fuel at reasonable cost is one of the drawbacks to mining development. Any metallurgical operation becomes so expensive as to be impractical. Lack of fuel is one of the chief reasons why ore or concentrates are exported for reduction elsewhere rather than refined in the country. The fuel difficulty, of course, will be partly met if large quantities of petroleum are found and production becomes significant—a possibility that is altogether likely.

Transportation on the Plateau.—Bolivia has upward of 2,500 miles of roads on which automobiles may be used during parts of the year; but only a few roads are first-class motor roads, and they are in detached stretches leading to a mine or extending a short distance out from some city, especially La Paz (Fig. 67). Concrete highways would cost nearly as much to build in Bolivia as railroads, and there are very few vehicles to use such highways. The greater part of the transportation of goods, other than by railroads, is done by mules, burros, and llamas. Bolivia is too poor to build both good roads and railroads, and railroads are given the preference, and properly so at this stage. In all Bolivia, there are fewer wheeled vehicles than would be found in one small city in the United States.

In the building of railways, Bolivia has made notable progress, when the tremendous difficulties involved are taken into account. This inland country is connected by three railways to the Pacific coast and by a fourth to the railway system of Argentina and thence to the Atlantic. The total railway mileage is about 1,300 or 1,400, very nearly all of which is on the plateau. The principal lines focus upon La Paz. The extension of the Southern Railway of Peru by way of Lake Titicaca connects the Bolivian plateau with the Peruvian port of Mollendo, but this route is the least used for Bolivian traffic of the three that reach the Pacific. The shortest route is the Arica-La Paz Railway, 281 miles long. It has frightful grades, and for 22 miles is compelled to use a cograil system. But the fact that the route is much shorter than either of the other lines to the Pacific gives it an advantage that is diverting an increasing quantity of traffic to it. In fact, it is, at times, taxed beyond the capacity of its limited equipment, and shippers complain of the long delays (Fig. 67).

The longest route is the Antofagasta and Bolivia Railway, a narrow-gauge privately owned British line that obtains a very large traffic from the copper mines and nitrate fields of northern Chile as well as from the tin mines of Bolivia. This line traverses

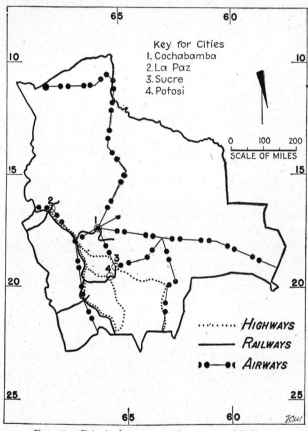

FIG. 67.—Principal transportation routes of Bolivia.

almost the whole length of the Bolivian plateau. Several lesser lines connect this important railway with cities and mining camps on the plateau, and one, completed in 1925, connects with the Argentine system at the boundary of that country and gives Bolivia an outlet to the Atlantic by way of Buenos Aires. The fact that all the overseas commerce of Bolivia must pass through ports belonging to foreign countries is objectionable to Bolivia, but the inconvenience is less than might be expected (Fig. 67).

Air lines connect various parts of the plateau, the plateau with outlying areas, and Bolivia with other countries (Fig. 67). Bi-weekly airplane service is provided to and from the United States. An air line runs from Arica via La Paz to Córdoba, Argentina. Although these air lines give mobility to passenger traffic, they are of little or no value in the movement of bulky commodities.

The Problem of Obtaining Capital.—In modern society, capital is an extremely mobile industrial resource. In Bolivia, as in many South American countries, securing necessary foreign capital for the development of mining properties depends in large measure upon the attitude of the government toward foreign investments. Capital will flow into Bolivia in any quantity necessary, if the laws and their administration are just, if a stable government is maintained, and if there is opportunity for profit. Since the country possesses great mineral wealth, actual and potential, the "opportunity for profit" is present; but there remains much exploratory and developmental work to be done. It would seem that wealthy corporations who could absorb certain necessary losses without facing bankruptcy would be the logical ones to carry on this work. In view of these conditions, it is difficult to justify Bolivia's policy of withdrawing all foreign concessions and by so doing antagonizing foreign companies.

Urban Centers of the Plateau.—Most of the towns of the plateau are mining centers. Some, like Potosí, have attained international fame, but only one today is of such size or importance as to deserve special attention—the city of La Paz.

The City of La Paz.—La Paz is politically, socially, intellectually, and financially the center of the country and the focus of its transportation lines. Founded by the Spaniards in 1548, the city has grown slowly to a population of about 200,000. It has trolley cars and electric lights, a telephone system, waterworks, and fairly well-paved main streets. The University of La Paz has several hundred students, most of whom are enrolled in law and medicine. There are also five departmental colleges, only one or two of which enroll as many as 100 students. La Paz has a few manufacturing establishments; and, as a mercantile and trading center it ranks first in the republic (Fig. 68).

At an earlier date, Sucre (30,000) was made the legal capital of the republic; but its out-of-the-way location has caused it to be replaced by La Paz, which is the actual capital. Lying in its sheltered and sunny valley, La Paz has a much more agreeable climate than is found on the wind-swept plateau.

The capital city of La Paz has the most unusual setting of any city in South America. In a recent geologic period, a river cut a profound gorge or gulch in the deep gravels that fill the valley

Fig. 68.—Sunday open-air market on a street in La Paz.

south of Lake Titicaca. The modern successor of that stream now flows through the city and eastward to a branch of the Amazon. The gorge, 1,500 feet deep at La Paz, is still deeper farther downstream and has a width of 2 miles or more. On nearly all sides of the city, the partly cemented gravels stand in pinnacles, towers, and massive walls of striking colors. The railways that wind and loop their way from the plateau down to the city constitute two of the most expensive pieces of railway building in Bolivia.

THE EASTERN SLOPES AND PLAINS

Although much larger in area than the plateau, this eastern region of Bolivia is of only minor importance in the economy of the country (Fig. 60). The region is composed of two major sub-divisions: (1) the eastern slope of the Andes, or the Yungas region, and (2) the Eastern Plains and Foothills. The most advanced portion of eastern Bolivia is the Department of Cochabamba with its important city of Cochabamba. Within the department are included a small part of: (1) the plateau, (2) the lofty Cordillera Real and its eastern slope (Yungas), and (3) the densely forested plains of the Amazon valley (Figs. 60 and 62). The human activities and character of the department thus give some idea of the transitions that occur between the plateau and the eastern portion of Bolivia.

The Department of Cochabamba is, next to La Paz, the most populous in Bolivia; and the city of Cochabamba is second in population only to La Paz. The city was one of the earliest founded in Bolivia by the Spaniards and is regarded as having an exceptionally fine climate, lying as it does at an intermediate altitude. Its population of 40,000 people is largely Indian and cholo but includes also a fair proportion of whites. It is connected with the main line of the Bolivian Railway at Oruro by a recently completed railroad, and two electric lines connect the city with other towns in the region. The department has more miles of roads that can be used by motorcars than any other in the republic, and regular motorbus service is maintained over some of these roads during the dry season.

Agriculturally, Cochabamba is the leading department of Bolivia and has the largest population to the square mile. Because of the exceedingly wide range of altitude and rainfall, almost every known crop can be grown somewhere in the department. Several thousand acres are under irrigation during the dry season. Corn is the leading crop in the Cochabamba valley, and three-fourths of it is used in making an alcoholic drink (*chicha*) of which the Indians and cholos are very fond. From both sugar cane and grains, alcohol is made to the extent of 70 million quarts a year in the single department of Cochabamba. The Indians are exceedingly fond of alcoholic drinks and welcome feast days, which both men and women celebrate by getting drunk. In 1919, there were 1,500 *chicha*-making places in the department and 1,400 *chicha*-selling places in the single city of Cochabamba. Every city and town abounds in liquor-selling shops. Drunkenness among the Indian laborers in the mines is such an evil that prohibitory regulations have been put into operation in the leading mining centers.

A small quantity of wheat is grown and is cut with the sickle and threshed by driving oxen over the straw, as is customary throughout the Andes. It is mostly ground into coarse flour in small water-driven mills of crude construction. Modern mills exist in the cities of Cochabamba and Sucre. Barley is the chief cereal of the drier lands, especially on the plateau. It is mainly used for making beer in breweries located in the larger cities. Cochabamba has a brewery that markets a million bottles of beer yearly.

One of the principal potential resources of eastern Bolivia is petroleum. Oil seepages and also the finding of oil by drilling have led to the belief that petroleum in paying quantities exists in this region. Up to 1930, practically no oil had been produced, but active exploration and drilling were in progress. The efforts to develop these petroleum resources illustrate well the important part that capital and experience must play in the great industrial undertakings and indicate how essential to the development of the resources of South America are the capital and experience that have already been acquired in more advanced countries.

The first serious efforts to locate and develop the oil resources of Bolivia were made by a Bolivian syndicate which was able to provide upward of $1,000,000. But even this large sum made only a beginning, and the syndicate had to seek financial aid abroad. In the course of time, the promised aid was secured, and $200,000 more was invested, when the project collapsed because of lack of funds. Another effort to secure capital in Europe was made, and a third company entered upon the project of finding and producing oil in Bolivia. This effort also failed, and a fourth company (foreign) was organized to take over the undertaking. It proceeded a short way in the work when its funds ran out, and again the enterprise stopped. Various men and groups of men who had interested themselves in Bolivian oil now controlled about $3\frac{1}{2}$ million acres of prospective oil lands in eastern Bolivia but did not have either the capital or the experience necessary to carry forward the expensive enterprise. Finally, the Standard Oil Company (of the United States) acquired the rights and interests of the largest of these stranded companies, made a contract with the Bolivian Government for 55 years, and, with its enormous capital, experience, and organization, began systematic exploration and drilling in this remote region hundreds of miles from railway or deep waterway. The undertaking cost millions of dollars and up to 1930 had not resulted successfully.

Petroleum production in Bolivia in 1938 amounted to about 150,000 barrels. Commercial production is confined almost exclusively to a zone along the eastern Andes where they border the eastern lowlands. This zone extends from the Peruvian border southeast and south to the Argentine border. The area, known as the Sub-Andean zone, was developed by the Standard Oil Company which, as was stated previously, lost its concession in March, 1937. What effect will this have on future production and foreign investments is largely problematical. That capital will be attracted into the industry on any but a concession basis seems doubtful.

In addition to petroleum there is also great likelihood that other minerals are present in the mountainous portion of the east. Little is known in detail of their distribution, and none are exploited. Until better transportation facilities are provided, it seems highly improbable that there will be any marked economic development in this region. The Yungas area would seem to afford a more favorable environment than the plains area.

The Yungas Region.—The country of heavy rainfall and forests on the eastern slope of the Andes, usually called the montaña, is called the Yungas in the region east of La Paz. The valleys and slopes lying between the altitudes of 5,000 and 8,000 feet have a delightful temperature and abundant moisture and are excellently suited to semitropical agriculture. Much of the land is held in large estates, small parts of which are worked by Indians under major-domos employed by the owners to manage the estates. The larger haciendas have a half-million acres and more, but only a very small fraction of the land is under cultivation. Agriculture is almost the only occupation in the Yungas, but it is carried on by the same inefficient and antiquated methods that prevail in the Andes. The small local market for farm products leads to the cultivation of those products for which there is an active demand among the Indians and cholos, who make up most of the population. The main crop of the Yungas, and almost the only one to which serious attention is given, is the coca shrub. This is planted in terraces on the mountain sides and is grown for the leaves from which cocaine is made (Fig. 69). The greater part of the coca leaves, however, are used directly by the Indians, who chew coca almost universally. Small quantities of coffee, cacao, sugar, cotton, and other warm-climate products are grown in little patches. Well-beaten trails connect the valleys of the Yungas with La Paz and other parts of the plateau, and a relatively active trade is carried on. It is reported that 5,000 mules a day pass along the main road between La Paz and the Yungas.

FIG. 69.—Terraced mountain slopes in the Yungas of Bolivia. On these terraces the coca shrub is grown.

The delightful climate, marvelous scenery, and great potential productivity of this region lead Bolivians to regard it as the future garden spot of the republic. But its remote situation and difficulties of access must delay its development. A narrow-gauge railway is slowly building from La Paz toward the Yungas and will eventually assist in opening up the region.

The Eastern Plains.—More than half the area of Bolivia is included in the foothills and plains of the Amazon and Paraguay Rivers. A section in the southeast was in disputed ownership between Paraguay and Bolivia until 1938. A large part of this section is dry country, covered with grass and scrub, somewhat used for cattle grazing but very sparsely populated. The two large departments of Santa Cruz and Beni are partly forest and partly park land where great herds of wild cattle pasture. Beni and the Territory of Colonies contain extensive rubber forests and have supplied most of the rubber that has been exported from Bolivia. The high point of exportation was reached in 1917 (about 6,000 tons); but the high point in value was reached in 1910, before the great drop in price that was caused by the competition of plantation rubber from the Far East. The recent production of rubber in Bolivia has been only about one-half as great as it was in 1917. The Amazon plains are low, wet, and jungle-covered, and are of little present value.

Chapter VII. Chile: The Country as a Whole and Its Northern Mineral Region

CHILE AND NITRATES

The development of modern Chile is intimately associated with the nitrate industry. Upon its success rested the social, political, and economic structure of the Chilean Republic. Until early in the twentieth century, nitrate paid up to 68 per cent of the costs of government and allowed the ruling class to maintain large landholdings without taxation. In recent years, the nitrate industry has suffered a series of reverses which threatened the very life of the republic. Partial collapse of the Chilean nitrate market has necessitated a rapidity of readjustment in the social and economic structure that has probably never been equalled in any other country.

Soon after the Spaniards conquered Peru, they made sporadic attempts to utilize this nitrate in the manufacture of gunpowder. This proved unsatisfactory, for the sodium nitrate takes up moisture from the air and makes powder manufactured from it damp. It was not until 1809 that the idea of utilizing Chilean nitrate for agriculture was conceived. The idea gained ground slowly. A shipment of 110 tons was made to England in 1831, and exports increased to 56,000 tons by 1860. As far as Chile is concerned, the real history of the nitrate industry began in 1880. Previous to that time, the deposits were in either Bolivian or Peruvian territory. In 1879 to 1883, Chile was victorious in the War of the Pacific against Peru and Bolivia and, as an indemnity, took from Bolivia its only strip of seacoast and from Peru a portion of its southern coastlands. In this acquired territory and south of it are the world's only known large deposits of nitrate of soda (Fig. 70).

Location and Nature of the Nitrate Deposits.—The Chilean nitrate deposits extend from latitude 19 to 27°S., a distance of about 450 miles. They lie at altitudes ranging from 4,000 to 9,000 feet in an irregular belt 5 to 40 miles wide in the "Pampa" between the coast range and the main Andes. For the most part, they are situated on the eastern side of the coastal range and are connected by rail with some 10 ports, from Taltal in the south to Pisagua at the north. The beds are not continuous but are most irregularly distributed (Fig. 71). Within a given deposit, the nitrate-bearing

Fig. 70.—Electric shovels removing overburden in nitrate fields.

layers may vary in thickness from a few inches to many feet, may lie at the very surface of the desert or as much as 25 feet below, and may carry all the way from a mere trace of nitrate up to as much as 40 per cent.

The nitrate exists as a cementing material in the rock waste that, in the geologic past, has been eroded from the mountains and carried down into the valley between the ranges. Whence the nitrate came and why it is here are questions still unanswered,[1] but it clearly was brought by percolating waters and crystallized in the upper layers of the loose sand and gravel where it has been

[1] For discussion of theories of origin and accumulation, see Miller, B. L., and Singewald, J. T., "The Mineral Deposits of South America," pp. 293–296, 1919.

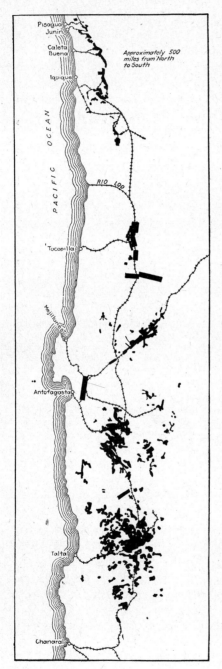

preserved by the extreme dryness of the region. So firmly does the nitrate cement these materials that they are resistant rocks and usually require explosives to break them up (Fig. 72). The richer of the nitrate-bearing layers are termed the *caliche*. Formerly only deposits that contain upward of 12 per cent nitrate were used, but a new process has made poorer deposits profitable to work. The physical obstacles to the production of nitrate are many, and the overcoming of these adverse conditions requires great labor and expense. Fresh water for the *oficinas* (factories) must be piped from the Andes 100 miles or more; and food, supplies, animals and feed, structural steel, timbers, machinery, fuel, and men must be brought from other areas (Fig 73).

Importance of the Nitrate Deposits to Chile.—Chile has several important

Fig. 71.—Nitrate fields, railways and shipping ports of Chile. The principal producing areas are east of Tocopilla and northeast of Antofogasta. (*Engineering and Mining Journal, Jan. 12, 1924.*)

mineral resources; but, of these, nitrate has been the most important of all. For many years, it constituted more than half the total exports of the country, and the export tax on nitrate (about $12 per ton) collected by the Chilean Government not only formed the largest item in the revenue of the nation but at times exceeded all other revenues combined. There is no other important country where national revenues came so largely from a single source as was the case in Chile. The economic health of the country has been dependent upon the condition of the nitrate export trade. When the nitrate *oficinas* were busy, Chile pros-

Fig. 72.—Nitrate workings in the desert of northern Chile.   (*Courtesy W. R. Grace and Co.*)

pered; when their activity lagged, Chile was depressed. One of the most serious financial crises experienced by the country followed the drop in the exportation of nitrate after 1921. The government was overthrown and found itself unable to meet its financial obligations. Synthetic nitrate, made in Europe and the United States, began to compete disastrously with the Chilean product.

"In 1900, the Chilean producers had a practical monopoly of the supply and the rest of the world was worrying lest the Chilean deposits would soon be used up, first sending the nitrate up to a prohibitive price level, and then making it unobtainable. Now it is evident that a permanent supply of combined nitrogen is available, and the Chilean

FIG. 73.—View of the nitrate oficina of W. R. Grace and Co. in the desert of northern Chile. (*Courtesy W. R. Grace and Co.*)

producers are faced with the necessity of selling their product at a price lower than that of the other forms of fixed nitrogen if they wish to continue as producers."[1]

Many *oficinas* closed and all lost money (Fig. 74). In 1932, the industry was completely demoralized, and although several reorganization plans have been developed the outcome cannot be predicted. Not only was the nitrate industry important to Chile as a source of governmental revenue, but it gave employment to some 40,000 workmen (57,000 in 1917), employed hundreds of millions of dollars of Chilean and foreign capital, provided the chief traffic for several railroads, and formed one of the chief markets for Chilean farm products.

Ownership of Oficinas and Erratic Production.—The capital invested in the Chilean nitrate industry has been derived from several

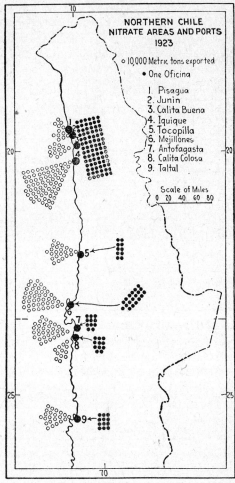

Fig. 74.—Nitrate ports and groups of nitrate oficinas which are tributary to them. The black dots show the number of oficinas, but not their exact locations. Many of these are not now in operation.

different sources. In 1879, the plants engaged in nitrate pro-

[1] Bain, H. Foster, and Read, Thomas Thornton, "Ores and Industry in South America," p. 232, Harper & Brothers, New York, 1934.

duction had an annual capacity of about 17,000 metric tons, and the capital invested in them at that time was nearly 60 per cent Peruvian, less than 20 per cent Chilean, 14 per cent British, and about 8 per cent German. By 1901, the production capacity had more than doubled and the financial relationship greatly changed. Of the invested capital in 1901, 55 per cent was British,

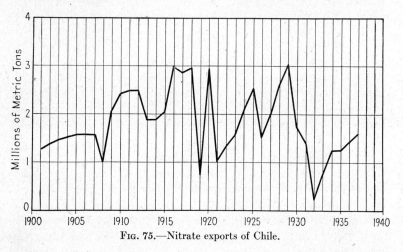

FIG. 75.—Nitrate exports of Chile.

15 per cent Chilean, 14 per cent German, 10 per cent Spanish, and all other 6 per cent. By 1921, the capacity for production had increased forty times, and the Chilean capital had reached 51, British 34, Jugo-Slav 5, German 4, American 2½, and Spanish 2 per cent.

The number of *oficinas* has also varied greatly. In 1894, there were 51; in 1909, 113; and, at one time, 125 were regarded as going concerns. When the situation became again desperate in 1930, there were about 45 firms engaged in nitrate production. At that time, 40 of these firms and the government formed the corporation known as the Compania de Salitre de Chile ("Cosach"). In this agreement, the government of Chile became a partner in the industry and in return agreed to remove the export tax. This scheme did not produce results anticipated, and further reorganization became imperative. Although the production increased from 1933 to 1938, the government has been compelled to make rapid readjustments in order to bring about a solution of the serious problems that had been created by the too great dependence on the nitrate industry for its economic stability. Figure 75 shows the fluctuations in production of nitrate in the present century. Manifestly, the Chilean nitrate industry is an erratic one, attended with heavy risks as well as with possibilities of large profits.

Reserves for the Future.—The existence of the nitrate in the Atacama desert has been known since early colonial times, and production dates from about 1825. There is no reliable knowledge concerning the nitrate that still remains in the ground. Most of the unproved lands, but not all, belong to the Chilean Government; and tracts are sold from time to time. At one period, grave concern was expressed as to the life of the industry, but there is abundant evidence that an enormous quantity of nitrate still remains. The danger, as Chile sees it, is not the exhaustion of her nitrate but the successful competition of synthetic nitrates. Already, Germany (a former important market) is manufacturing nitrate fertilizer more than sufficient for her needs. In the United States and other areas since the World War, there has been a notable increase in the manufacture of nitrogen compounds that actively compete with Chilean nitrates. It seems evident that (1) Chilean nitrate has lost a natural monopoly of an essential material and (2) the government of Chile can no longer count on the large revenues formerly obtained from the nitrate industry. In spite of these conditions, the output of nitrates in Chile again exceeds well over 1 million tons a year.

PHYSICAL FEATURES

The Shape of the Country.—The shape of Chile is unique, for the country has a length of 2,600 miles and an average width of only 110 miles. The unusual shape of the country as a political unit grows out of historic and physiographic causes. The desert of Atacama at the north separated the Spanish colonial settlements in Peru from those which grew up farther south in the valley of Chile; and this separation foreshadowed that, whenever the Spanish colonies should become independent nations, this desert would separate two of those nations. Following the same logic, the main range of the Andes, another natural barrier, became a boundary between the west-facing settlements of Spain on the Pacific coast and the east-facing settlements that grew up around the estuary of the River Plata.

The main range of the Andes was accepted from the beginning of the independence of Chile and Argentina as their boundary, but it was not until 1902 that the award of King Edward of Great Britain determined the exact line of international boundary. In the main, then, Chile's peculiar shape is the logical outgrowth of its unusual physical features.

The shape of Chile might seem to be a disadvantage to the economic development and safety of the country; but, under all the conditions as they exist today, it does not appear that it is. Natural influences, such as a genial climate and fertile soil, have concentrated the population of Chile in the Central Valley, which occupies only 600 miles of the 2,600 of the country's total length. The arid region that forms the northern portion of Chile is somewhat detached from the Central Valley and under conceivable circumstances might be drawn into sympathetic relations with Peru or Bolivia if either of those countries could offer better protection or greater commercial advantages than Chile offers. But such is not the case and probably never will be. Chile is the stronger and more progressive nation; and this fact is likely to hold the northern desert, with its great mineral wealth, firmly under Chilean domination. The southern third of Chile is a mountainous, rain-drenched, forest-clad land in which few people will care to make their homes for a long time to come. The only country that touches this region is Argentina, and it is scarcely conceivable that Argentina or any other country will covet this strip of land. If Chile had powerful and greedy neighbors, the shape of the country might cause concern; but the excellent army and navy and the longitudinal railway combined with the natural defenses seem to guarantee full safety.

Coast Line and Harbors.—Half the west coast of South America belongs to Chile, and the northern two-thirds of the Chilean coast has not a single well-protected harbor. The southern third of the country has undergone a sinking which has transformed the coastal mountains into islands and the valleys into straits and channels. In this part of Chile, protected harbors are numerous, but there is little commerce, for the back country is undeveloped and much of it unexplored.

Chile has about 50 ports which regularly carry on ocean commerce, coastwise or foreign; but only the ports in the southern third of the country have sufficient natural protection from storms to entitle them to be called harbors. Of the ports regularly used for foreign commerce, Talcahuano, near the city of Concepción, is the best protected by nature, but it is too far south to serve the populous part of the valley. Valparaiso is the principal port and receives more than half the total imports of the country; but it is unprotected from the westerlies, and, at times of storms, the transfer of cargoes from ships to lighters or lighters to ships is difficult or impossible. A similar condition exists along the entire Chilean coast from Valparaiso northward; and on the frequent "surf days," no transfer of cargo is attempted in most of these ports. It is noticeable that the great majority of the ports are located on the northern side of small promontories or projecting points of land that afford a little protection from the prevailing winds. Ships usually anchor some distance from land and load or unload freight and passengers by means of lighters and launches. This involves delays and added cost, but it does not appreciably diminish the volume of Chilean commerce. If certain of these harbors were spacious and well protected, they would draw to themselves a greater part of the ocean commerce of the country, but they probably would not increase the total commerce. Good harbors are unquestionably an advantage, for they expedite and protect shipping operations. In some ports, breakwaters, which give some protection, have been built at great expense and difficulty because of the deep water. Chile well might wish for a coast line with good harbors, but there is no evidence that, in and of themselves, these would greatly increase the commerce of the country.

The Geographical Regions.—Chile is a ribbon of land between the ocean and the crest of the Andes. The country has a well-defined coastal range on the west and the Andes on the east with a depression between, consisting of low plateaus in the north which give way southward to a well-defined valley. The country's great expanse of latitude leads to definite differences in climate. These climatic contrasts are far more effective in influencing the economic activities of the country than the topographic features. Based for the most part on the climatic conditions, the country may be divided into three well-defined geographical regions:

1. The arid northern mineral region.
2. The Mediterranean central agricultural valley.
3. The wet southern forest and grazing region.

1. In the dry and mountainous northern half, between the coast range and the main Andes, there is a poorly defined valley, much interrupted by mountain spurs and peaks. Here, in a strip some 450 miles long, are the famous nitrate beds scattered over the "Pampa." The extreme northern end of Chile contains no nitrate beds, however, and the controversy between Chile and Peru over the disputed provinces of Tacna and Arica has not involved the possession of nitrate lands, for those were definitely taken by Chile after the War of the Pacific in 1879 to 1883. The southern end of the nitrate zone is near Chanaral, some 600 miles north of Santiago. The intervening region is very mountainous but contains a few valleys where irrigated crops are raised and livestock is kept. The Central Valley does not become well defined until the latitude of Valparaiso is reached. The mountainous character of this northern half of Chile, combined with the very low rainfall, excludes nearly all forms of industry except mining; but the minerals are so important that the adverse influence of the mountains and desert is offset by the mineral wealth which exists there. A desert climate and a mountainous topography, which ordinarily are unfavorable to man's activities, have here become favorable influences in the country's production of wealth, for the soluble nitrates would long since have disappeared in a moist climate. As pointed out elsewhere, nearly half the revenue formerly collected for the support of the government was derived from the export tax on nitrate, and the largest mining center in South America is the great copper camp at Chuquicamata, in the heart of the northern desert.

2. The second geographic province of Chile is the Central Valley, or Vale of Chile, already mentioned. This valley between the low coast range and the lofty cordillera, together with the adjacent coast, contains about 90 per cent of the inhabitants of the country. It is this agricultural valley that makes possible a real nation.

3. Still farther south lies the third geographical region, the deeply indented, island-fringed coast, flanked by forest-clad mountains. It is too wet and rugged and disagreeably cold in winter to attract settlers, but its wealth of timber will some day give rise to larger lumbering interests.

The economic life of Chile is peculiarly affected by the highly accentuated features of its topography, so different from the plains of its neighbor Argentina, on the opposite side of the Andes.

Influence of Climate.—Chile extends from latitude 18 to 56°S., a distance of 38 degrees. The northern end of the country lies within the tropics, and the southern point is in a latitude 7 degrees higher than the northernmost part of the United States, not including Alaska. Moreover, in altitude, the land reaches from sea level to mountain tops wrapped in perpetual snow. Thus Chile has so great a range of temperature that it is able to raise nearly every crop known to man. As a matter of fact, however, the tropical portion is so dry that nothing can be grown without irrigation, and the great scarcity of water restricts even this to a few narrow strips along mountain streams.

The rainfall in the north and south differs as widely as the temperature, for it ranges from next to nothing in the desert of Atacama to upward of 100 inches in the mountains of the south. In the Central Valley, the rainfall is moderate but comes mainly in the winter months. In the northern end of the valley, most of the 20 to 25 inches of rain falls in the winter months of May, June, July, and August; in the southern end, rains are frequent every month of the year but very heavy from April to September.

The abundance and excellence of the grapes that are grown, the wide variety and high quality of other fruits, the specialization in wheat as a field crop, and the great sheep-raising interests of the far south are all a direct response to the climatic peculiarities of the respective regions, as such phenomena are the world over. On account of its great variety of climate, Chile is, or might be, a nearly self-sufficient country, so far as food production is involved.

A more significant influence is that of the climate upon the characteristics of the people. Throughout the west coast of South America, the characteristics of the indigenous Indian races have had much to do in determining the character of the present population, for the great majority of the people north of Chile and a very large number in Chile have Indian blood and manifest the traits of their Indian ancestors. In the tropical lands, the conquering Spaniards found it easy to reduce the Indians to virtual slavery and to use them as laborers. Consequently, large numbers of Indians remain, and there is a generous admixture of Indian blood in the mestizo population. These countries are more largely

Indian than Caucasian, although the Caucasian element rules. In South America, as elsewhere, the native tropical races have lacked sustained fighting spirit and have become the servants of the conquerors.

In Chile, however, the Spaniards encountered not a docile people, but one of the most virile and warlike Indian races of the Americas—the fierce Araucanians. Again and again throughout more than 300 years, these unyielding warriors defeated the invaders; but their personal courage did not make up for the inferiority of their arms, and gradually they were pushed southward. Finally, the white man's military science, but still more the white man's liquor, conquered; and, in 1882, a treaty was made with the Araucanians under which they have submitted to Chilean rule. Some of this fighting blood of the Araucanians, has worked its way through intermarriage into the veins of the present Chilean people and partly, though not wholly, accounts for the aggressiveness and military tendencies so evident in the Chileans. The long struggle between the whites and the Araucanians reduced the numbers of the Indians, but their fierce spirit prevented their being reduced to servility as the natives were in tropical South America. The result is that the whites have not learned to depend upon Indian labor in Chile to the same extent that they have in Bolivia, Peru, and Ecuador; and the stimulating qualities of their own climate have aided in making the Chileans a vigorous people, fond of activity, and unafraid of work. Thus has a variety of influences, growing directly and indirectly out of the climate, contributed to the formation of the energetic Chilean character. So marked is this difference between the peoples of tropical and those of temperate South America that there is no room for doubt that climate is a leading cause.

LAND UTILIZATION

The Limited Extent of Farm Land and Cultivated Land.—Of the 289,796 square miles of land in Chile, about one-fourth (50 million acres) is classed as actual or potential farm lands, available for crops or pastures. By way of comparison, it may be pointed out that this is more farm land than the Japanese Islands contain and more than the actual acreage included in farms in California. However, less than 2 million acres, or between 1 and 2 per cent, are actually in farm crops as compared with 6 or 7 per cent in pastures. Illinois, for example, has more than ten times as much land under the plow as Chile has.

In considering agriculture, the first noteworthy point is the small percentage of the land of the country that is actually used for crops and pastures. This is the result of three main causes: (1) the lack of rainfall in the north, the excessive rainfall of the south, and the dry summers in the Central Valley; (2) the exceedingly mountainous character of the country; and (3) the small population and large landholdings, with the consequent incomplete utilization of the land that might be put to agricultural use. Chile is capable of greatly increased production of foodstuffs, certainly as great as Japan or Italy, with their large populations and high standing as world powers.

Agriculturally as well as physiographically, Chile must be divided into three portions: (1) a northern third, which is almost totally desert; (2) a middle third extending from Santiago southward to Valdivia, the northern half of which has a moderate rainfall in the winter but which depends much upon irrigation; and (3) a southern third made up of mountains and islands. It is evident that such agriculture as is practiced must be carried on in the middle portion of the country, the rich valley of Chile, the only extensive agricultural area on the west coast of South America.

THE NORTHERN MINERAL REGION

The Great Importance of Minerals in the Economic Life of Chile.—Because of her mountains, her deserts, and her limited area, Chile cannot be a great agricultural nation like her neighbor Argentina. Much more food can be produced in Chile than is now produced, and a population several times as large as the present can be fed from the land. But it is to their mineral resources that the Chilean people look for the upbuilding of the future nation. At one time, 80 per cent of the value of all exports from Chile were nitrate and copper, and the reserves of both are enormous. Iron is abundant, and coal is available; and, upon these two, the manufacturing of the future may be built. No other South American country except Brazil has such well-balanced resources as Chile; and, among these, her mineral wealth is most significant. The Chilean nitrate industry and its importance have already been discussed. But one of the by-products of the nitrate operations is of such importance that it needs special mention here.

The By-product Iodine.—The *caliche* contains the valuable drug iodine, obtained as a by-product of the nitrate-refining process. So great is the quantity of iodine which can be recovered that any one of the largest companies could supply the world's demands. Only a small fraction of the quantity that could be obtained is actually recovered, for the total quantity could not be sold. To prevent competitive sales among the companies and the consequent demoralization of prices, the iodine-producing capacity of each company is calculated and the company is assigned its quota; and when the year's sales have been determined, each nitrate company is paid its quota or percentage of the total income from iodine, no matter whose iodine was actually sold. The sales in 1916 reached $8,000,000; and in 1932 they declined to $1,500,000. The United States has usually taken upward of $1,000,000 worth annually. However, the future of iodine production in Chile has been greatly affected by the extraction of iodine from petroleum products in California. So important has the development in California become that it may be that the market in the United States (about one-third of the world's consumption) may be permanently lost to the Chilean producers of iodine.

Salt and Borates.—Northern Chile is dotted with basins (*salares*) large and small which, in the past, have contained lakes. The floors of these old lake basins are sometimes composed of nearly pure salt, many feet in thickness. One of these (the *Salar Grande*) near the coast is connected to a port by an aerial tramway and supplies Chile with the greater part of its common salt. There are various other salt workings in the country, and the possible production is enormous.

Another type of *salar* contains borates from which borax is made. There are upward of 25 of the borate *salares* in the desert of Chile and others in Bolivia and northern Argentina. All owe their existence to the accumulation of the salts in shallow basins by means of surface and ground water, the later evaporation of these waters, and the preservation of the salts by the arid climate. Chile has been an important producer of borax and at one time reached the rate of 40,000 tons per year. Production in the United States during and after the World War practically stopped production in Chile. Greater uses for borates or cheaper production in Chile may cause that country again to become an important producer.

Copper.—The Andes of Chile, like those farther north, were producers of copper before the Europeans came, and the Spaniards began production in a small way in 1601. But Spain took little interest in copper, partly because it was not then sufficiently in demand to awaken interest. In the latter half of the nineteenth century, Chile was the leading copper producer in the world and,

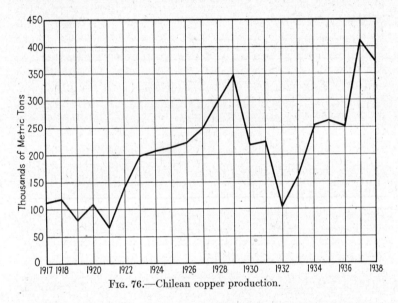

FIG. 76.—Chilean copper production.

in 1876, yielded 38 per cent of the world's supply. Then the great developments in the United States placed its producers in complete control of the copper market. Chilean production fell off; in 1906, it supplied only 4 per cent of the world's copper. In 1929, it had again risen to 16 per cent, and Chile ranked next to the United States as a copper producer.

As a rule, large copper deposits are found either in rocks that are themselves of igneous origin or in those that are closely associated with igneous rocks. The first great range of the Andes, after passing the low coast range on the west, is highly volcanic, as its many towering cones testify. Volcanic activity was vastly greater in the past than it has been recently, and, during that more ancient period, the great deposits that are now being worked were accumulated. The largest of the known deposits, though containing a vast wealth of copper, do not carry rich ores. Rather are they quite low in the percentage of copper that they contain, usually a little under 2 per cent. It is due to the great magnitude of the ore bodies and to the relative cheapness with which they are worked that three mining camps in the Andes have become leading producers among the world's copper mines. Yet even these ore bodies had to await the discovery and perfecting of improved processes of mining and extraction and a time when very large amounts of capital were available before they could become profitable producers of copper. Chile's production in 1913, the last year before the World War, was only 40,000 tons. After this, the production rose to 350,000 tons in 1929 and fell to 100,000 tons during the depression of 1930 to 1936 (Fig. 76).

Control by Three United States Companies.—Although there are many copper-mining companies in Chile, more than 90 per cent of the copper is produced by three North American corporations. Most of the other producers are Chilean companies that operate on a small scale and with small capital. The North American copper mines in Chile are controlled by powerful and experienced copper-mining corporations. It is interesting to note that Americans dominate the copper, petroleum, and iron industries in South America, lines in which they have become very proficient at home. Until recently they did much less in tin mining or nitrate production, two activities in which they have had no opportunity to gain experience in the United States, for neither of these minerals is found in quantity there.

Mine of the Chile Copper Company at Chuquicamata.—This is the leading copper-producing property of South America. It was acquired and developed by the Guggenheim brothers, who later sold a controlling interest to the Anaconda Copper Company. The property is valued at upward of $100,000,000. It is located in the desert of northern Chile about 100 miles inland and 165 miles northeast of the ports of Antofagasta and Mejillones to which it is connected by the main line of the Bolivia and Antofagasta Railroad. The ore body itself is one of the many mountains of this region and is mined, or rather quarried, by blasting and power-shovel work (Fig. 77). No underground workings exist; but the face of the mountain is blasted off at various levels, and the ore is moved to the crushers near by in train loads at the rate of over 40,000 tons a day.

As already indicated, the ore is of low copper content (a little under 2 per cent), but the operations are conducted on such a vast scale and so cheaply that the refined copper is produced at about the lowest cost ever attained. The crushed ore is leached with sulphuric acid, which is itself made as one of the by-products

FIG. 77.—View of Chuquicamata copper mine.

of the process. Later, the copper-bearing solution is treated electrolytically, and the copper is deposited in sheets on massive copper-silicon anode plates from which it is stripped, melted, refined, and cast into bars or ingots of practically pure copper (Fig. 78). The powerful electric current (60,000 horsepower) that is required for this process and for driving the machinery is generated with fuel oil at a point on the seacoast (Tocopilla) 100 miles away and is transmitted by wires to the mines. It is cheaper thus to transmit the electric current than to transport the oil or coal to the mines. This is another of the economies which the company has been able to effect. The copper still remaining in this ore body is the largest reserve known and is conservatively estimated at 134 billion pounds, for copper is sold by the pound, not by the ton. The output can be raised as rapidly as the market conditions will justify it.

Fig. 78.—Copper ingots in the storage yards of the Chile Copper Company at Chuquicamata in northern Chile. (*Courtesy Chile Copper Company.*)

The Equipment of the Mining Camp.—Another factor enters into a great enterprise like that at Chuquicamata, namely, providing for the comfort and contentment of the large army of laborers and other employees. If men are to be attracted to the desert and held there in a reasonable degree of contentment, life in the camp must be made endurable and even enjoyable. This is especially true when there is a shortage of labor as there is in Chile, with the near-by competition of the nitrate fields. There are 13,000 to 15,000 people at Chuquicamata, of whom 700 to 800 are engineers, chemists, metallurgists, machinists, etc., and their families. These employees are mainly from the United States and are employed on contract at good salaries. Most of the other workers are Chileans of the *roto* class, strong, energetic, and efficient, if working on a piece system or bonus system. They are provided with living quarters, medical service, and opportunities for pleasure and recreation. They live in two- or three-room houses, systematically arranged on improved streets, well sewered and provided with water and electricity. Their living conditions are decidedly superior to those of the working class, generally, in Chile or other South American countries.

The salaried employees have neat homes, tennis courts, baseball and football fields, moving pictures, and a $100,000 clubhouse that is more attractive and better equipped than one finds in many good-sized American cities. Two kinds of water—one for drinking purposes and the other for industrial uses—are piped in from the mountains 80 miles back. One of the very best hospitals on the whole west coast is maintained. There are schools, a guesthouse, hotels, stores maintained by the company and also by outsiders, and an efficient police and sanitary staff. It is probably the model mining camp of the world.

AN EXAMPLE OF IMPORTANT PRINCIPLES IN ECONOMIC GEOGRAPHY.—As an example of a modern mining camp of the most advanced type, Chuquicamata deserves more than passing notice, for it illustrates impressively certain principles with which our study is concerned.

The existence of the ore body was known long ago, and efforts to mine it profitably had been made but had failed. Of the many factors that had to be taken into account in mining, refining, and marketing the copper, all but one were unfavorable. The favorable factor is the abundance of the ore lying at the surface of the ground. Opposed to this are many unfavorable elements, namely: (1) the low percentage of copper in the ore; (2) the remoteness of the region from the great centers of copper consumption in Europe and the United States; (3) the absolute desert that surrounds the ore body, and the complete absence of everything necessary to the operation of the mine. There is no drinking water or water for the industrial operations; no fuel of any kind within many hundreds of miles; no timber, no food nor any chance to raise it—in short, Chuquicamata is an unqualified desert within the tropics in a very out-of-the-way part of the world.

A generation ago, there began a series of events that gradually changed the whole aspect of the problem and brought about the present highly successful and profitable development of this remarkable ore body: (1) The Antofagasta and Bolivia Railroad was built, and passed within a few miles of the mine. (2) During this same period, the long-distance transmission of high voltage electric current was perfected. (3) Methods of leaching ores and separating the copper on a large scale by an electric current were developed. (4) The world's consumption of copper had risen rapidly. (5) Certain copper-mining companies in the United States had acquired a wealth of experience and had amassed large capital. One of the ·most wealthy of these companies believed the time was at hand when the low-grade ores at Chuqui-camata could be mined and marketed at a profit. (6) In 1914, the Panama Canal was opened, giving a direct route to the eastern United States and Europe. By this series of changes, the *time* be-

Fig. 79.—View of operations at the copper mine of Portrerillos. (*Courtesy of Andes Copper Company.*)

came propitious for investing a huge sum of money in this great enterprise. The only people who had had long and successful experience in mining copper on a large scale under somewhat similar conditions were the mining men of the western United States, and a group of these acquired the ores at Chuquicamata. Thus was the second essential provided, namely, the *people* capable of carrying the enterprise forward with probability of success.

The geographical factor in this triangle of *place*, *period*, and *people* is that of *place*. The existence in this particular region of an ore body is a geographical and geological matter. But the sur-mounting of the difficulties by which the ore is mined and delivered to the world's industries is a matter of human initiative and human achievement; it was an enterprise, however, that had to await a time when it could be successfully undertaken, as it could not have been at an earlier date. The right *place*, the right *period*, and the right *people* had to come into conjunction.

In the southern end of the northern region of Chile are the important mines of the Andes Copper Company at Potrerillos (Fig. 79). The ore body is large, but the ore is lean (1.5 per cent). These American-owned mines rank third in copper production in Chile (Fig. 80).

Iron Resources and Production.—Chile has two known iron-ore bodies of large size, containing in the neighborhood of 1 billion tons of high-grade ore. One of these is in Atacama, near the port of Huasco, but it is not an active producer. The other is a little back from the coast near Coquimbo on the Bay of Cruz Grande and is actively worked by a subsidiary of one of the largest steel corporations of the United States, the Bethlehem Steel Corporation. Modern shipping docks similar to those at the head of

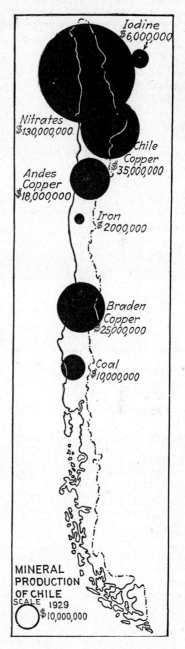

Iodine
$6,000,000

Nitrates
$130,000,000

Chile
Copper
$35,000,000

Andes
Copper
$18,000,000

Iron
$2,000,000

Braden
Copper
$25,000,000

Coal
$10,000,000

MINERAL
PRODUCTION
OF CHILE
SCALE   1929
$10,000,000

Fig. 80.—Approximate location and output of the chief mineral regions of Chile in 1929. In recent years copper has become more important than nitrates as an export commodity.

Lake Superior have been erected. An electric railway leads down from the mines to the docks; and the loaded cars, coming down, generate power that hauls the empty cars back. Specially designed steamships of large capacity receive the ore and carry it by way of the Panama Canal to the eastern United States. In active years, the shipment of ore from this port has averaged about 1,500,000 tons. If a method of coking Chilean coal is found or, lacking this, if coke can be brought back cheaply in the ore boats from the United States, there appears to be no reason why, at some time in the future, Chile should not develop an iron and steel industry of its own. This will be an important step toward that economic independence which nations greatly desire.

Miscellaneous Minerals.—At times in the past, Chile has been a large producer of the precious metals, especially of silver; but its present output is small. In recent years, Chile has supplied a very small fraction of the world's silver, all mined in the northern third of the country. The gold output is valued at $1,000,000 to $2,000,000 a year, mainly derived from the working of copper and silver ores. Sulphur, manganese, lead, and zinc are obtained in varying but small quantities.

Chapter VIII. Chile: The Central Valley and the South

THE CENTRAL VALLEY

Between the extremes of desert on the north and the excessively rainy, forested area of the south lies central Chile. In most respects, this Central Valley *is* Chile. It could easily be made a self-dependent unit. More than 80 per cent of Chile's population is concentrated here. With the exception of some of the mining centers of the north, practically all the wealth of Chile is here. It is here that the Chilean culture and educational facilities are best developed. The Central Valley is a rich agricultural district abounding in cereal and fruit production. Probably 99 per cent of all the agriculture is carried on in the valley, and 90 per cent of the manufacturing industries are centered here. It contains the two most important cities—Santiago and Valparaiso. This development is due largely to climate, soil, and irrigation.

Agriculture.—Physical conditions in the Central Valley make irrigation necessary and easily feasible. The narrow (25- or 30-mile) 600-mile-long valley is a great trough partly filled with the gravels, sands, and clays that ages of erosion have carved from the mountains (mainly on the east) and have deposited in the trough between (Fig. 81). Much of this deposit is fertile and easily worked. Large parts are nearly level, but with a prevailing slope toward the west. Many permanently flowing rivers fed by rainfall and melting snows of the Andes flow across the valley floor and cut through the coast range to the sea. Central Chile corresponds in extent of latitude to the eastern coast of the United States from northern Florida to southern Maine. Central Chile is more uniform in temperature, however, as it is not so warm at one end or so cold at the other. The eastern coast of the United States is affected by the Labrador Current and the Gulf Stream.

199

Central Chile is affected throughout by the cool Humboldt Current, a more even temperature being thus maintained and mild winters prevailing throughout. It has been pointed out above that most of the valley has a Mediterranean climate, but it must be kept in mind that the precipitation varies from a few inches in

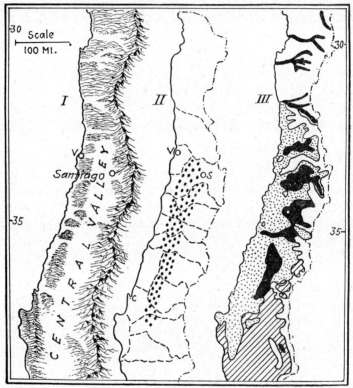

FIG. 81.—*I*, topography of Central Chile. *II*, irrigation. Each dot = 25,000 acres. (*After D. S. Bullock.*) *III*, irrigated and unirrigated farmlands. Black, irrigated land; stippled, unirrigated farmland; cross-lined, forests. (*After Mark Jefferson.*)

the northern end of the Central Valley to 86 inches at Puerto Montt. Since warmth and water at the same time are necessary to the growth of crops, it follows that the Chilean farmer in the northern part of the valley must find a way to supply his land with water during the warm but dry months of summer. A partial solution of his problem lies in diverting water from the streams that flow across the valley. The Indians did this anciently, the Spanish did it in the colonial days, and the Chileans have still further extended the irrigation works. The greater part of the land that is actually cultivated in the northern 200 miles of the Central Valley has to be irrigated.

Government officials exercise the necessary supervision over the use of irrigation water; yet most of the irrigation works have been built gradually in the past by the landowners themselves. As a rule, these works are simple and relatively inexpensive. There are few large dams and reservoirs such as those in the western United States. For the most part, the irrigation works consist of canals which tap the rivers at convenient points and lead the water along the higher lands of the estates or farms, whence it is distributed by branch canals and ditches to as much land as can be watered. Few great engineering feats have been attempted, and there are only two government irrigation projects of large size. Yet these irrigation works are effective, because the streams fed by the rains and melting snow and ice of the mountains are perennial. Under the present system, the country produces most of the foodstuffs that its people require and a small surplus of some products. Only a minor fraction (5 per cent) of the total land in the central provinces is actually reached by the ditches, and the total of irrigated land in all Chile is placed at 2,800,000 acres, or 4,375 square miles. California has 4,250,000 acres under irrigation. Yet so valuable is this irrigated land of Chile, lying near the chief cities of the Republic, and so productive is it that its importance in the agricultural life of Chile is much greater than its small area might suggest.

The official estimates state that 1,800,000 additional acres are capable of irrigation, but at an increasing unit cost; for, naturally, the lands most easily irrigated have been the first to be supplied with water.

Large Landholdings.—Most of the desirable land in the Central Valley has passed in very large holdings into the possession of families that became the land aristocracy of Chile. Over 500 great estates still exist, and these include more than half the agricultural land of the country. It is an impressive fact that one-half of 1 per cent of the people own 59 per cent of the farm land. Farms of 500 acres or larger make up over 90 per cent of the total land included in farms. This necessarily means that agriculture as an industry is conducted on an extensive rather than an intensive scale. Owners of the large estates are away from their estates a great deal and usually live in the larger cities. City life is more attractive than the isolated country life on the estates. A farm manager is employed and is given a free hand. The owner is concerned mainly with the net return that he may depend upon and prefers to avoid annoyances and disagreeable details. He desires to retain the estate in the family, but he is not fond of giving his personal attention to the farming operations. Under such a system, farming goes on as it always has; progress is slow, and production per acre is low.

But this is not the whole story of farming in Chile, for the country has a homestead law that has placed many farmers on small pieces of land. Through social legislation, attempts have been made to break up the large estates. Most of the recently created farms have been developed in the southern, or pioneer, portion of the valley or from estates whose owners were willing to sell. From time to time, large estates are divided among the heirs, and parts of these are sold to small holders. By one means or another, some 76,000 farm holdings of less than 125 acres have come into existence, and most of these are operated by their owners.

Chile thus has two distinct types of landholder, but the fact remains that 90 per cent of the farm land is in holdings of over 500 acres. The holders of the big estates form a powerful group in the politics of the nation. Naturally, they are conservatives; naturally, they oppose any considerable taxation of farm land; naturally, they do not look with favor upon expensive public improvements, such as modern roads, the cost of which must fall heavily on the landholders. They are interested in keeping the cost of agricultural labor low and generally view with skepticism very much education for the children of their laborers.

Farm Labor.—In southern Chile, farm laborers receive $1\frac{1}{2}$ to 4 paper pesos a day. In 1930, for example, this represented from 18 to 45 cents. In middle and northern Chile, wages are somewhat higher. Those receiving the lowest wages also get a hut to live in and a little piece of ground to till. They usually labor from sunrise to sunset and are willing and industrious workers. The wooden, two-wheeled farm cart, the one-handled plow, and the patient, plodding oxen form a characteristic sight on Chilean farms. Horses are used relatively little. Where wages are so low, time does not greatly count, and oxen are economical. On the great estates, *inquilinos* are the usual farm laborers. They are half-breed or Indian peons who are closely attached to the estate, cannot leave it if they have any debts due to the owner, and quite commonly spend their lives on the estate, as their fathers and grandfathers have done. The living conditions of most of these laborers' families are pitiably primitive, even more so than those of the Negro of the southern United States. Yet it is by no means sure that those who leave farm labor and go to work in the mines and nitrate fields better their condition, all things considered, although they receive larger pay and may have better living conditions. The number of laborers on the farms exceeds the total of those engaged in mining and manufacturing combined.

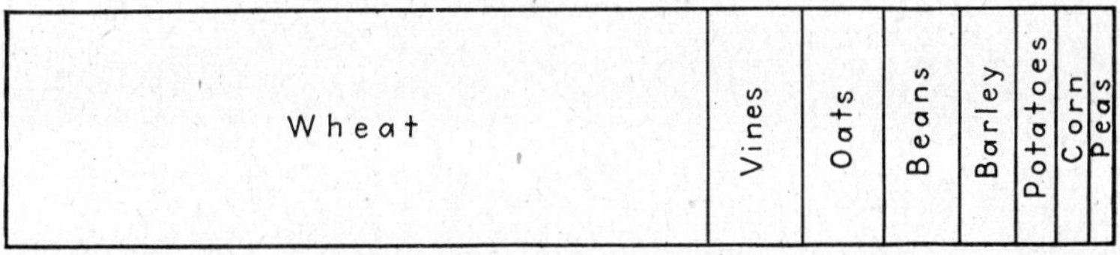

Wheat		Vines	Oats	Beans	Barley	Potatoes	Corn	Peas

Fig. 82.—Relative acreage of the chief crops of Chile—three-year average, 1935–1937.

Wheat, the Chief Cereal.—For a number of reasons, wheat is the principal crop of Chile: (1) The Chileans prefer wheat bread to any other kind, and this preference provides a home market for most of the grain. (2) There is nearly always a foreign market at reasonable prices for any surplus that may be exported. (3) The climatic conditions are especially well suited to wheat growing (Fig. 82).

It will be recalled that the valley of Chile has a rainy season and a dry season. Wheat is a grain that calls for plenty of moisture during the early stages of its growth but ripens best in a dry period. It thrives on a relatively low rainfall, as it does in the Great Plains of the United States and Canada and in Australia. These habits of the wheat fit it ideally to the climate of the Central Valley where practically all the Chilean crop is raised both with and without irrigation. In the latter case, it is customary to plow part of the land in spring, allow it to lie fallow during the dry summer, cross-plow or harrow it in the fall, and sow the seed with the coming of the early rains which occur in May and

June. So mild are the winter months that the wheat grows during the winter and spring and matures in the dry, sunny summer and early fall. In other cases, the seed is sown in the early spring, grows with or without artificial irrigation during the summer, and is harvested in the autumn. Wheat is the principal crop throughout the valley, but it is especially important in the provinces of Malleco and Bío Bío, in the general region of the Bío Bío River near whose mouth is the important city of Concepción. The acreage devoted to wheat is fairly uniform from year to year. The average is about $1\frac{1}{2}$ million acres, giving a yield of 28 million bushels, or 19 bushels to the acre, somewhat above the average yield in the United States. The average exports amount to 8 to 10 per cent of the crop; but the exportation of wheat and flour will not continue far into the future, for the increasing home demand will soon overtake the supply.

To a considerable extent, wheat is still threshed by driving horses round and round in a circle on a threshing floor until the grain is tramped out. On the larger farms, modern threshing machines are used. The wheat is shipped in sacks; and, in the late fall, the warehouses along the railroads and all available cars are piled high with sacks of wheat. It is the only cereal grown in Chile in a large way. More land in Chile is devoted to wheat than to all other crops. Wheat occupies four times as much land as is devoted to all other cereals combined and supplies two-thirds of the cereal products of the country. The wheat crop of Chile is about one-eighth that of Kansas in a good year, and the country ranks about sixteenth among the wheat-growing countries of the world.

Cereals Other than Wheat.—Oats and barley are of minor importance in Chile, and corn (maize) forms only 5 per cent of the total production of cereals. Rye production is insignificant. The German population in the southern portion of the valley and the breweries that they have built are responsible for a part of the production of barley, which is used in making malt. The small production of corn and the small number of swine raised in Chile are two facts that doubtless have some causal connection.

Vegetable and Other Minor Crops.—Throughout Latin America, beans of various kinds form an important item in the diet, especially in that of the poorer people. The same is true to a lesser degree of peas. These two vegetables supply the nitrogenous element in the food, the element that is provided by meat in the diet of people who can afford or prefer this more expensive food. All legumes raised in Chile occupy only 10 or 12 per cent as much land as wheat alone.

Potatoes are not a large crop; the average yield is only about 12 million bushels, or 3 bushels per capita of the Chilean population. This compares with 4 bushels in the United States and 20 bushels in Germany. The potato belt of Chile is at the southern end of the valley and on the large island of Chiloe where the cooler temperature and fairly well-distributed rainfall are favorable to this crop.

Truck and garden crops of practically every variety known in temperate and semitropical climates grow in Chile. Melons are of many kinds and of delicious flavors, and considerable numbers are now exported. The mild climate of the valley permits hardy vegetables to grow throughout the winter, and it is not uncommon to obtain four crops a year from the irrigated land.

Tobacco is a crop of only minor importance.

Alfalfa is a crop on the irrigated land, though far less important than it is in Argentina. It is grown mainly in four provinces near Santiago. Clover and grasses are extensively grown; and baled hay, clover, and alfalfa are sent to the mining camps and nitrate fields for feeding the horses and mules.

Fruit Growing and Wine Production.—The Valley of Chile was designed by nature for the production of fruit, and almost every known variety grows there. It is the California of South America, for the Valley of Chile grows nearly the same fruits with the same profusion. There are no extremes of heat or cold; sunshine is abundant, and irrigation water is applied as it is needed. Among the subtropical fruits are oranges, lemons, olives, and figs; all these fruit crops are typical of Mediterranean climates. No such development of general fruit growing, however, has taken place in Chile as in California, partly because the Chilean fruit grower has not a market for any large quantity of these fruits. He is not part of a nation of 125 million people, as the California fruit grower is; and even the latter finds his major problems in transporting and marketing his crop rather than in growing it. Apples, pears, peaches, plums, apricots, cherries, and all kinds of berries are raised. Strawberries are grown throughout the summer and late into the fall. They are cheap and delicious. Apples and peaches are inferior to those grown in the western United States, owing to the more backward state of this industry in Chile as compared with California and Washington. Next to grapes, apples are the fruit to which the most attention is given, and an

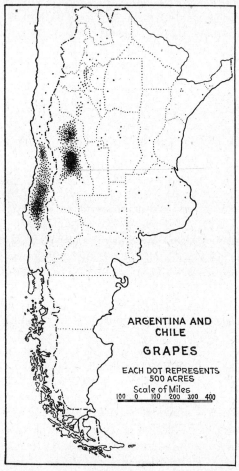

ARGENTINA AND
CHILE

GRAPES

EACH DOT REPRESENTS
500 ACRES
Scale of Miles
100 0 100 200 300 400

Fig. 83.

effort is being made to establish some 10 or 12 of the best North American varieties in Chile. Shipments of Chilean fruits to the United States by way of the Panama Canal have been sufficiently profitable to encourage the belief that a small fruit trade with the United States can be maintained. Among the nuts grown on a commercial scale are almonds and walnuts; the latter have become an important item of export. For a country situated far from the great consuming centers, nuts as an export crop are superior to the perishable fruits.

The high development of vineyards and of wine making in Chile is a response to two main causes: (1) the ideal climate and (2) the wine-using habits of Latin Americans. Moreover, wine is a

FIG. 84.—Picking grapes in Chile, south of Santiago.

concentrated and valuable commodity and does not require marketing at a particular time as fruit does.

More than twice as much land in Chile is devoted to grapes as to all other fruits combined, and about one-third of the annual crop of 15 million pounds is grown under irrigation. Two-thirds of the vineyards are in the northern section of the valley between the Bío Bío River and Santiago (Fig. 83). About every known variety of grape grows excellently, and the size of the individual grapes and of the clusters is astonishing. Clusters weighing several pounds each are common. In the city markets and at the railway stations, this delicious fruit is offered for sale at prices as low as 2 or 3 cents a pound. Upward of 1½ million pounds of raisins are made, but the industry is not yet a large one; it easily might become so, for climatic conditions are favorable. The greater part of the grapes are made into wine, and Chilean wines have attained real excellence (Fig. 84). In the region surrounding Santiago and immediately south are situated the principal wine-making establishments, some of which are very large and involve the investment of millions of dollars capital in land, plant, and equipment. The fact that the better wines are stored for years before they are marketed adds greatly to the amount of capital

Fig. 85.—Hacienda Las Palmas, Chile.

required for conducting the industry. Most of the wine is consumed in Chile (Fig. 85).

As in California, so in Chile, the drying and preserving of fruit is becoming an industry of importance, and fruits thus preserved are exported to the extent of about $1,000,000 annually in addition to supplying practically the entire home demand.

Horses and Oxen.—In its use of horses, Chile differs widely from its neighbor Argentina, on the opposite side of the Andes, for Chile is in no sense a land of horses. Rather may it be called a land of oxen. In the entire country, there are less than 400,000 horses, or 1 to each 10 of the human population of the country, as contrasted with 1 to 1 in Argentina. Saddle horses are commonly used both for riding over the extensive estates and for traveling over the country roads, many of which are poorly suited to wheeled vehicles; but horses are much less used than oxen as draft animals. Oxen are less expensive than horses, are more cheaply kept, require an inexpensive yoke instead of an expensive harness, and, at the end, may be used for meat.

Goats.—Goats are not raised on a large scale anywhere in Chile, yet there are more goats than horses in the country. They are raised mainly in the dry lands north of Santiago and Valparaiso.

Swine.—Swine are even less numerous than goats, there being only about 300,000 in all Chile. Single counties in Iowa have that number.

Cattle.—Cattle are raised practically everywhere in the farming section, but no part of the country specializes in them. In fact, not enough are raised to supply the beef required by the country, and large numbers are driven over the mountains from Argentina for slaughter in the mining camps and nitrate fields. There are regular routes followed by the cattle drovers, and the industry is of considerable importance.

Dairying is unimportant, and such butter and cheese as are made are practically all produced on the farms under none too sanitary conditions. In the southern half of the Central Valley and in many of the smaller valleys in the mountains, dairying could thrive and eventually will do so. At present, Chile imports butter and cheese, mainly from Argentina.

Sheep.—Sheep are raised in many parts of Chile, but more than three-quarters of the wool grown in Chile comes from the extreme south.

Minerals of Central Chile.—It has already been pointed out that South America is extremely poor in coal, in fact, the poorest of the continents. Of all the South American countries, Chile alone produces coal on a commercial scale, but in small amounts. The only mines of importance are situated on the coast not far from the city of Concepción, in the southern half of the country. The best veins are those worked at Lota and Coronel. About 12 or 14 mines are operated, and the annual output is a little more than 1 million tons a year. In quality, the coal is a low-grade bituminous, not suited to coking by present methods. Four companies mine about three-fourths of the total output. Mining is done by inefficient methods; and the cost is high, so high that the use of the coal is restricted and fuel oil is coming more and more into use in mining and nitrate operations. Only the state railways are large buyers of the native coal. However, the fact that Chile has coal well situated for mining is a matter of national importance and may play a significant part in the future industrial development of the country. One of the foremost needs of a modern nation is sources of mechanical energy, either coal, oil, or water power. Chile has the coal and potential water power, and they are two of her great assets. Chile is both an importer and an exporter of coal, and the two movements nearly balance, although the increasing use of fuel oil is cutting down the importation of British coal, which formerly came in return cargoes in the ships that carried away the nitrate. It is an interesting fact that, when coal is shipped to the interior, it is usually shipped in sacks to save it from pilferage, and, even then, some 7 or 8 per cent of it disappears in transit. Ordinarily, imported British coal costs no more at the nitrate ports than does Chilean coal, and the former is superior.

About 60 miles south of Santiago, at El Teniente, is one of the great copper camps of Chile (Fig. 80). The mines are at an elevation of over 8,000 feet in the mountains back of Rancagua, a station on the Central Railway of Chile connected with El Teniente by the company's railroad. Over $50,000,000 of United States capital has been invested in land, mines, hydroelectric plants, aerial tramway, mill, smelter, machine shops, dwellings for employees, hospital, schools, clubs, railway, locomotives, cars, and miscellaneous equipment. Snowstorms are heavy, and many miles of snowsheds are needed to protect the railway. The mining operations are underground; the ore is low grade, averaging only a little under 2 per cent copper, but the proved ore body has over 250 million tons, enough for 50 years to come. So efficient are the operating methods that copper is produced at 7 to 9 cents a pound. This mine and that of the Chile Copper Company at Chuquicamata are among the leaders of the world in cheapness of production.

Manufacturing.—Nearly all the industrial development, with the exception of lumbering and activities relative to mineral extraction and concentration, is found in the Central Valley. Like other South American countries, Chile has not yet reached the industrial stage. Manufacturing must develop slowly in a country of small population and small capital. Chile is still primarily an exporter of the products of the land, including the minerals, and an importer of manufactured goods. But Chile is seeking to be as little dependent as possible upon imported goods. By 1914, there were slightly over 6,000 establishments engaged in some form of manufacturing. Most of these were workshops rather than factories, for the average number of persons employed was only eight to the establishment. The smallness of the manufacturing industry may be seen from two comparisons: (1) The total number of persons employed in all forms of manufacturing throughout the country was about the same as the number employed in the nitrate *oficinas* alone when they are running at their maximum. (2) The total power used in manufacturing in 1914 was almost exactly the same as the Chile Copper Company alone is now using for its operations at Chuquicamata. The World War stimulated manufacturing somewhat, and, by 1928, the value of manufactured products had increased 80 per cent. The growth is better shown by noting that the power employed quadrupled in the 14 years. This indicates a movement away from the workshop type of manufacturing in the direction of factory manufacturing. Yet the average number of persons to the manufacturing establishment is only 25, and the average production per factory is valued at less than $60,000, United States money. The census of 1930 shows 22.1 per cent of the population as engaged in industry, but at the present time (1939) probably 30 per cent is so engaged. By 1930, there were in Chile upward of 3,500 establishments that might be called mills and factories, though only a small proportion of these employed as many as 200 persons. About one-third of these actual mills or factories are in or near Santiago, and half as many are in or near Valparaiso. The provinces of Concepción and Valdivia, in the southern portion of the Central Valley, are the other manufacturing regions. It should be noted that the smelting and refining of copper and the extraction of nitrate are classed with the mining rather than with the manufacturing industries.

Chile has made notable progress in the manufacturing of shoes, using the most modern American machinery in the leading factories. Fabrication of shoes increased by about one-third from 1929 to 1937. Exports of shoes to Peru and Bolivia are of increas-

ing importance. Over 300 tanneries supply leather. The manufacture of wine, alcohol, and liquors is a large industry. About
200 plants are engaged in making electricity. Flour mills provide
practically all the country's needs in this line; six good-sized
woolen mills and a large number of cotton-textile mills have been
established. Production of textiles in 1937 was about seven times
as great as in 1929. The paper output more than doubled, and
manufactures of paints, explosives, cement, and chemicals
greatly increased from 1929 to 1937.

Chile seems the best endowed of all the South American
countries, except possibly Brazil, for becoming a manufacturing

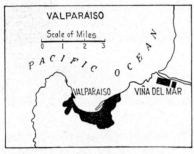

FIG. 86.

nation. Its invigorating climate, its energetic people, its
resources of coal, iron, copper, and water power; its
wool, hides, wheat, fruit, and
other raw materials; its progressive policies and increasing capital are all in its favor.
Its protective tariff may enable it to develop the manufacturing of goods for its own
people, but there are only a few million of these; and it can
scarcely be expected that Chile will export manufactures, except
to its less developed neighbors. Placing the value of Chile's manufactures at $180,000,000, it is to be remembered that many a
single corporation in the United States, England, or Germany
has an output larger than this.

Cities.—There are but two cities of over 100,000 population
in Chile, and they are found in middle Chile. Valparaiso is the
port for the northern part of the Central Valley and the most important seaport in the country (Fig. 86). The harbor is open to
the west winds but has been improved by an expensive break-
water so that ships can now dock at the port. The city is beauti-
fully situated on the narrow plain bordering the sea and on
several neighboring hills. Including Viña del Mar (a resident
section and pleasure resort), it contains over 260,000 people.

Santiago is the capital and the most important center from a
commercial, industrial, and social as well as political standpoint.
It is the fourth largest city in South America, with a population

of approximately 800,000. It is distant 116 miles from Valparaiso with which it is connected by fine train service and a motor road.

Fig. 87.—Santiago from San Cristobal—Santiago lies in the flat filled plain of the Central Valley.

Fig. 88.—Entrance to the beautiful park of the Cerro Santa Lucia in Santiago, Chile.

The city is situated in a plain, 1,700 feet above sea level, with a magnificent view of the snow-capped peaks of the Andes (Fig.

87). Splendid views of the capital may be obtained from Cerro San Cristóbal at the edge of the city or from Santa Lucia Hill—a small rock eminence which has been ornamented with balustrades, balconies, and gardens (Fig. 88). The capital has fine government buildings, residences, and beautiful boulevards. Practically all the important commercial, financial, manufacturing, and mining organizations of Chile have their head or branch offices in Santiago. It is the principal manufacturing city of the Republic as well as the most important retail emporium. It is the educational, social, and cultural center of the country.

THE SOUTHERN GRAZING AND FOREST REGION

The southern half of the Valley of Chile is submerged beneath the sea. From Puerto Montt southward, the hills that form the southern continuation of the coast range become a chain of islands. The sinking of this coast has depressed the valleys below sea level, and they have become arms of the ocean. Many glaciers still occupy the high valleys of the Andes in the far south. Larger glaciers once occupied these valleys and eroded them deeply. A part of the depressions thus eroded are now occupied by beautiful lakes, similar to the glacial lakes of Switzerland. The overdeepened lower valleys on the coast have become fiords, similar to those of Alaska. The heavy rains that the westerly winds from the Pacific precipitate upon the mountain slopes cause the growth of dense forests which completely clothe the Pacific side of the Andes in this region. So heavy are the rainfall and snowfall that the ground is saturated with water. The winters are wet and disagreeable, and very few people live in this part of Chile. Still farther south, practically at the end of the continent, are grasslands which constitute the principal sheep pastures of Chile.

The southern forest belt of Chile occupies one-third of the length of the country, forms one-seventh of its total area, and contains nearly four-fifths of its saw timber.

The Forest Industries.—Southward from the latitude of 38 degrees, Chile was a heavily forested land when the white men came. In the northern end of this forest belt, the fierce Araucanians made their last stand. The forests have now been nearly cleared from the southern end of the valley, and productive farm lands have taken their place. South of Puerto Montt, where the railroad ends and the island-fiord region begins, the country is clothed in a forest of hardwoods and conifers. So wet and spongy is the ground that the few roads are usually sloughs of mud, and six or eight oxen may be needed to haul a log to the mill. Rains are so frequent and so heavy that lumbering operations are carried on under difficulties and are confined mainly to the three least rainy months. In this mountain region, the proportion of large, straight trees suitable for saw timber is small. Of some 39

Fig. 89.—Volcano Osorno, Chilean lake region. (*Courtesy of the Departmento de Turismo, Chile.*)

million acres of original woodland, only one-eighth contains commercially valuable timber. The remaining seven-eighths is suitable for pulp, posts, poles, firewood, and second-rate lumber or consists of land that has been cleared or burned over. So long as tariff duties on lumber were moderate, Chile imported the major part from the west coast of the United States, but a recent increase in the tariff duties has led to a larger use of the native woods.

In spite of the climatic and topographic difficulties under which lumbering is carried on, the forest and wood-working industries rank third (after mining and agriculture) among Chilean industries. Between 600 and 700 small sawmills are in intermittent operation, and forest products form a leading item of traffic on the railway in the southern half of the valley. The forests of Chile are a national asset in that they can, if necessary, supply the wood, lumber, and timber which the country requires, and thus they contribute to the self-sufficiency of the nation.

FIG. 90.—Lake Todas los Santos, Chilean lake region. (*Courtesy of the Ministerio de Fomento, Chile.*)

But there is no comparison between the forests of Chile and those of the coast of Oregon and Washington.

Sheep Raising.— Sheep raising as an industry is of two distinct kinds in Chile. The sheep are raised in moderate numbers throughout the farming sections, and their wool constitutes a product of the general farming operations. But in the far south, in the Territory of Magallanes, sheep raising has become a specialized industry of dominating importance, as it has on the Argentine lands across the border. The Andes are progressively lower as one proceeds toward the south and disappear under the sea at Tierra del Fuego. Here, in the latitude of about 50 degrees, the climate is sufficiently cold to give the sheep thick, heavy fleeces of very fine quality. Pasture land is inexpensive, and some of the largest sheep ranches in the world are found. As a rule, the sheep-raising companies are corporations that conduct their ranches as capitalistic enterprises. In the Chilean part of this region, there are some 50 large ranches, controlled partly by

Chilean and partly by British capital, but commonly in charge of Scotch managing shepherds. The majority of the large ranches carry 20,000 to 50,000 sheep, but one company has 1,300,000 which is more than one-fourth of the total number in all Chile. This company is capitalized at $8,000,000, and its shares of stock have been quoted at four or five times their par value, an evidence of the large profits that at times have been realized.

Most of the sheep are crossbreeds, raised both for wool and for mutton. Owing to the cold climate and to the selected breeds,

Fig. 91.—Mt. Tronador, Chilean lake region. (*Courtesy of the Ministerio de Fomento, Chile.*)

fleeces of 8 or 10 pounds of wool are secured—a very high average. Of some 30 million pounds of wool annually shipped from Chile, nearly 80 per cent goes from Magallanes Territory, and most of it goes to England, whose ships run regularly to this region, especially to the port of Magallanes, where both Chilean and Argentine wool is assembled for oversea shipment.

In addition to wool, large quantities of chilled or frozen mutton are also shipped from a half-dozen freezing plants that have been erected in the Magallanes region. An interesting by-product of the sheep-slaughtering industry is the preparation of sausage casings from the intestines of the sheep; 1½ million of these are sent annually to the United States. Sheep products, including wool, frozen mutton, sheepskins, and sausage casings, constitute the third largest export of Chile, being exceeded only by nitrate and copper.

Scenery and Recreation.—Near the southern end of the Central Valley and in much of the south there are spots of rare scenic beauty. Fiorded coast, glaciated mountains, volcanic and glacier covered peaks, and alpine valleys are here found in a combination unexcelled in the world (Fig. 89). On both the Chilean and Argentine slopes of the Andes are valleys containing beautiful lakes which have abundant fish for the sportsman. Of these, perhaps Lake Todos los Santos is the outstanding gem (Fig. 90). Colonel Holdich wrote some thirty years ago:

"When a man who has travelled far and seen many lakes in many countries, sets himself down to write of the most beautiful lake he ever saw in his life, he finds it difficult to choose superlatives in the British tongue which may serve to paint the picture with all due force and without detriment to the perfect harmony of his ideal perspective. Perhaps the superlatives are better omitted. . . . Todos los Santos! May all thy saints preserve thee from pollution of base utility, and keep thee an artistic joy forever for the teaching of Nature's truths!"[1]

This region promises to develop into a continental playground for South America—a Switzerland for this southern continent (Fig. 91).

TRANSPORTATION IN CHILE

Railways.—The railroad pattern of Chile is governed by the peculiar shape of the country. Whereas the railway system of Argentina is essentially a great fan with its handle at Buenos Aires, that of Chile may be compared to a herringbone. A central line extends from north to south throughout the greater part of the length of the country, and many short lines branch off to the seaports or to places in the foothills of the cordillera. The extreme northern link is not yet completed, but there is continuous rail connection north and south for upward of 1,500 miles. In all, the country has around 6,000 miles of railway, over half of which is owned by the government. Nearly all the privately owned lines belong to British companies. These are mainly in the northern part of the country, particularly in the nitrate

[1] Holdich, Col. Sir Thomas Hungerford. "The Countries of the King's Award," Hurst and Blachett, London, 1904.

region. The oldest existing railway in South America is in Chile.[1] Unfortunately for the efficiency of the railway system, six different gauges are in use, ranging from $2\frac{1}{2}$ feet for the Antofagasta and Bolivia Railroad to $5\frac{1}{2}$ feet for the state-owned Central Railroad. The longitudinal lines north from Cabilda are of meter gauge and are built for strategic reasons rather than with any expectation of profit for a long time to come. Taken as a whole, the state-owned lines are operated at a loss, but the privately owned lines return a profit.

The transcontinental line, extending from Valparaiso on the Pacific to Buenos Aires on the Atlantic, 886 miles, is one of the famous railways of the world. The narrow-gauge mountain section employs a rack-rail system for a 20-mile stretch where the grade reaches 8 per cent. It passes the summit level by a tunnel at an elevation of over 10,000 feet. The cost of this mountain railway was staggering, and its present capitalization is at the rate of $317,000 a mile. The road carries little freight, and the passenger fares are extremely high. Financially, the line is a failure. The scenery is truly grand, but less grand than that along the Central Railroad of Peru. The Transandean Railway has serious trouble with heavy snows and snow slides, and miles of snowsheds are required. On the principal railway lines of Chile, modern sleeping, dining, and parlor cars are operated. The Central line from Valparaiso to Santiago is electrified, and further electrification is under way. Next to Argentina, Uruguay, and the coffee district of Brazil, the railway facilities of Chile are the best in South America.

Highways.—In the northern half of Chile, the desert and its sparse population preclude the building of good roads, and only an occasional short stretch near some city exists. In the rain-soaked forest region of the south, good roads are next to impossible. Even in the rich and populous Central Valley, the roads are little more than broad trails, deep in dust in the dry season and deep in mud in the rainy season, as they were in the United States not long ago. Very little hard surfacing has anywhere

---

[1] The line from the port of Caldera to the mining center of Copiapó was built in 1849 by an American, William Wheelright. He also founded the Pacific Steam Navigation Company, one of the principal steamship lines serving the Pacific ports of South America. Wheelright was also builder of the first railway in Argentina.

been done, but the number of better surfaced roads is gradually increasing. Ox carts are the chief means of hauling products to markets or to railway stations. In country roads as in farming methods, Chile is in a backward condition.

Airways.—As in most South American countries, air transportation has had a relatively rapid development. Regular service from Santiago to Buenos Aires and from Santiago northward and intermittent service from Santiago southward is maintained.

COMMERCE OF CHILE

Foreign Commerce.—Certain characteristics of the foreign commerce of Chile stand out prominently:

1. The balance of trade is regularly in favor of Chile, and usually it is heavily so.

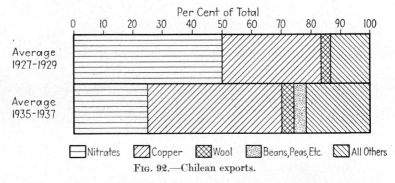

Fig. 92.—Chilean exports.

2. Mineral products constitute about 80 per cent of the value of all exports, whereas agricultural products, animal products, and manufactures form less than 15 per cent. Nitrate and copper are classified as mineral products, but they are also semimanufactured.

3. The combined trade of Chile with three countries—the United States, Great Britain, and Germany—is greater by far than that with all the other countries of the world combined.

4. About 25 per cent of the foreign trade is with the United States, but Chile sends to the United States much more in value than it buys from this country.

5. The value of foreign trade fluctuates widely even from one year to another, depending so heavily as it does on the exportation of one product, nitrate.

6. The value of exported products per capita of the population averages about $40 a year as compared with $14 per capita for Peru and $8 or $9 for Brazil.

Invisible Imports in Chilean Commerce.—New countries that possess large natural wealth of soil or minerals and have relatively small populations, as is true of Chile, Uruguay, Australia, and Canada, may become heavy exporters of raw products. Since their respective populations are small, the value of their exports per capita of the population is large. Chile has a small population (about $4\frac{1}{2}$ million) but has two articles of export of large annual

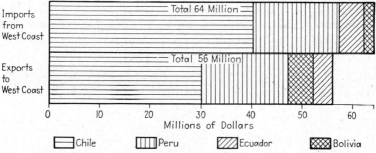

Fig. 93.—Trade between the United States and the west coast of South America (average, 1935–1937).

value—nitrate and copper (Fig. 92). The major part of the value of Chilean exports consists of copper, nitrate, and iron, mined by companies financed with foreign capital and paying the larger part of their dividends to foreign stockholders. In spite of an almost uninterrupted favorable balance of trade, Chile has largely increased her national debt to foreign bondholders, and hence a very substantial part of the value of her exports does not return to the country but remains abroad to pay the interest on these obligations.

Character and Sources of Principal Imports.—Like all South American countries, Chile is, in the main, a buyer of manufactured products. With few exceptions, her own manufacturing establishments have not reached the stage where they can produce economically articles which are made by complex and expensive machinery or those in which quantity production is essential to economical production. The greater part of the mining machinery, electrical apparatus, industrial machinery, automo-

biles, locomotives, passenger and trolley cars, and similar manufactures used by Chile must be built abroad, generally in the
United States, Great Britain, or Germany, but also in France
and Belgium.

The United States has become the largest source of Chile's
imports, with Great Britain a close second (Fig. 93). The depressed value of Chilean money in relation to United States
money has at times worked against importations from the United
States and in favor of German, French, and Belgian goods, and
to a lesser degree in favor of British goods. The fact that the
United States takes about as large a proportion of Chilean exports as do all European countries combined is likely to keep the
United States in first place as a source of Chile's imported goods.
It is worth noting that the little island of Puerto Rico buys about
twice as much in value from the United States as Chile buys and
that the Hawaiian Islands, with one-eighth the population of
Chile, buy twice as many goods from the United States.

Chapter IX. Argentina

Argentina appears to be a land of paradox and inconsistency. It is at once an old and a young country—old in its settlement which predates the landing of the Pilgrims in New England by a half to three-quarters of a century, young in its stage of economic development. It is a land of primitive *gauchos* and of mundane, sophisticated, cosmopolitan, wealthy landholders. In Argentina is the largest city south of the equator, a city as well supplied with all the accouterments of modern western civilization as New York, London, or Paris; and yet Argentina is strikingly nonurbanized—a land of few cities, sparse population, and vast, almost empty plains (Fig. 1).

Argentina, among South American countries, is also one with many unique characteristics. It is a "white man's country" both in climate and in population. It is the only part of South America with extensive plains in temperate-zone areas (Fig. 94). Not all of Argentina is so favored, but at least one-fourth of its more than 1 million square miles is a flat plain in a climatic region suited to temperate-zone crops. Argentina also differs from most South American countries in that the population is almost entirely of European origin. The mestizo, the mulatto, and the Negro are unimportant elements in the population. Native blood, likewise, makes up an insignificant proportion of the total. Nearly 80 per cent of the 12 million people who inhabit the country are of Spanish ancestry. The balance are predominantly Italian. A further unusual quality of Argentina is that the present heart of the country, the area of the Pampa and especially that portion adjacent to Buenos Aires, was not the only nucleus from which the country evolved. Expansion took place from at least three nuclei. One center was the arid mountains of the west and northwest

Fig. 94.—A herd of fine beef cattle on the Argentine Pampa. Argentina is the leading beef-exporting country. (*Copyright Ewing Galloway, N. Y.*)

where Incas from Peru had established irrigation agriculture. Another center was in the north where an Indian population gained a livelihood by hunting, gathering forest products, and raising patches of corn. A third included the present territory of the Pampa and the area southward to the tip of the continent. This region was peopled by nomadic Indians who lived by hunting guanacos and other wild native animals. The present Argentine Republic is essentially an amalgam of these three centers and their activities, but the aboriginal peoples who inhabited these areas have in large measure been displaced or exterminated, rather than assimilated.

Although many of the activities and unique characteristics of Argentina seem incongruous and incomprehensible in the present economic pattern, they become consistent and understandable when viewed in the light of historical evolution. The changes that have taken place in the economic life of the country are indicated by a study of Argentina's past and present foreign trade, for Argentina is above all else a commercial nation. An analysis of her trade and the reasons for the changes that have come about help to explain the present activities in Argentina, give evidence of the variety of the country's environment, and indicate possible future lines of development.

ARGENTINA'S FOREIGN-TRADE PATTERN

Historically, Argentina's foreign trade, on the basis of commodities shipped, direction of flow, and general character of the trade, may be divided into three major periods: (1) the Spanish colonial, (2) readjustment, and (3) modern. Although it is rather difficult to give exact dates to these various periods (since they overlap to a certain degree and each presages its follower and carries forward in some measure into the new stage), in a general way the first (the Spanish colonial) extends from the effective settling of the colony (1560–1580) until the time of Argentina's declaration of independence of Spanish rule in 1810; the second (the period of readjustment) from 1810 to 1868; and the final (the modern) from 1868 to the present.

The Spanish Colonial Period.—Argentina's trade, so long as she remained a colony of Spain, was exceedingly small. Commodities that were permitted to enter trade were regulated by

Spain as was the direction of their movement. Spain was not interested in a colony that could produce and trade in food products, the one activity for which Argentina was preeminently suited. Spain's interest was in precious metals which could be shipped to the motherland and used to help defray the costs of her frequent wars and pay for the luxuries from the Orient to which her aristocrats had become accustomed. Moreover, colonies were looked upon as personal possessions of the king and not as states with certain inalienable rights. They were administered for the benefit of the crown and not for the people who inhabited them. Immigration was largely prohibited so that the much-needed labor for pioneer development was not forthcoming. Food production and trade in agricultural commodities were further handicapped because of the route that Spain decreed had to be used for the movement of goods from Argentina. Illogical as it seems, all trade had to move up over the Bolivian plateau and then down to the Pacific coast from where it was shipped to the Isthmus of Panama, transferred by pack animals across to the Caribbean side, and then, in Spanish bottoms, shipped to Spain. Despite the severe penalties of death and confiscation of property that Spain imposed for disobeying this decree, contraband trade was rife in Buenos Aires. It has been estimated that at least one-third of Argentina's exports during this period was carried by smugglers.

One of the most important areas of legitimate trade during this time was from the irrigated foothills of the northwest. Here a food-producing area complemented the economic pattern of another, and at that time more important, Spanish colonial possession: the Bolivian plateau. The plateau was an area of important mining activity, but its high barren wastes were largely unsuited to agricultural production. Food had to be imported, and animals were needed for transport. This need was one of the driving forces behind the advent of the Spaniards into this portion of Argentina. Spanish *conquistadores* subdued the Indians of the northwest and set themselves up as feudal lords on their irrigated lands. The Indians lost their lands but not their lives, for they were needed as farm laborers. The area became an important livestock region, producing cattle for beef and mules as draft animals for the Bolivian mining camps. Return cargoes, mostly of Spanish origin, included guns and ammunition, clothing, and various other supplies. The district prospered accordingly, because it fitted into the economic pattern of the time and was able to take advantage of its agricultural assets.

Elsewhere trade in Argentina was not particularly significant. Some agricultural commodities and livestock products moved from the rich Pampa, across the arid *monte*, and on to the Pacific, but the hazards and expense of the trip were retarding influences. Ferocious Indians harassed the caravans, scarcity of water was an omnipresent problem, and travel was slow and costly by this "backdoor" route. Other areas of irrigation agriculture in the western foothills were acquired by Spanish penetration, but they did not become regions of important commercial production. Mendoza, for example, was early occupied from the Chilean side, but there was little or no market for its products. In Chile, similar commodities were raised, and eastward was a barren, arid, and largely uninhabited waste. Mendoza, therefore, developed subsistence rather than commercial farming.

Under the hampering influence of unfavorable trade regulations, lack of precious metals, and isolation from the mother country, Argentina drifted toward revolution. Spain was so occupied with wars in Europe, and especially with Napoleon, that she had little opportunity to devote herself to the needs of the colony. The climax came in May, 1810, when an armed assembly of Argentine Creoles in Buenos Aires declared their independence of Spanish rule. This revolutionary spirit soon spread and swept Spanish rule from the whole South American continent.

Although change in political control relieved Argentina of many of the shackles that had held her in economic servitude, neither peace nor prosperity came immediately. Instead, there followed a period of readjustment stretching over half a century.

Period of Readjustment.—Trade during the 50 years following the declaration of independence continued stagnant. This state of affairs had its roots in political instability, in economic conditions, and in the natural environment of the country.

With the same shortsighted policy that had characterized Spanish rule, the new government established in Buenos Aires took little account of the needs of the entire country. Provincialism rather than nationalism guided the leaders in Buenos Aires. The western irrigated farming districts, in particular, were neglected. This became the more serious, because this region had been cut adrift from its markets in the old Spanish mining towns of Bolivia. As a consequence, internal strife developed, and separatist tendencies were prevalent in nearly all the provinces; presidents succeeded one another on the wave of revolutionary activity. Not until 1868, when Sarmiento, "the school teacher president," assumed office, did a period of relative political quiescence come to Argentina. It was he who launched the country into the so-called modern period of economic development.

Partly because of the unsettled political conditions, trade did not increase significantly, and population remained almost stationary at around 1,000,000. So long as attention was focused on political problems, there was little effort devoted to building up the economic resources of the country or to expanding its trade. Moreover, during this same period, the United States with its vast lands, its rich resources, and its stable government was a more attractive area for immigrants and was proving to be too powerful an adversary for Argentina in the competition for European markets.

In addition to political strife within the country and competition from without, Argentina was faced with other serious problems that hampered trade expansion. Indians were a constant menace over vast areas, and transportation facilities were lacking for the movement of commodities to the seaboard cities. Lack of navigable streams in the Pampa, and the absence of road-building material in the deep alluvial soil of much of the area resulted in economic isolation and retarded trade.

As a result of this combination of conditions, the period of readjustment appears, at first glance, to be one of stagnation in which the general outlines of the pattern differ little from that of the 300 years that had preceded it. Actually, though, the bases for rapid and significant change were laid during this time. Once political stability became an established fact, the way was open for the solution of many internal problems. This, in turn, made it possible for Argentina to take advantage of foreign markets which were suddenly thrown open to her by our Civil War and the period of readjustment that followed. Technological changes were also coming about, such as the development of refrigeration and more rapid transport, which were to enable the country to take advantage more fully of its rich agricultural resources. Though seemingly a period of stagnation, these years stand out as a time of readjustment and as an age of transition from the old colonial economy to the new world-scale commercial activity of modern Argentina.

The Modern Period.—In the years since 1868, Argentina has evolved from a country of minor importance to one whose foreign trade places her among the 10 leading commercial nations of

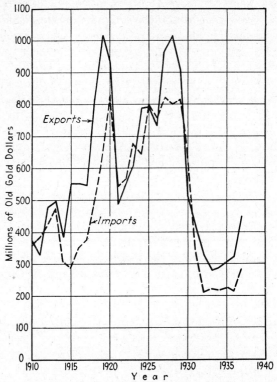

FIG. 95.—Export and import trade of Argentina.

the world. In half a century, Argentina has become one of the world's leading sources of cereals, meat, oilseeds, and wool. From a total of around $750,000 in the 1870's, trade increased in value to over $1,500,000,000 in the early 1920's. With some variations, total trade held around $1,000,000,000 to $1,500,000,000 until 1932 when, along with declines in all parts of the world, it began to drop. At no time did it fall below $500,000,000, though, in 1934, it amounted to only $508,000,000. Since then, there has been some revival. In 1937, total trade amounted to almost $750,000,000 (Fig. 95).

An interpretation of these statistics discloses many facts about Argentina. A somewhat detailed analysis of these figures indicates more than expanding production and consequent increased purchasing power in the country. For trade to reach these totals, there is the implication of vast and far-reaching economic transformation within Argentina itself, of international readjustments of trade patterns and of internal economies, of technological changes, and of population movements. The whole problem is so complex and its ramifications are so great that no simple or complete explanation is possible here, though some idea of the situation can be obtained from a study of a few of the items in Argentina's foreign trade.

Several prerequisites must be fulfilled before a product can enter international trade. There must be present, first of all, suitable natural conditions for the production of the commodity.[1] Mere capacity to produce, however, does not ensure the growth of trade. Markets and transportation ways to reach those markets must be available; the manufacture or import of various kinds of equipment to aid in production and trade is necessary; the "state of the arts" must be such as to enable a country to take advantage of its resources; and an adequate personnel to supply the labor requirements must be present. Internal and external changes, therefore, must be viewed and analyzed before the rapid growth of Argentina's trade can be comprehended.

Expanding Markets for Argentina's Products.—Almost contemporaneous with the end of Argentina's period of readjustment, world markets were opening up for her products. The United States had passed through a devastating civil war and was more concerned with internal problems than with foreign trade. Many European countries were evolving new economies that made them more dependent on the outside for foodstuffs and raw materials of a kind Argentina could supply. England had become a great manufacturing and commercial nation with little agricultural production. Denmark had passed from more or less extensive cereal production to the more intensive form of agriculture

---

[1] It will be assumed here, for the sake of simplicity, that Argentina possesses a natural environment suited to the production of certain articles. Later, in the regional analyses, this point will be treated in greater detail.

that dairy farming represents. Not only did she cease to be a supplier of cereals for European markets, but she became an importer of them. Industrial development, more intensive types of farming, and population growth in other European countries likewise led to greater demands for imports of food and raw materials, and Argentina shared in this expanding market. Even today, over 70 per cent of the country's exports go to European markets.

The effect this condition in Europe had on Argentina is illustrated by the expansion of wheat trade. In 1877, Argentina did not produce enough wheat for its own needs. In 1878, the country exported 2,500 tons, twenty years later 600,000 tons, and two decades later $3\frac{1}{2}$ million. By 1929, exports had reached over 7 million tons. Since then, there has been some decline. In 1934, export amounted to around 5 million and in 1937 to about 4 million tons.

Foreign Trade and the Development of Transportation and Manufacturing Industries.—Increase in trade was accompanied by rapid development of transportation facilities and the growth of certain kinds of industry. In fact, each of these activities helped to stimulate the other and aided in its progress.

ROADS.—As Argentina became more densely populated and as more and more products moved into world markets, the need for roads became great. Unfortunately, even today the country cannot boast of good highways. There are at present some 132,000 miles of roads, but less than 1 per cent of this amount is surfaced. The roads serve primarily as feeders to the railroads and do not form a well-defined system (Fig. 96). Two big handicaps, one natural and one human, retard highway development. The heart of the country, the Pampa, which most seriously needs good roads, is lacking in road-building materials. Over vast stretches, the fine soil contains scarcely a pebble, and bedrock lies deeply buried. Shipping ballast hundreds of miles from remote sections makes road-construction costs almost prohibitive. Lack of money also hinders the realization of a good system of roads. A general land tax was proposed for road improvement but did not meet with the approval of the large landholders on whom it would have fallen most heavily. A small income is realized from a 3 per cent tax on the receipts of railroads, but this yields only about $500,000 per year. Government appropriations for roads are frequently

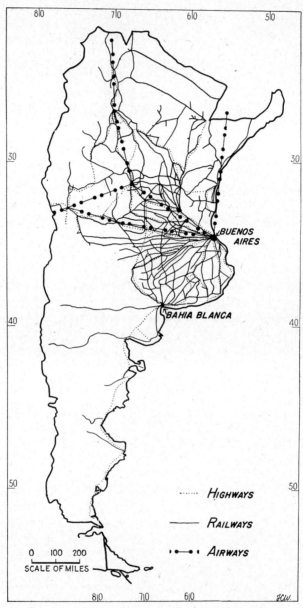

Fig. 96.—Major transportation lines in the Argentine.

less than the amount expended by many single states in the United States.

Since no real road system exists, each landowner finds it necessary to have a right of way from his land to a railway station. Owners have set aside and fenced broad strips, usually two or three times as wide as roads in the United States, to be used as thoroughfares (Fig. 97). Ponderous wagons, drawn by 4 to 12 horses with sometimes four or six drivers abreast are used in hauling farm crops. This is, in part, the explanation of the exces-

Fig. 97.—Gauchos on one of the wide unsurfaced roads of Argentina.

sive width allowed for the roads. Partly because of the poor quality of the highways, motor trucks are used to only a limited extent. In periods of good prices, grain is hauled profitably as much as 30 or 40 miles to a railway station, though 25 miles is generally considered the maximum distance of profitable hauling. Hauling is commonly done by contract at a price of ½ to 1 cent per bushel per mile. In general, it costs more to move grain from the farm to the railway than to ship it from Buenos Aires to Liverpool. Since roads do not satisfactorily meet Argentina's requirements, waterways and railroads are relied upon to move products to seaboard cities.

WATERWAYS.—Although the rivers of Argentina play a far more important role in the commerce of the country than do those of the United States, they do not afford adequate commercial highways for the country. Nearly all the overseas trade passes through the Rio de La Plata (River Plata estuary). Three navigable rivers, the Paraná, the Paraguay, and the Uruguay, which join with the Rio de La Plata to make up the *River Plata system*, complete the major navigable waterways of the country. Although of great importance in the movement of commodities into and out of the areas they serve, these rivers only touch the periphery of the heart of the country, the Pampa, which supplies the bulk of Argentina's export commodities.

The River Plata with its tributaries is the second largest river system of South America and one of the great systems of the world. The Paraná is longer than the Mississippi and is larger in volume. All-year freight service up the Mississippi ends at St. Louis, 1,300 miles[1] from the sea, but it extends up the Paraná-Paraguay 1,700 miles.[1] The lower Paraná is a river of great size, carrying ocean vessels of 26-foot draft to Rosario, one of the principal ports of Argentina, situated nearly 400 miles from the ocean. Its great headwater tributaries penetrate such widely separated regions as the coffee district of Brazil on the east and the Andes of Bolivia on the west. Only a few rivers of the world drain a larger area than the Paraná or carry a larger volume of water.

The Paraguay River is of utmost importance to the landlocked country of Paraguay, whose capital Asunción, 1,000 miles[1] up from Buenos Aires, is regularly reached by large steamers. During the 3 months of high water, 1,000-ton boats ascend 1,700 miles[1] to Corumbá in Brazil, and smaller steamers navigate the river throughout the year. A moderate amount of dredging at a few critical points would enable ocean vessels of 2,000 tons to reach Asunción throughout the greater part of the year. Even in its present unimproved condition, the river is one of the highly useful rivers of the world. In its course through Paraguay, the river has a width of $\frac{1}{4}$ to $\frac{1}{2}$ mile and is unbridged at any point. Steamship entries into Asunción reach 1,500 a year, and a large number of other freight-carrying boats, large and small, enter the port. The downstream traffic is much larger than the upstream, causing an unbalanced condition that partly accounts for the high freight rates. It commonly costs more to ship products 1,000 miles by river steamer than to ship them 7,000 miles to

[1] Distance following the windings of the river.

North America or Europe by ocean vessel. Although the rivers of this undeveloped region are of great usefulness, the cost of transportation on them is much higher than railway rates in the United States. Yet, without these rivers for navigation, a large section of South America would be practically cut off from contact with the outer world, for railways could not profitably penetrate the more remote regions for a long time to come. The one railway that does reach into Paraguay is continuously in financial difficulties and, at the best, can serve only a portion of the country.

There are three forest products of this region that supply the greater part of the river traffic: (1) the pine lumber of the lower Paraná basin; (2) the yerba maté;[1] (3) the quebracho[2] logs and extract obtained mainly from Argentina and the Paraguayan Chaco. The greater part of the yerba and quebracho is carried southward on the rivers, and a smaller proportion of the lumber. The production of quebracho extract is centered in a limited number of factories strategically located for shipping their products; but yerba is supplied by hundreds of small as well as some large producers, scattered along many rivers and branches. The river boats transport practically all the quebracho—over 200,000 tons a year. Moreover, such other products—tobacco, hides, oranges, meat—as this section produces in excess of its own needs are shipped to the outer world mainly by way of the rivers. Even on the small rivers, specially built light-draft boats are propelled from point to point, carrying a few tons of freight. The greater part of the imports is also carried by some one of the river steamship lines which send their boats regularly or intermittently into this interior region.

The bulk of the river traffic has passed into the control of a British company that has bought up most of its competitors and nearly monopolizes the river shipping. It is a well-managed, substantial company giving better service than the smaller lines, but the high rates charged cause complaint. The river steamers that reach Asunción during the low water draw only 6 or 8 feet when loaded, and in a very dry season even less.

[1] Yerba means herb and maté means a gourd. The yerba maté tree produces a leaf similar in appearance to holly. The leaf is dried and used in making a tealike beverage which is customarily served in a small gourd.

[2] Quebracho is a species of tree very rich in tannic acid.

The principal passenger steamers between Buenos Aires and Asunción depart from each city twice weekly. The upriver trip requires 4 or 5 days and the down trip about 3 or 4 days. On the lesser rivers, the steamers may make only 50 to 60 miles a day, stopping anywhere that freight or passengers are to be obtained, using 3 hours or more daily to take on wood for fuel, and possibly tying up at night. Where there is no competition with railroads, rates and fares are high.

A Brazilian company has, at times, operated a line of steamers by way of the Paraná-Paraguay to bring down manganese ore from mines in Matto Grosso. The navigation of the upper Paraná, above the point where it is crossed by the International Railway, is less important than that of the Paraguay, for the region is very sparsely settled, most of the population of Paraguay living along the Paraguay River or not far from it. It is a region of many enormous landholdings and of great waterfalls, including those of Guayra and of Iguazu which, at times of flood, rival Niagara in grandeur.

AIR LINES.—Airway routes effectively serve the northern portion of Argentina (Fig. 96). Airplanes provide a valuable supplemental means of transportation for quick movement to distant areas but, of course, are unimportant in the shipment of bulky commodities. It is primarily in the field of passenger travel, rather than freight movement, that this means of transportation can be considered significant.

Since roads, waterways, and air lines do not adequately serve or effectively reach the heart of the country, Argentina depends on railroads as the primary carrier of her export commodities. The rapid growth of a railroad system is indicative both of the need for and the adaptability of the railroad to the country's transportation requirements.

DEVELOPMENT OF RAILROADS.—Increase in trade was accompanied by the rapid development of railroads. In 1857, there were only 6 miles of railroad in the country. In 1937, the figure exceeded 25,000; a large percentage of this amount is located in the heart of country which is not well served by other types of transportation facilities (Fig. 96). Today, Argentina is the only country of South America with an extensive and well-defined railway net.[1]

[1] It should perhaps be noted that, though Argentina has a well-developed railroad net, service is very infrequent on many lines.

The level topography of the Pampa which has so favored the agricultural and pastoral industries has no less favored the construction of railway lines. For miles, there is not a cut or a fill or a bridge. The cost of upkeep of the lines is low in comparison with the cost in most parts of South America. There is little or no snow in winter; no washouts due to violent floods; and the great producing area is compact and lies near the sea. Furthermore, the quantities of cereals and animal products that are to be transported are exceedingly large. These facts would seem to ensure low cost of building and operating railways; but building materials, rolling stock, replacements, and much of the fuel had to be imported and still are imported from Europe or the United States. The English are economical builders and operators of railways; yet the capital investment is so large that profits have been relatively small, averaging for many years 4 to 6 per cent but more recently reaching 6 or 7 per cent.

Aside from the fact that Argentina has the best railroad system of South America, four other facts concerning the railways of the country are important: (1) The railroads are mainly British-owned and -operated. Somewhat more than 20 per cent of the total mileage is owned and operated by the Argentine Government. (2) The roads are of three different gauges: meter (3.28 feet), standard (4 feet 8½ inches), and broad (5½ feet), with the broad gauge predominating. (3) All the great systems focus upon Buenos Aires, with Rosario and Bahía Blanca as secondary ports (Fig. 96). (4) The passenger and freight service are of good quality but are more expensive than in the United States.

There are three major railway systems, each having upward of 3,000 miles of line: (1) the Central Argentine, (2) the Buenos Aires Great Southern, and (3) the Buenos Aires and Pacific. These are all British-owned lines and are broad gauge. The first railway (6 miles long) in Argentina was opened in 1857. The growth of lines was gradual until 1900 when the total mileage reached 10,000. In the next decade, it nearly doubled and, in 1930, had reached about 25,000 miles, by far the greater part of which is in the Province of Buenos Aires (Figs. 96 and 98). Over $1,000,000,000 of British capital is invested in Argentine railroads.

The passenger trains between the principal cities are frequent and modern, including dining-car and sleeping-car service. The electric suburban trains in and out of the capital are among the

best to be found anywhere. Over 500 passenger trains leave
Buenos Aires daily, and the terminal stations in that city are
palatial. The time schedules of the through trains are fast, and

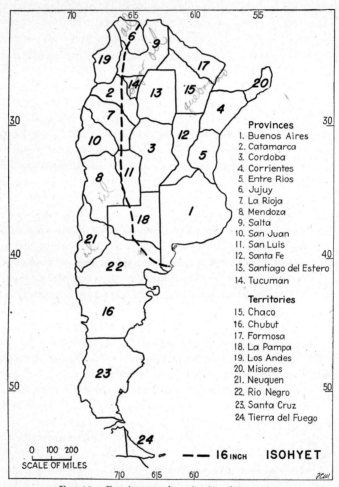

Fig. 98.—Provinces and territories of Argentina.

trains are prompt in arriving and departing. The government
lines have been built mainly in the outlying parts of the Republic
for the purpose of promoting the development of those regions.
As a rule, these lines have been operated at a loss. Extensions of
both private and government lines are going on steadily. In spite

of the 23,000 miles of railway, the country needs double the present mileage, for there are great areas of productive land that are still 30 or 40 miles or more from a railway station.

Narrow-gauge, light railways can be laid on the level *pampa* for less than the cost of good highways, and some *estancias* are being connected with the main railways by these "decauville," or light railways, built and operated by the large landowners for their own use.

The Argentine-Chile Transandean railroad is one of the world's famous railways. It was opened in 1910 after long years of struggle on the part of many engineers to conquer the defiant Andes. The Argentine portion of the line was the less difficult to build, for the slope is less precipitous; the ascent is spread over 110 miles, whereas an equal ascent to the famous Uspallata Pass from the Chilean side is made in 40 miles. Gradients of 8 per cent (8-foot rise to 100 feet of track) are necessary, and locomotives climb such grades by use of the cog device known as the rack and pinion. At the highest point (10,452 feet), the railroad passes through a 2-mile tunnel. The railroad is a masterly piece of engineering, extremely difficult to build, and very costly to protect from the heavy snows, avalanches, and landslides of the Andes. Miles and miles of concrete and timber snowsheds have been built, and only since 1919 has the line been kept open throughout the winter. The Chilean section, which cost over $300,000 a mile, has had to receive generous government aid and can never return a profit on the present capitalization. The twice-a-week International Pullman train is excellent; it covers the distance of 900 miles from Valparaiso to Buenos Aires in 36 hours and charges $100 United States currency, or about 11 cents a mile. There is very little freight traffic. The Argentine portion, now consolidated in one company from Buenos Aires to the summit of the Andes, is part of the Buenos Aires and Pacific, a British system. The Chilean Transandean railway is privately owned but receives government aid. Thus, there are three links in the transcontinental line: (1) the broad-gauge Chilean portion, (2) the meter-guage mountain portion, and (3) the broad-gauge Argentine portion from Mendoza to Buenos Aires.

The statue of the Christ of the Andes, erected as a pledge of enduring peace between Chile and Argentina, stands at the pass of the Andes under which the railway tunnel is built (Fig. 99).

An Argentine railway reaches to the boundary between Bolivia and Argentina, and Bolivia has completed a line to the same point. This gives rail connection between Buenos Aires and

La Paz and thence by three different railroads to the Pacific. It is a long route through thinly settled regions and will be little used for years to come.

One railway line extends to Asunción, the capital of Paraguay, and thus connects that city with the Argentine railway system. Railways have also been completed that connect Buenos Aires and Montevideo with the Brazilian railroads that reach São Paulo and Rio de Janeiro. These are relatively new lines, badly graded and poorly equipped. As yet, they are little used for international traffic.

Fig. 99.—Statue of the Christ of the Andes, on the Argentine-Chilean boundary at the crest of the Andes.

Though Argentina's growing export trade was one of the principal incentives to the expansion of railways, the development of rail transportation modified the import-trade pattern. As rail lines were extended, there arose the need for fuel and for iron and steel and their products. This fact gives a further insight into the character and resources of the country. That these items are still significant in the import trade is indicative of one of two conditions. Either Argentina has failed to make use of available resources within the country or else she does not possess them. Unfortunately for Argentina, the latter is primarily the case.

FUEL AND POWER SUPPLIES.—Fuel supplies account for some 10 per cent of the total imports of Argentina today. The need for these imports is in part the natural result of increased demands as railroad and industrial development have taken place and in part the result of inadequate supplies within the country. Although wood provides fuel requirements in some sections, it is on coal, oil, and water that the country must depend in most areas.

Coal. Coal of valuable grades, from all present indications, is almost entirely lacking in Argentina. Deposits that have been discovered have all been of poor grade, small in size, or too remote from areas of consumption to be of value. The best deposit so far located is near Lake Epusjen in the Territory of Chubut (Fig. 98); but it is low grade and must be washed before it can be used, and even then it is only about half as good as imported coal.

Because of an almost total lack of coal, Argentina has had to depend on imports for most of her needs. Rail lines toward the northeast were able to utilize wood in that forested section; but elsewhere, and particularly on the treeless Pampa, no such supplies were available. Increases in railway mileage and expanding commodity movements brought about increased imports of coal. In 1900, about three-fourths of 1 million tons were brought into the country. By 1914, imports had increased to over 4 million. During 1917 and 1918, there was a sharp drop back to the 1900 level. By 1928, imports had expanded to $3\frac{1}{2}$ million tons but since then have declined, falling to 3 million tons in 1930, 2.4 million in 1932, and 3 million in 1937.

Here, again, is evidence of the complexity of the problem and of changing world conditions that have striking repercussions in a country as dependent on world trade as is Argentina. The decline in 1917 and 1918 was not due to factors within Argentina. Demand for coal had not lessened. If anything, if total trade can be taken as a measure, there was a greater demand than ever for fuel. The falling off of coal imports during these years is to be accounted for by the World War. England had long been the major source of Argentina's coal. During 1917 and 1918, Great Britain found herself without men to mine the coal and without ships to transport it. Argentina suffered dire shortage and was forced to burn more wood, asphaltic residues from oil seeps, and even corn to meet her fuel requirements.

Perhaps even more interesting than the wartime shortage is the postwar decline. Whereas the former is indicative of a short period of maladjustment resulting from outside causes, the latter implies a long-run tendency that is bringing about profound changes in the trade pattern and, consequently, in the internal economy of the country. The postwar decline might be assumed to have resulted from the general world depression. This doubtless had something to do with the situation, but reduced imports of coal were in evidence before trade in general declined. Moreover, despite greater total foreign trade in the postwar than in the prewar period, coal imports never regained the place they held before the sharp decline of 1917 and 1918. More efficient use of imports would also help to explain a decline in the amount needed. Although Argentina has learned to be very frugal in the use of fuel, even the most efficient utilization would not account for the sharp drop from the prewar level. More important than either the world-wide depression or the more efficient use of available supplies has been the substitution of fuel oil for coal in many instances.

Petroleum. Oil imports in 1916 amounted to just a little over 100,000 metric tons; by 1923 they had increased to 700,000, by 1929 to 1.3 million, and by 1937 to 1.7 million. Since 1 ton of oil has approximately the heat equivalent of $1\frac{1}{2}$ tons of coal, about $1\frac{1}{2}$ million tons of coal have been displaced by imports of oil. In addition to increased imports of petroleum from abroad, there has also been a growing production of oil in the country. Petroleum is one mineral that Argentina possesses in significant amounts. The combined output of all wells in the country, which in 1937 amounted to over 16 million barrels, is sufficient for one-half to three-fourths of Argentina's needs, but expansion in production seems possible and probable.

Oil was first developed for lighting purposes in Argentina in 1886, but early oil companies were unsuccessful. In 1907, oil was discovered while drilling a water well in Chubut at Comodoro Rivadavia. Today, this field is the most important in Argentina and yields over one-fourth of the country's requirements of fuel oil and gasoline. Operations, as is true in all the oil fields of Argentina, is under government control. Argentina has two other and at present much less important producing areas. One is located in the extreme northwestern part of the country in the provinces of Salta and Jujuy (Fig. 98) and the other farther south in the provinces of Neuquén and Mendoza (Fig. 98). Oil from the former field is high grade, but production amounts to only about 2,500 barrels per day. It is moved to Buenos Aires for refining. Production in the Neuquén-Mendoza field amounts to some 5,000 barrels per day. Most of it is produced in Neuquén province and shipped to Bahía Blanca for refining.

Water Power. The only other mineral source of power that Argentina possesses is water. It has been estimated that the country possesses a potential water-power reserve of 5,400,000 horsepower. Of this, only about 67,000 horsepower has been developed. The retarded development is primarily due to the location of the power. The market for electricity is, of course, in the eastern coastal cities, but many of the principal power sites lie in the west on the eastern slope of the Andes. Between the two areas is a vast stretch of undeveloped and largely undevelopable territory. The single most important water-power site in the country is at Iguazu Falls on the northeastern boundary. It is estimated that 350,000 horsepower could be developed here, but isolation from the heart of the country (Iguazu is 800 miles north of Buenos Aires) has prevented any development, except for preliminary surveys and agreements with neighboring countries as to water rights.

As this brief analysis of Argentina's fuel resources has shown, there are likely to be changes in the detail of the present import-trade pattern, but the general outlines will probably remain much the same for some time to come. Coal imports will probably never again attain the importance they once held, not because of increased production in Argentina, but because of the substitution of oil for coal as fuel. Oil will also, in all probability, continue to be an imported commodity of some significance. Judging from the past developments, it seems unlikely that domestic production will meet all the needs of the country. Assuming that need for fuel will continue to increase, local production will have to become greater to supply the same percentage it now furnishes. Unless Argentina devotes more effort in the future than she has in the past to make herself independent of outside sources, it is highly improbable that production will increase sufficiently to meet all her needs. It also seems most unlikely that the country will be able to supplement her present fuel needs to any significant degree through the use of water power.

METALS AND METAL PRODUCTS.—A discussion of Argentina's imports of iron and steel and their products will help to give, as did that on coal, an understanding of the requirements of a modern commercial nation dependent for its existence on the sale of raw materials in world markets. The importation of iron and steel is an expression of the need for these materials in railway construction and maintenance and in the development of certain industrial activities that are a requisite of present-day commercial enterprise.

Argentina lacks workable deposits of iron ore, and this fact, together with the absence of adequate supplies of coal, largely precludes the development of a blast-furnace industry. Deficient supplies of these minerals, however, do not prevent the growth of an iron and steel industry. It should be borne in mind that iron and steel production is composed of two major steps: (1) the blast-furnace activity which transforms the ore into metal; (2) the fabrication of this metal into usable articles. It is in this latter phase of the industry that Argentina can engage. That she does is indicated by the important place that partly fabricated iron and steel products occupy in the import trade.

The resmelting and reshaping of iron and steel are favored in Argentina by several factors. First of all, scrap iron can be used. Although there is a certain loss due to rust, there is a large portion that is recoverable and it is well suited to the production of open-hearth steel. Moreover, scrap supplies can be supplemented with low-cost imported "pig" which gives the country a favorable differential over the high-cost steel and steel products manufactured elsewhere. Finally, it is not necessary to use coking coal in making steel. A great variety of fuels, including electricity, can be used. On the other hand, carbon, in the form of either coking coal or charcoal, must be used in the blast furnace. Since Argentina is largely dependent on the outside for her coal supplies, a choice of fuel is an added incentive for her to enter the fabricating rather than the blast-furnace phase of the industry.

A number of small iron and steel foundries and machine shops have grown up in Argentina as a response to the need for these products and owing to the advantages that the country possesses for their manufacture. Nearly all the railroads maintain small foundries for the reclamation of scrap. In Buenos Aires and in nearly all the large cities, there are similar establishments, and there seems to be no reason why the industry should not expand and, as the country matures, become more diversified. That this is likely is revealed by the fact that rolling-mill operations have already begun in Buenos Aires. Two mills, with a combined capacity of 21,000 tons, produce material used in the fabrication of agricultural machinery and equipment. This type of manufacturing represents a somewhat more advanced stage of industrial development than the simple processing done in machine shops and foundries.

That Argentina will not develop a blast-furnace industry, at least for a long time to come, seems to be indicated by a brief analysis of her iron-ore deposits. Although iron ore has been reported in some fourscore places in the country, none of them is of economic importance. Magnetite in the northwest, magnetite sands along the seacoast at Mar del Plata, hematite on the eastern slope of the Andes, and laterites in Misiones Territory are the only deposits worthy of mention. All these present serious problems in their utilization. They contain foreign materials (which increases the difficulty of smelting), are inaccessible, and are too small in size or too low grade to warrant their development.

The "modern period" of Argentina's development brought with it the need for imports of fuel and iron, and there seems to be little indication that the character of the country's trade in these items will be greatly modified in the near future. The fuel situation has already been discussed. In the case of iron and steel, certain changes in the type of product imported have taken place, but iron and steel will doubtless continue to be important items of trade. Several factors lead to this conclusion. There is a decrease in the amount of metal recovered each time scrap is re-used. This will need to be made up by imports. It also seems reasonable to assume that the need for iron and steel in the country will continue to increase. Argentina, at least for a long time to come, will probably be unable to meet her needs for all types of iron and steel products. Her small fabricating industries will probably not be able to meet the country's demands for mass-production items, large articles, or those items of a highly specialized nature which can be produced more cheaply in other areas. Iron and steel and their products, therefore, seem destined to continue to play an important role in the foreign trade of the country.

MANUFACTURING INDUSTRIES OF ARGENTINA[1]

Industry	Oct. 31, 1935		July 1, 1934–June 30, 1935 Value of products, paper pesos (000,000 omitted)	Per cent of total, value
	No. of estab.	No. of workers, (000 omitted)		
Food, beverages, and tobacco.....	11,564	121	1,267	37
Textiles and manufactures........	4,712	82	536	16
Forest products and manufactures	3,932	31	102	3
Paper, cardboard, etc............	214	7	34	1
Printing and publishing..........	2,180	27	140	4
Chemicals, drugs, oils, paints.....	929	15	137	4
Petroleum, coal, and subproducts..	57	5	133	4
Rubber and manufactures........	46	3	25	1
Leather and manufactures........	1,076	19	92	3
Stone, earth, glassware, and china.	2,248	17	59	2
Metals and manuf. (not mach.)...	3,739	42	195	5
Machines and vehicles...........	4,995	51	229	7
Electric-power stations..........	898	9	193	5
Building contractors.............	1,527	34	123	3
Oil fields, quarries, and mines.....	195	13	79	2
Miscellaneous...................	2,055	38	98	3
Totals......................	40,367	514	3,442	100

[1] Adapted from "*Commercial Travelers' Guide to Latin America*," Part II, p. 11.

As was stated previously, one of the needs of a modern large-scale commercial nation is equipment of various kinds to aid in production and trade. In view of the size of Argentina's foreign trade and the small number of people in the country, laborsaving types of machinery become the more essential. Argentina imports large amounts of agricultural and general machinery, electric goods, automobiles and trucks, and various types of specialized equipment. These products are, for the most part, either types of commodities not manufactured in Argentina or not produced in amounts sufficient for the country's needs. As such, they are a key to the productive resources and consumption needs of Argentina.

OTHER MANUFACTURING INDUSTRIES.—Though some industries are not economically suited to the resources of Argentina, certain types of manufacturing, other than those already mentioned, have developed. This industrial growth is reflected in both the import and the export trade of the country. Whereas nearly all manufactured articles were imported a half century ago, many of the country's needs are now met by home industries using local or imported raw materials, and some of the products of Argentina's factories move into world markets.

The leading industries of the country are those which utilize local raw materials (see table, page 246). An estimate made by an official Argentine bureau[1] indicates that 71 per cent of the products manufactured in the country are made from local raw materials. Especially significant are food, beverage, and tobacco manufactures which account for over one-third of the total value of all manufactured products (see table, page 246). The principal items in the food and beverage group are sugar, wine, packed and preserved meats, flour, and dairy products; of these, meat, flour, and dairy products are important articles of export. The textile industry has grown rapidly since 1930. It is estimated[2] that local mills supply most of the country's knit goods, 80 per cent of the woolens, 60 per cent of the linen, and about $33\frac{1}{3}$ per cent of the cotton cloth. Two rayon plants are also in operation.

The industrial census of 1935 lists some 40,000 manufacturing establishments employing 514,000 workers and producing goods valued at approximately $3\frac{1}{2}$ billion pesos (paper) or, translated into American dollars at the present rate of exchange, approximately $1,000,000,000. This means that the average plant in Argentina employs about a dozen workers and turns out about $25,000 worth of goods per year. Though not an entirely reliable measure, these figures do indicate something of the small scale of operation of many of the plants. Over 70 per cent of the

---

[1] Naciones Utiles sobre La República Argentina, 1924.

[2] "Commercial Travelers' Guide to Latin America," Part II, p. 10.

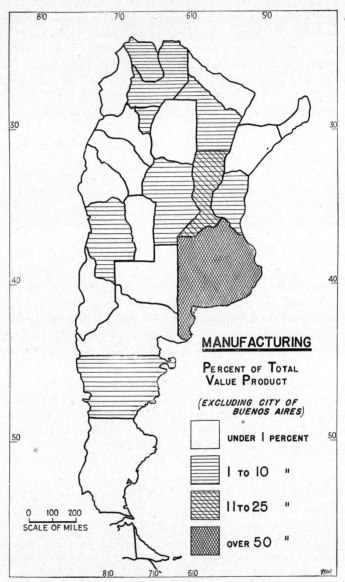

Fig. 100.—Manufacturing in Argentina.

country's manufacturing is concentrated in the city and province of Buenos Aires (Fig. 100). About 43 per cent is in the city of Buenos Aires alone. The balance of the country's manufacturing is in provinces or territories immediately contiguous to the leading center or in outlying sections where specialized production has resulted in some manufactural development, as wine in Mendoza, sugar in Tucumán, quebracho extract in Chaco, or oil refining in Chubut (Figs. 98 and 100).

Although Argentina has shown considerable industrial growth, it should not be overlooked that most of her industries have been fostered by high import duties, strong nationalistic feeling, and exchange restrictions, policies that seem in the long run inevitably to conflict with the free movement of her exports. Though Argentina may desire to reduce her dependence on imported goods and become a more self-contained nation, it would seem that the country could attain this goal in only a moderate degree. To pursue it at the expense of export markets seems a dangerous course to follow.

Much has been written concerning industrial expansion in Argentina. Some writers have drawn comparisons between the various periods of economic development in that country and our own. They have pointed out that in each case there was a pioneering stage, during which the land was wrested from the Indians and settled. A period of economic adolescence followed, during which the country depended in large measure on the export of raw materials and began industrial development. In the United States, this second phase was followed by rapid growth of factories and evolution toward a balanced economy. On the basis of the similarity of the first two stages in the two countries and because of the recent and rapid rise of industry in Argentina, some writers contend that Argentina is on the verge of great manufactural expansion. Without belittling the significance of the growth of factories in Argentina, it should not be overlooked that the country does not possess the rich mineral resources of the United States, especially coal and iron. Nor does Argentina have rich resources of other metals. Tungsten deposits yielding a small percentage of the world's supply are worked in the north-central part of the country. Unimportant quantities of gold, silver, copper, lead, and zinc have, from time to time, been mined in the mountains of the west; but these mining efforts have been largely unprofitable, and production is trifling when compared with the major industries of the country. Since Argentina lacks most minerals, it seems highly improbable that the country's economic development will parallel or even closely resemble that of the United States, particularly in the field of heavy industry and mass production. New discoveries and technological changes of far-reaching importance, of course, may alter present conditions. But of these we know nothing, and to forecast on the basis of such remote possibilities is to deal in pure fancy. Until and unless such changes come, imports of various kinds of machinery and equipment seem destined to occupy an important place in the country's trade. Though individual items may be removed from the list by the development of home industries, the general character will probably not be greatly modified in the near future.

Technological Changes and Foreign Trade.—That improvements in technology do work profound changes in a country is demonstrated by Argentina's foreign-trade history. In colonial days, hides and skins were important exports. Animals, in the form of meat, did not move into world markets except dried or salted. With the discovery of refrigeration and the application of it to ships in the 1880's, marked changes came about in the country's trade. As a result of rapid transportation and refrigeration, frozen and chilled meats became important export commodities as did dairy products. Today, trade in meats and dairy products, which is directly dependent on refrigeration, accounts for at least 15 per cent of the country's total export trade. Technological changes also came in other fields. Of particular significance were those in agriculture. The development of various kinds of farm machinery and their application to the vast, fertile, and sparsely populated plains of Argentina made possible much greater production per man and thus added much to the exportable surpluses of the country.

Technological changes, however, are meaningless unless put to use, and one of the essentials for the application of new techniques is an adequate personnel. The million or so people of colonial Argentina could not have, by themselves, built up the great trade volume that the country enjoys today. More people were needed, and the rapid growth of trade reflects the migration of peoples and the growth of population.

Population Growth and Trade.—For reasons already mentioned, the population of Argentina increased very slowly until orderly government was established. After that, European immigration increased rapidly. In 1895, the population was nearly 4 million; in 1915, it had doubled again and stood at 8 million. During the World War and in the years immediately following, the increase was slight. In fact, for 5 years, more persons departed from the country than came in. In 1935, the estimated population was 12 million. The country needs immigrants, and the government takes active measures to induce European immigration. In the 10 years from 1904 to 1913, the United States admitted about 10 million immigrants; Argentina, 2.4 million; Canada, 1.5 million; and Brazil, 1 million.

Among the immigrants into Argentina, the Italians are the most numerous, with Spaniards ranking second. An increasing number of Germans, Poles, and other non-Latin Europeans are arriving; there are few Asiatics. Under Argentine laws, the children born of foreign parents in Argentina become automatically citizens of the country. The half-breeds (Indian and white) known as the *gauchos* are disappearing and now number scarcely 200,000. There are about 36,000 civilized Indians and a few small tribes of uncivilized Indians. Of all the countries of the Western Hemisphere, Uruguay and Canada possibly excepted, Argentina has the largest proportion of people of European stock, mainly south European, whose languages are similar and who learn Spanish readily.

Illiteracy among the immigrants is high. Schools for the children exist in the cities and villages; but, in the open country with its long distances and sparse population, schools are few, except on *estancias* that have a considerable number of colonist families. Here, some sort of schooling may be obtained.

In Buenos Aires alone lives 20 per cent of the entire population of the country, and this city attracts and holds an altogether disproportionate part of the population. Neat farmhouses and well-kept rural villages which are so conspicuous in the farming regions of the United States are notably lacking in most of Argentina. The country people are still, in a large degree, a tenant and migratory population. Over most of the area, population density is still less than 15 per square mile (Fig. 101), and there is a great need for more people in many sections.

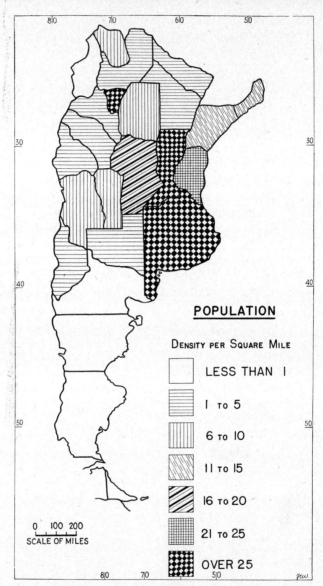

Fig. 101.—Population density in Argentina.

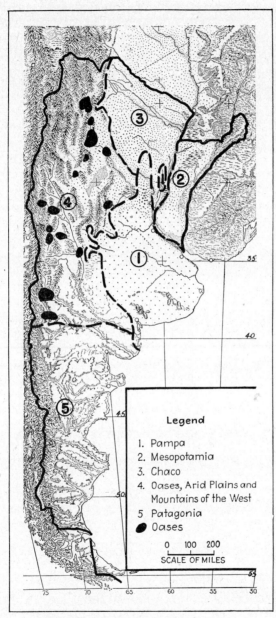

Legend

1. Pampa
2. Mesopotamia
3. Chaco
4. Oases, Arid Plains and Mountains of the West
5 Patagonia
   Oases

0   100 200
SCALE OF MILES

FIG. 102.—Regional map of Argentina.

The growth of population, though, has done much to increase the trade of the country. Without immigrants, the country would have been unable to reach the high stage of commercial importance it now enjoys.

Agriculture and Trade.—In the discussion that has preceded, the items that are most important in Argentina's foreign trade have purposely not been emphasized. Although the data on trade in certain of the commodities discussed give an insight into the character of this South American nation, it is on agriculture that the commercial importance of the country rests. Grains, meats and animal by-products, wool, and oilseeds are the major products of the country. They alone account for over 90 per cent of all exports. It is to the production of these commodities that the whole economic life of the country is geared. The importance of the trade in these products indicates the dominantly agricultural status of the country. But an understanding of the agriculture of Argentina necessitates detailed regional analyses. The products and problems of the various sections are so different and so vital that each must be viewed separately in order to gain an understanding of the whole. On the basis of human activities and natural environment, five major regions are discernible. The heart of the country and most important region is the Pampa (Fig. 102). The other regions might be thought of as an appendage to this heart, regions that supplement the products of the Pampa and round out the economy of the country. They include: (1) Mesopotamia; (2) the Chaco; (3) Oases, Arid Plains, and Mountains of the West; and (4) Patagonia (Fig. 102). It is in terms of these regions that the productive resources will be analyzed in the remaining chapters on Argentina.

Chapter X. The Pampa

The 250,000 square miles of grassy, level plain to which is given the name of *La Pampa* is by far the most important region of Argentina. Frequently, it has been stated that "the Pampa is Argentina," and there is considerable justification for this characterization. The Pampa is the heart of Argentina. It is the most highly urbanized and densely populated portion of the country (Figs. 102, 1, and 101). The region, as has been noted previously, is responsible for at least three-fourths of the country's manufacturing and has more than 75 per cent of the country's railroad mileage. In the Federal District of Buenos Aires is located the political capital, and here and in the other cities of the region is localized most, of the commercial activity of the country. The primary importance of the region, though, results from its agricultural productivity. Over 80 per cent of the cultivated land of Argentina is in the Pampa.

From the vast and fertile plains of the Pampa comes a large proportion of the commodities that give Argentina its place among the great commercial nations of the world. About one-fifth of all the world's wheat and flour, over one-fourth of the meat, nearly one-third of the hides and skins, about two-thirds of the corn, and nearly three-fourths of the world's flaxseed that enter world trade come from this region.

The Pampa occupies nearly one-fourth the area of the Republic, extending for some 700 miles north and south between the thirtieth and fortieth parallels and reaching westward 400 miles, in its broadest extremity, to about the line of the 16-inch isohyet (Figs. 102 and 98). Beyond the western boundary, the level land so characteristic of the Pampa continues, but the grass cover gives way to the xerophytic vegetation of the *monte*, or bushland.

255

The flat structure of the plain also extends north of the Pampa, but heavier rainfall here has produced a forest vegetation which differentiates this area from the almost treeless Pampa. The southern boundary, for the most part, coincides with the northern limit of the plateau structure of Patagonia.

Regional unity of the Pampa is based essentially on a similarity of human activity throughout the area. It is a region in which the basic economic activity is commercial agriculture, in the form of either commercial grain farming or commercial livestock ranching. Although these two types of farming are not dependent upon each other, one does supplement the other to some degree. It is the exception rather than the rule to find farms in the Pampa that do not engage in both types of agricultural production. Ranches devoted primarily to livestock almost always raise some crops, at least as supplemental feed for the animals, and almost every "dirt farmer" raises some livestock. Around this dual-phase agriculture, the economic life of the Pampa is built, and to it almost all the activities of the region are related.

In view of the outstanding importance of the Pampa as the major source of the country's exports, it is not surprising that population should be concentrated in this area. Labor is needed, not only to carry on agriculture, but also to handle the varied commercial activities associated with the export trade. This concentration of population is in part responsible for the development of manufacturing. Likewise, the relatively high degree of urbanization in the Pampa has created a market for certain specialized types of agricultural products such as milk and fresh vegetables. As a result, dairying and truck farming have become important; and, in the case of dairying at least, the activity has outgrown local demands and now contributes to the exportable surplus of the country (Fig. 103).

Although there is regional unity in the Pampa as to the type of agriculture carried on, there are many and striking local variations in crops grown or animals raised and in production methods. In a broad general way, the agriculturalists of the Pampa may be classed as farmers specializing in cereal production or as ranchers devoting themselves to raising livestock. But even within this broad classification there is specialization as to the kinds of cereals grown and even, though perhaps not to such a marked degree, the kind of animals raised. Differences in climate, drainage, distance to market and transportation facilities available, and other natural and human factors are all important in explaining the human-use pattern, in interpreting the localization of particular activities within the broader economic structure of pampean agriculture.

FIG. 103.—Creamery on dairy estancia, Buenos Aires region.

COMMERCIAL CROP FARMING

Despite the fact that less than half of the Pampa is under cultivation, at least two-thirds of all the exports of Argentina come directly from the plowed lands of the Pampa. In addition, certain cultivated crops are almost indispensable to the livestock industry, since they provide supplemental feed for the animals. Well over half of the 74 million acres under cultivation is devoted to cereals; wheat alone occupies slightly over one-fourth of all the cropland. In total acreage, it is rivaled only by alfalfa. The land in alfalfa is, in most years, somewhat greater than that in wheat, though the two are of about equal importance. Almost one-fourth of the cultivated land is devoted to corn and flax, with the former occupying some 14 per cent and the latter between 9 and 10 per cent of the crop area. Oats, barley, and rye are the other leading grains. Together they account for about 10 per cent of the total and are about equal in importance.

Although these grains are widely produced throughout the Pampa and although there are few districts devoted exclusively to a single crop, there has developed a striking pattern of specialization in certain of the crops. Differences in drainage, particularly underground, in soil, and especially in climate are important in an interpretation of the crops-land pattern. The moist and warm conditions of the north are favorable to corn and flax; the cooler and drier environment and the lighter soil of the center and west are suitable for wheat and alfalfa; barley, oats, and rye are adaptable to the cooler conditions and shorter growing season of the south. It must be clearly understood, however, that, although these districts specialize in the production of the particular crops mentioned, these grains are merely the leading ones in those areas, not the only ones.

The vast, level stretches of fertile land, enriched by humus from the original grass cover, the almost complete absence of stumps and stones, the scarcity of labor, and the immense size of most of the landholdings combine to favor the development of extensive farming in the Pampa. Large-scale operations and the wide use of laborsaving machinery are characteristic. This system of agriculture is well illustrated in the case of wheat. Wheat raising is not the only example of extensive farming, but it is typical of most of the agriculture of this economically youthful country.

The Wheat Crescent.—The chief wheat area forms a giant crescent 600 miles long which stretches from Santa Fé in the north to the coastal margin east of Bahía Blanca in the south (Fig. 104). Climate, soil, and drainage help to confine wheat within its present area of production. Toward the north and northwest, rainfall conditions are unsatisfactory. This section is one with wet summers and dry winters (Figs. 8 and 9). As a consequence, there is too much moisture for good wheat production in the summer season and not enough in the winter. Expansion to the west and southwest faces the unsurmountable handicap of increasing aridity. The 20-inch rainfall line defines the arid margin of the main portion of the wheat belt, the 16-inch isohyet its limit. In a few cases, wheat can be grown with less moisture, but the distribution must be such as to provide full utilization of all that falls. The driest land on which wheat is now grown is in the southwest where most of the rain comes in the spring and autumn, at the times of the year when it is most beneficial to the crop. Wheat raising has not spread eastward of the crescent to any marked degree. This area is low, poorly drained, and has a heavy clay soil, a combination of conditions not favorable to wheat production.

Throughout the wheat belt, other crops are also raised, though crop rotation is not commonly practiced. In the south, oats and barley are outstanding; in the north, corn and flax attain importance; cattle and alfalfa are prominent in the landscape of the entire area. The relative importance of wheat varies considerably in different parts of the crescent. In Córdoba[1] and southern Santa Fé, wheat occupies 20 to 40 per cent of the land and, around the little town of Villa Maria in central Córdoba, as much as 40 to 50 per cent. North of Bahía Blanca, in southern Buenos Aires, densities similar to those of Córdoba and Santa Fé are also found. Elsewhere throughout most of the belt, wheat occupies 10 to 20 per cent of all the land.

FIG. 104.—The principal wheat lands form a crescent on the western and southern sides of the Pampa. (*U. S. Dept. of Agr.*)

Wheat is sown from May to August, and harvest begins in November of the following spring. Harvest progresses with the season from north to south. Most of the operations of plowing, planting, and harvesting are done with machinery drawn by horses or oxen, though some tractors are in use. Although some combines are used, most of the threshing is done by migratory outfits which move from one farm to another. The wheat is generally run from the thresher into jute bags and hauled immediately to the nearest railroad station in huge, heavy carts carrying 4 to 6 tons each. There are no elevators at these interior

[1] For location of provinces, see Fig. 98.

stations; so the grain is stacked in the open on platforms and covered with tarpaulins to protect it from the weather until ready for shipment to the seaboard cities (Fig. 105). Although all the wheat belt is within 400 miles of the sea, the method of hauling the grain and stacking it, the time involved, and the large amount of labor needed all add to the cost of getting the wheat to market. Despite these costs, Argentine wheat can be sold profitably in Liverpool below the price of North American wheat.

Fig. 105.—Piles of bags of wheat at a railway station in Argentina. Since there are practically no country elevators in Argentina, grain is handled in bags. (*Photograph by H. G. Olds.*)

Nearly all pampean wheat is grown by three types of farmers. On the large *estancias*, *shareworkers* may contract to farm 400 or 500 acres in return for an even division of the proceeds from the sale of the crop. The owner provides the land, the machinery, and the seed; the shareworker gives his labor. The shareworker usually stays in one place only a few years, generally only until the native fertility of the soil has been much reduced. He then plants the land to alfalfa, returns it to the owner, and moves on to a new tract. In this way, the wealthy landholders get their range land planted to a good forage crop at relatively little cost. At one time, about three-fourths of all the country's wheat was grown in this way. Many in Argentina who possess a little capital with which to buy equipment and seed rent a tract of land. These *tenant farmers* live a life similar to and practice a system of extensive one-crop agriculture much like that of the share-

workers. The major difference is that they get a larger share of
the proceeds because they furnish their own machinery and
seed. More important today than either the shareworker or the
tenant farmer in the production of wheat is the *colonist*.
The colonists of Swiss, French, and Italian origin are
landowners. They account for most of the wheat grown in the
northern section of the crescent. Although most of the wheat
of Argentina is raised in one of these three ways and despite the
wide use of agricultural machinery, there is not sufficient local
labor to meet the harvest demands. This problem is solved by
migratory workers, called *golondrinas* (swallows), who come to
Argentina from Italy and Spain for the harvest season. In
some years, these number as many as 180,000. Fortunate it is for
Argentina that these workers are available and that her Southern
Hemisphere location brings her harvest at a different time of the
year than that in the area from which these *golondrinas* come.

Largely owing to the extensive methods of farming, wheat
yields in Argentina are relatively low. In most years, the average
is around 13 bushels per acre. Great differences in the amount of
rainfall from year to year, unseasonable precipitation, frost, insect
pests, and other handicaps to stable agricultural production, which
will be discussed in greater detail later, also cause great variations
in the yield and consequently in the amount of wheat raised.
On the average, about 60 per cent of the wheat crop is exported.

The "Corn Belt."—The Argentine "Corn Belt" differs mark-
edly in at least one respect from its counterpart in the United
States. Corn in the Pampa is raised principally for export (about
80 per cent) and for human consumption and *not* for local animal
feed. The familiar corncrib and silo of the United States are
almost entirely absent from the pampean Corn Belt landscape.
The relative position of corn in the export trade of the two countries is shown by the trade and production statistics. Argentina
produces less than one-tenth as much corn as the United States
but exports over ten times as much.

The major section of production is in an area 120 miles long
in northwestern Buenos Aires, southern Santa Fé, and eastern
Córdoba (Fig. 106). The belt occupies the territory east of the
wheat crescent and west of the Paraná River and is the most
fertile area of the Pampa. Production has not spread east of the
river to any marked extent, largely because of inadequate

transportation facilities. In the west, the Corn Belt encroaches on the wheat area. In fact, corn has become an important crop in an area once devoted primarily to wheat and cattle. Wheat was the first crop grown by the colonists who settled along the Rosario-Córdoba railroad, but corn had almost completely displaced wheat in this section by 1910.

ARGENTINA, URUGUAY, AND CHILE
CORN (MAIZE)
ACREAGE
EACH DOT REPRESENTS 5,000 ACRES

FIG. 106.—(*U. S. Dept. of Agr.*)

In at least one respect, the Argentine Corn Belt resembles that of the United States. Corn is not the only crop grown in the belt, although it does occupy over one-half of all the land in crops. In some sections, particularly along the river, north and south of Rosario, as much as 75 per cent of cropland is in corn. Wheat, alfalfa, and flax are also important in the Corn Belt.

Most of the corn raised in the Pampa is the flint type and not the more familiar dent corn of our Corn Belt. Flint corn has several advantages over the dent variety for the Argentine farmer. The flint type contains less moisture and therefore keeps and ships better; the kernels are smaller, and thus it is better suited for poultry feed. It is also sweeter and, consequently, is preferred for horses. As a result of these assets, flint corn usually sells for 8 to 10 cents more per bushel than dent. It should be noted that, although flint corn has certain advantages, it is less satisfactory as food for hogs and cattle and gives lower yields per acre. Although the flint type predominates, some dent corn is also raised.

The climate of the Corn Belt is well suited to the crop's production. Although drought is a threat, the area receives, on the average, 30 to 40 inches of rain with an early summer maximum. In some years, there is excessive rainfall late in the summer which interferes with the ripening, harvesting, and shipping of the corn. Summer temperature conditions are quite similar to those in the United States Corn Belt with averages around 71 to 75°F. Winters, though, are much milder and permit winter plowing, a further advantage that the Argentine corn farmer enjoys. Land is usually plowed during July, August, and September, and planting may continue until December. This long planting season enables the farmer to avoid sowing his crop at undesirable times. If weather conditions are not satisfactory, for example, he can delay planting until they are more favorable.

Harvesting is done principally by migratory contract corn pickers. The harvest season lasts through the autumn months of March, April, and May. The ears of corn, after being broken from the stalks, husked, and hauled to the farmhouse, are stored in great cylindrical heaps (*trojes*), enclosed in wire netting and cornstalks and usually, though not always, thatched with cornstalks. This crude method of storing results in much of the corn spoiling, especially if the harvest season is rainy. The stored corn is eventually shelled by machine and put in old wheat sacks for shipment. The shelling is done by crews who travel from one farm to another in much the same manner as the wheat threshers.

In relatively few cases do the Corn Belt farmers own their land. Most of them are sharecroppers or tenant farmers. The explanation of this goes back to the historical development of this area. As was stated previously, this section is one in which livestock production was once very important. When crop production displaced the grazing industry as the important activity of the region, the lands were not divided into smaller holdings. So, despite the changing cultural landscape, there has been little modification of the land-ownership pattern with the advent of crop agriculture.

The Argentine Corn Belt enjoys one marked advantage over that of the United States. The Pampa has easier access to the sea and consequently to world markets than its northern competitor. This advantage, combined with nearly ideal conditions for production and general lack of demand within the country for the crop, has been instrumental in making Argentina the unrivaled leading exporter of corn and in enabling corn to become the principal export commodity of the country in recent years.

Flax.—The principal area of flax production in the Pampa coincides with the Corn Belt and the northern end of the wheat crescent (Fig. 107). The zone also extends across the Paraná into Entre Rios where it is the chief crop of that province. Flax in the Pampa is grown not for its fiber but for the seed which furnishes linseed oil, so valuable in the manufacture of paint. The crop, although it makes heavy demands on the fertility of the soil, is drought- and heat-resistant and well suited to the environment in which it is raised, since high temperatures and variability in the precipitation are characteristic of this northern

region. Flax is sown in the late autumn and harvested in the early summer. It is harvested and threshed in the same manner as wheat.

Much of the flax grown in Argentina is raised on rented land by immigrant farmers. These people plant flax for 3 or 4 years on land owned by wealthy land-holders. As part of the rent for the use of the land, the tenant, just as in the case of wheat sharecroppers, is required to plant alfalfa the last year he farms the land. Flax grown for seed has increased rapidly in importance since the turn of the century; today, Argentina is the world's leading producer and ex-porter. In 1900, production amounted to only 9 million

FIG. 107.—(*U. S. Dept. of Agr.*)

bushels; by 1929, it had increased tenfold; since 1929, there has been a decline to around 70 million bushels. Exports average over 90 per cent of total production.

Other Cereals.—The pattern of other cereal crops (oats, barley, and rye) corresponds rather closely to that of the southern end of the wheat crescent. These grains tend to be localized in the cooler southeastern portions. Oats, barley, and rye are of minor significance as compared with corn, wheat, or flax, but they are increasing in importance. If more scientific agriculture and the wider practice of crop rotation are introduced into pampean farming, these grains will undoubtedly be more widely grown.

At least one-third of all the oats grown in Buenos Aires Province is used as green winter forage. At present, these grains are confined primarily to areas of poorer soil or districts with other less favorable natural conditions than those found in the sections devoted to the leading cereal crops. Today, they occupy more or less a supplemental position in the pampean agricultural economy rather than an integral part of it.

Alfalfa.—Alfalfa is a crop grown almost entirely for home consumption. It is, in a sense, a *liaison* product which joins together the two great agricultural economies of the Pampa—crop farming and the livestock industry. As has been pointed out, alfalfa is frequently the crop planted on rented lands before they are returned to their owners. As will be indicated in more detail later, alfalfa is a basic crop used in the rearing and fattening of animals.

The major region of alfalfa production is somewhat larger than the Corn Belt, but it occupies the same general portion of the Pampa. In northwestern Buenos Aires and southwestern Córdoba, alfalfa covers 15 to 25 per cent of the total area. The crop has also spread westward into the Province of San Luis and into the central and western portion of the wheat crescent. The zone of production is rather confined by the requirements of the crop. Ideal conditions are: a high ground water table, and a light soil through which the roots of the plant will penetrate easily. Since alfalfa has deep roots, it can be grown in areas where grain crops will not mature, but much of the land in alfalfa is also suitable for wheat. Production has not spread eastward to any extent, for the strong native grasses of this area soon destroy the alfalfa.

Alfalfa possesses many advantages in the dual-phase agricultural system of the Pampa. It has a feeding value for animals about four times as great as the native grasses. This enables the ranchers to fatten and get their animals to market about 1 year sooner than was possible with the use of the natural pastures. One planting lasts a long time, sometimes as much as 15 years. Because the roots are so deep, the plant stays green through the dry conditions of late summer after native grasses have turned brown. The crop is also valuable because it enriches the soil, since it is a nitrogen-fixing plant. As a result of the type of agricultural economy that has developed in the Pampa, there has evolved a cycle of long-term crop rotation in the alfalfa areas.

New land is broken and planted to wheat, flax, or some other crop for a period of years. Replanting continues until the native fertility of the soil has been reduced. The land is then planted to alfalfa and left in this crop for 5 or 10 years. During this time, the fertility of the soil has been restored in some measure, and the whole cycle begins again.

Truck Farming and Fruit Raising.—Although fruit and vegetable raising is widespread throughout the Pampa, the area of commercial production is confined to a section within a 100- or 200-mile radius of Buenos Aires, particularly in the coastal strip from La Plata to north of Buenos Aires. Localization in this section is primarily due to the market that the eastern seaboard cities provide and to the excellent transportation facilities of this district. These vegetable and fruit areas provide a wide variety of the common garden vegetables and nearly all types of temperate fruit, except grapes and citrus fruits. It is on the truck farms that the only example of intensive agriculture in the Pampa is found. Owing to the length of the growing season in this region, fresh vegetables are obtainable most of the year and no canning industry has developed to meet off-season demands.

Crop Hazards.—Some indication of the risks the pampean farmer faces in producing his crops has already been given. The danger of drought is serious and relatively frequent. It becomes greatest in the areas of lowest rainfall, the western margins, in those regions where slight fluctuations are of great importance. In some years in the past, the wheat crop has been so badly damaged that many of the farmers did not even have grain for seed. Some idea of the degree of variation can be seen in the following figures. In October, 1866, 9 inches of rain fell in Buenos Aires; in the same month in 1867, only $\frac{1}{4}$ inch fell. In September, 1884, Buenos Aires received 13 inches and a year later 1 inch. Twenty inches of rain fell during 1893. In 1900, there was this much in the single month of March. Droughts cause great fluctuation in the crops. Wealthy landowners are able to average good years with bad ones and derive a profit from their lands; the tenant who has no reserve may find himself in worse condition after a year of hard work than he was at the beginning.

Drought is not the only weather hazard in the Pampa. Late frosts in the spring are a rather common occurrence. Hot winds from the north are very damaging and blow not infrequently.

To meet these vagaries of the weather, the Argentine farmer has attempted to adapt his crops to the environment. Flax is raised in areas where drought or hot winds are likely. Special varieties of drought-resisting wheats are also grown to reduce the hazard of low rainfall. Although these measures help somewhat, the results have not been too encouraging.

Another hazard that confronts the farmer (and the stockman too) is the danger of the locust. This pest visits the northern half of the country and does great damage to green crops. They are particularly bad for the corn crop because they arrive just when the ears are green and soft. In the spring, these creatures fly south in clouds from the Chaco and settle in the northern agricultural provinces. Here, the females deposit their eggs, and, about 3 weeks later, the young hatch. In the first five of the six stages through which they pass in their metamorphosis, they are crawlers and hoppers. In the sixth stage, they take on wings and fly away in a northerly direction, probably back to the Chaco. In the hopping stage, they travel over the country in countless millions and eat nearly every green thing they reach, covering belts 50 miles or more in width. So destructive are they that a special government organization for combating them has been established; 900 to 1,000 persons are permanently employed, and about 1,000 additional at times of special need. Ten million pesos a year have been appropriated to fight the locust.[1] Sprays, barriers, traps, and burning are all resorted to, but with very little effect. The number of locusts is so inconceivably great that the thousands of tons of them that are destroyed make little impression. They do not come every year and are much worse in some years than in others. In a bad year, the locusts may reduce certain crops by 10 to 25 per cent; and, in an especially dry year, the drought and locusts may reduce crops by as much as two-thirds.[2]

THE LIVESTOCK INDUSTRY

Until the twentieth century, the raising of livestock was the chief economic activity in Argentina. Though today it has de-

[1] In 1925, a United States steel company shipped 15 million galvanized-iron sheets to Argentina to be used in building barriers to protect crops from locusts. These 15 million sheets would build a barrier 14,000 miles long.

[2] An excellent account of a locust invasion is found in Chap. VII, pp. 118–135, of Walter Lardin's book, "Argentine Plains and Andine Glaciers," 1911.

creased in relative importance, as compared with cultivated products, it still holds a significant place in the economic life of the country. In fact, in at least one-third of the Pampa, the live-stock industry leads all other types of agricultural production. Cattle, both beef and dairy, sheep, and hogs are the principal animals from a commercial standpoint; and beef cattle far out-rank the others in importance.

ARGENTINA, URUGUAY
AND CHILE
CATTLE
NUMBER
EACH DOT REPRESENTS 5,000

Fig. 108.—(*U. S. Dept. of Agr.*)

Beef Cattle.—The beef-cattle industry is primarily localized in the Pampa and especially in the central and eastern portion of the Province of Buenos Aires. At least three-fourths of the 33 million cattle of Argentina are in the Pampa, and 40 per cent of them are in Buenos Aires (Fig. 108). It is chiefly in the eastern and central portion of the Pampa that the great *estancias* are lo-cated and seem destined to re-main (Fig. 109). The *estancias* are an inheritance from the colonial pastoral period when land was cheap and could be obtained in large blocks. The *estancias* con-tain several thousand acres each; some are measured in terms of hundreds of square miles. The breakup of these huge estates seems unlikely for several reasons. First of all, they are in an area ideally suited to the grazing industry, an activity the landed aristocracy desires to maintain, and a type of life the laborer pre-fers to the more confining crop agriculture (Fig. 110). The section occupied by many of the *estancias*, on the other hand, is not particularly well suited to raising crops. It is an area of low relief and consequent poor drainage, and this unfavorable condition is intensified by the heavy soils characteristic of the region.

Since the days when wild cattle were hunted on the pampean plain by half-civilized *gauchos* and hides were the principal item of export provided by the livestock industry, great improvements have taken place in the cattle industry of Argentina. The greatest changes have come about in Buenos Aires, and many things have been done to better the quality of the animals. Most of the large *estancias* have been fenced. This accomplishes two ends. It enables the stockmen to control breeding and improve the strain; it also prevents overgrazing, since animals can be kept off of ranges that might be damaged. Animals have also been improved by the importation of purebred stock for breeding purposes (Fig. 111). The English Shorthorn is favored in areas of

Fig. 109.—Example of high-grade estancia house near Buenos Aires.

good pasturage, and the Hereford is preferred in the rougher and poorer pastures. The great demand for blooded animals is shown by the fact that as many as 150,000 purebred animals have been brought into Argentina from England and the United States in a single year; at the stock shows in Buenos Aires, a purebred bull will bring $25,000 to $40,000. In addition to fencing the ranges and improving the quality of the animals by importing blooded stock, the ranges have been made to yield more food, as has been seen, by planting alfalfa. One of the handicaps that faced the early stockmen was lack of water. There are few streams in the Pampa, and in times of drought these are likely to dry up. To relieve the water shortage, wells were dug a few feet down to the high water level and windmills used to pump the water into storage tanks. In this way, a plentiful supply was ensured.

FIG. 110.—Scene on a cattle estancia on the Pampa of Argentina. (*Photograph by H. G. Olds.*)

With improvements in the range and in the quality of the animals, the cattle industry attained a highly favorable position. Nearness to the sea facilitates export; the mild climate favors year-round outdoor grazing; no buildings are needed to shelter the animals. The mean winter temperature at Buenos Aires, for example, is 40°F., and only 10 or 12 days out of the year does the temperature fall below 32°F. Snow is rare, and seldom is there a severe enough frost to kill palms in the city.

Fig. 111.—Breeding cows on a well-kept estancia.

Despite all these advantageous conditions, the cattle industry is not without its hazards. In northern subtropical Argentina, parasites and cattle diseases spread easily. North of the thirtieth parallel, the cattle tick abounds, and only native cattle are immune. From this region, no cattle are permitted to be brought south until they have been dipped in a tick-killing chemical. The tick breeds in wooded lands and decreases as the land is brought under cultivation. The dreaded disease anthrax often breaks out after a prolonged drought, and terrible epidemics of hoof-and-mouth disease occasionally sweep large areas. Cattle must be watched, also, for signs of tuberculosis.

A second handicap to cattle raising is its dependence on foreign markets. If European people seriously cut down their importation of meat, the export market collapses and prices drop to ruinous levels. This occurred in 1921 and 1922, and Argentina suffered a setback that shook the financial foundations of the country. On the whole, however, the industry is prosperous and profitable. Argentine cattlemen can deliver beef cattle in Buenos Aires at 60 per cent of the cost of producing cattle in the United States and delivering them in Chicago; Argentine beef is sold in London as cheap as American beef is sold in New York.

Dairy Cattle.—The dairy industry of Argentina is essentially a product of the World War. Before that time, the country had

Fig. 112.—Milking shed on dairy estancia.

depended in large measure on imports from abroad of condensed milk, canned butter, and cheese to meet its needs for dairy products. Today, the country is an important exporter. The stimulus given the industry when foreign supplies were cut off was sufficient to start its development. Natural and economic factors favored its growth. Dairying is localized in the area around and to the south and east of Buenos Aires. Rapid transportation facilities, a large local market, and access through the port of Buenos Aires to world markets all are important factors in bringing about the concentration of over one-fourth the dairy cattle[1]

[1] Most of the dairy cattle of Argentina are Holsteins, though some Jerseys have been introduced.

of the country in the area immediately adjacent to the capital. The industry is also favored by the mild climate and moderately heavy rainfall (40 inches per year) which provide outdoor grazing on good pastures. Few of the cattle are housed, and most of them are milked in corrals (Fig. 112).

Many of the dairymen are immigrants who rent part of a large *estancia*. They try to produce enough milk to pay the rent on their leased land and perhaps yield a small profit. A secondary profit comes from the sale of calves each year. The dairymen of Argentina are, therefore, partly dairy farmers and partly meat producers. There has not developed such a clear-cut distinction between the two phases of the cattle industry as in the United States. Although Argentina possesses many advantages for the dairy industry, there is not likely to be any great increase in production until herds are improved, larger markets (both foreign and domestic) are available, and more laborers are attracted to this type of agriculture.

Sheep Raising in the Pampa.—Sheep raising in Argentina has not retained the relatively important place it once held in the economy of the country. A half century after the first shipment from Argentina (1840), wool exports were equal in value to all cultivated crops. In 1937, wool exports were about one-third as valuable as wheat alone. In the years around 1895, Argentina had approximately 75 million sheep. In 1937, there were about 44 million. Despite the decline that has taken place, sheep raising is still a major industry of the country. Wool exports are second only to Australia; mutton shipments second only to New Zealand.

In addition to a decrease in the importance of sheep raising, other changes have taken place. The industry was first important in the area immediately adjacent to Buenos Aires. There are now almost no sheep in this district, since crop agriculture has displaced the livestock industry. In the early days, the sheep of the Pampa were raised for wool; today, nearly all pampean sheep are mutton type. The changes that have come about are the result of a combination of natural conditions, technological developments, and modification of local and world economies.

Wool production in the Pampa in the early days was favored by an almost ideal combination of natural and human factors. The extensive, flat, grass-covered, low-priced plains in an area of mild temperate climate provided excellent pasture lands. The sheep-raising industry, with its relatively small demands on labor, was one that could be carried on by the small population of the country. The product was one that kept almost indefinitely and could be easily shipped from remote areas. Simultaneously, industrial expansion was taking place in northwest Europe, and a large market was available. With the end of Spanish rule and the settlement of internal problems, discussed in the preceding chapter, Basque, Irish, and English shepherds, long-skilled in the art of sheep raising, migrated to Argentina and provided the much-needed labor for an expanding industry.

In the face of changing conditions, however, wool sheep on the Pampa were doomed. The higher per acre return that crop agriculture provided gradually pushed the sheep to the south and west and out of the more desirable portions of the Pampa. Although not in their optimum conditions, sheep can do well on dry, thin, and rocky pastures where crops cannot be raised and where cattle would starve to death. Sheep were unable to hold their own in competition with cattle on the alfalfa pastures; they graze the land so closely that they soon destroy an alfalfa range that will last for many years if grazed by cattle. Most sheep were, then, gradually displaced from the economy of the Pampa in the face of more intensive and more profitable forms of agricultural production.

While wool sheep were moving into outlying inferior areas, particularly the arid west and Patagonia, mutton sheep were growing in importance in the Pampa. The development of the refrigerator ship and meat-freezing and meat-chilling plants in the seaboard cities helped to stimulate the meat phase of the sheep industry in central and eastern Argentina. In some of the more remote areas, crossbreeds, producing both wool and meat, are raised. In the moist lands of the east, the Lincoln and Romney Marsh breeds predominate. Both of these are mutton sheep, originally bred on the wet downs of England.

Swine.—The raising of hogs is not a very important industry of the Pampa. There are only about 4 million in the whole country (most of them in the Corn Belt) as compared with the 50 or 60 million usually raised in the United States. Iowa alone normally produces three times as many as Argentina. The industry, though, is growing and is potentially important. Many of the same favorable conditions that have been noted in connection with the other livestock industries apply to hog raising—mild climate, abundant surplus-feed supplies, easy access to world markets, and consequent low-cost production. Pork products, for example, can be delivered to the eastern part of the United States from Argentina more cheaply than from Iowa or Illinois. Expansion is slow, though, for a number of reasons. The swine are subject to diseases, and many of them go to the packing plants only to be rejected. There is almost no local market for pork. The people of Argentina are beef and mutton eaters but consume almost no pork. Finally, hog raising requires a great amount of labor. The Pampa has not at present a surplus available that can be devoted to the industry. Despite these handicaps, though, the time is not far away when Argentine pork will be coming in quantities to the United States, unless it is excluded by a tariff wall.

Horses.—Horses are not important in the foreign trade of Argentina, but they play a significant role in pampean economy. There are more horses in Argentina than in all the rest of South America, and a high proportion are good horses. The great *estancias* have ever been the land of the man on horseback. On a single *estancia* may be found 1,000 to 2,000 horses. The most famous and wealthy club south of the equator is the Jockey Club of Buenos Aires, and horse racing is one of the most popular sports of Argentina. On some *estancias*, the owners make a specialty of breeding race horses and on others, draft horses. As a rule, the farm horses are not fed grain but live on forage, mainly in the pastures. They are usually worked only a half day, being replaced by fresh horses the second half day. Considering the quality, horses are cheap in Argentina.

COMMERCIAL FOCI OF THE PAMPA

The cities and towns of the Pampa are first of all and above all else commercial centers. It is to trade that they owe their original development, and it is on trade that their continued existence depends. True, some of them, like Buenos Aires, rely in part on manufacturing for their economic welfare; but industrial development occupies a definitely secondary place, and in all cases, factories are dependent upon commercial activity. On the basis of size, location, and character of function performed, the cities and towns of the Pampa are of two major types: (1) ports, and (2) inland market towns.

The Port Cities.—The largest and most important cities of the Pampa and those which have grown most rapidly are the following ports: Buenos Aires (90,000 in 1855; 663,000 in 1895; 2,317,755 in 1937[1]), Rosario (91,000 in 1895; 265,000 in 1922; 504,000 in 1937), Bahía Blanca (6,000 in 1895; 44,000 in 1914; 108,310 in 1937), Santa Fé (131,404 in 1937), and La Plata (190,577 in 1937).

Fig. 113.—View of the sky line of Buenos Aires.

Buenos Aires.—Few cities in the world dominate the urban life of their respective countries as Buenos Aires (Fig. 113) does Argentina. Buenos Aires is the focal point of the nation (Fig. 96). One person in every five in Argentina lives in the capital (Fig. 101). It is the focus of all important railway systems. It does more manufacturing than all the other cities. Through its inferior and congested harbor passes half the commerce of the nation (Fig. 114). It is a city of great wealth; of beautiful avenues (most famous of which is the world-renowned Avenida Alvear with its open-air restaurants), of parks (Fig. 115), residences, and suburbs; of expensive and extravagant living on the one hand and of

---

[1] All 1937 figures are from estimates in the *Foreign Commerce Yearbook*, 1938, of the U.S. Dept. of Commerce.

Fig. 114.—Scene along the water front of Buenos Aires, chief commercial port of South America. (Photograph by H. G. Olds.)

FIG. 115.—Plaza in Buenos Aires.

FIG. 116.—Municipal theater (Colon), Buenos Aires.

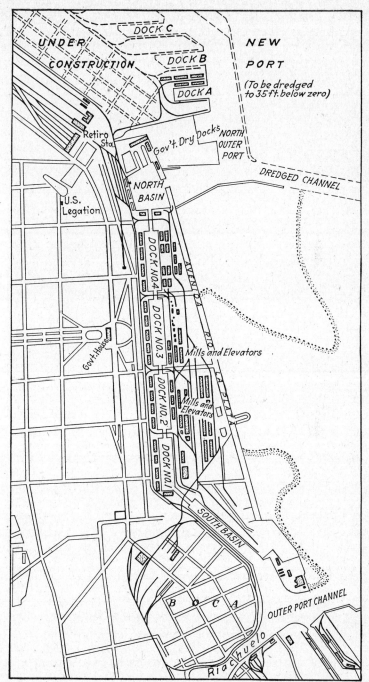

FIG. 117.—Port facilities of Buenos Aires, upon which a vast sum of money has been expended. (*U. S. Coast Survey.*)

poverty on the other, for wealth is not evenly distributed (Fig. 116). It is a city relatively free from smoke; yet it has all the most modern utilities.

The city is 155 miles from the open sea, near the head of the Rio de la Plata estuary, which is here 34 miles wide but very shallow. The city owes its location to the mouth of a little river, the Riachuelo, which offered the only site for an early harbor for

FIG. 118.—Swift's packing plant in Rosario.

scores of miles along this coast. The first port works were at the mouth of this river, but they were soon outgrown. Until the modern channels were dredged, steamers drawing more than 15 feet could not get within 12 miles of Buenos Aires but had to receive and deliver cargoes by means of lighters. The new docks are of the most modern basin type, equipped with warehouses and elevators, served by many lines of railway, and affording excellent facilities for handling sea-borne commerce. Yet, even these are inadequate, and very expensive new docks are under construction (Fig. 117). The harbor improvements will have cost $100,000,000 by the time present plans are completed. The river carries so much silt that constant dredging of the channels is necessary. The port of Buenos Aires is an instance of man's conquest of an unfavorable environment, for nature did very little toward providing harbor facilities for this city. In this respect, Buenos Aires is quite unlike Rio de Janeiro, New York, or Sydney, where nature provided such perfect harbors.

Rosario.—Two hundred miles upstream from Buenos Aires on the west bank of the Paraná is the second largest city and second port of Argentina, Rosario. Developed between the years 1853 and 1860, during the period of political isolation from Buenos Aires, the city has retained a high degree of economic independence. Its primary function is as a port of export for wheat, corn, and flaxseed, for it is readily accessible to the rich agricultural lands of southern Sante Fé and Córdoba. Rosario is also a meat-packing center (Fig. 118). Ocean-going steamships of 26-foot draft ascend the Paraná to the modern port works which a French company has installed at Rosario, and five railroad systems connect the port with the surrounding country. The Paraná, however, is not an easy river for ocean steamers to navigate, and Rosario is not likely to gain much in relative commercial importance.

Bahía Blanca.—Bahía Blanca, the third port of Argentina, is a modern city, developed to serve the southern part of the Pampa. Two hundred and fifty miles south of Buenos Aires on a well-protected harbor, it came into being primarily to relieve congestion at Buenos Aires during the autumn. Millions of dollars have been spent at Bahía Blanca for railway terminals and port works. A special rail line 400 miles long connects the city with Rosario. This line cuts across nearly every important railway of the Republic and serves as a great "outer-belt" line through the Pampa.

Santa Fé.—Santa Fé is an old town which has been revived by the modern "colonists." It lies 378 miles up the Paraná from Buenos Aires (298 miles by rail) and is an important commercial focus for northwestern Argentina. Although on the edge of the Pampa, its commercial life is primarily dependent on the outlying regions to the north.

La Plata.—La Plata, like Bahía Blanca, is a modern city. It was founded in 1882 as the capital of Buenos Aires Province when the city of Buenos Aires became the national capital. Its port facilities are entirely artificial. Located at the mouth of the

Plata River, 34 miles from Buenos Aires, it was hoped that the city would develop as a great outer port for the capital. Although there is some important commercial activity at La Plata, the great future that was anticipated for it has not been realized. In addition to its port activities, La Plata is an important center for meat packing (Fig. 119).

Fig. 119.—Loading a cargo of chilled meat at one of the large American packing plants at La Plata, Argentina.

The Inland Market Towns.—The vast Pampa, as has been pointed out in other connections, is not an urbanized area. It is a land of widely dispersed settlements and isolated dwellings; no agricultural villages dot the landscape. But here and there, scattered over the plain in almost clocklike regularity, are small centers of commercial activity that nearly always owe their existence to the crossing of rail lines. The pattern of distribution and size of these towns correspond almost exactly to the density-of-population pattern. In the more peopled portions of the plain, they are closer together and larger in size; in the more remote and more sparsely settled areas, they are smaller and farther apart. Together they form a great radial pattern which focuses on

Buenos Aires and loses in force and importance as distance from this center increases.

Some 10 or 15 of these towns can boast of a population of 15,000 to 25,000; another 50 fall into the 5,000 to 10,000 class. Five thousand or 25,000, though, they are all much alike in economic structure and in territory served; the functions they perform tell much about the agriculture life of the areas for which they are focal. The sphere of influence of each town covers an area within a 10- to 25-mile radius. The inhabitants consist primarily of bankers, grain- and stockbrokers, lawyers, agricultural-machinery distributors, and merchants who handle the various supplies needed by the farmers and stockmen; in short, these towns contain the type of people necessary to carry forward the commercial life of the Pampa and to aid in the production of the commodities that are so vital to the economic welfare of the area.

Chapter XI. Satellites of the Pampa

Argentina, away from the heart of the country, is made up of a number of regions whose development is dependent on the Pampa to a marked degree. Many of the products of outlying areas find their ultimate destination in the Pampa or move through it on the way to world markets. In many cases, the land is devoted to uses that are reminiscent of an earlier-day pampean landscape, indicative of the emigration of these activities from the Pampa in favor of other and more profitable types of land utilization. Though not entirely lacking in individual importance and independence, these outlying areas are so closely associated with the heart of the country that they may be thought of as economic satellites of the larger economic body—the Pampa.

These satellites differ from each other in most respects, but they do possess certain characteristics in common. In general, all are sparsely populated; all are relatively remote from the heart of the country; and, with the possible exception of the irrigated oases, all are less advanced economically and culturally than the Pampa. The boundaries that separate each region from the other are defined by differences in human activities or methods of production which vary with climate, soil, topography, and accessibility and with other natural or human conditions. On these bases, four major regions are distinguishable: (1) Mesopotamia; (2) the Chaco; (3) Oases, Arid Plains, and Mountains of the West; (4) Patagonia (Fig. 102). Together these regions form a pattern that completely encircles the landward margins of the Pampa.

MESOPOTAMIA

Mesopotamia occupies the 74,000 square miles between the Paraná and Uruguay rivers that make up the provinces of Entre

Rios and Corrientes and the Territory of Misiones (Figs. 102 and 98). The uniform topography, so characteristic of the Pampa, does not exist in Mesopotamia. In the southern portion, bordering on the lower course of the Paraná (southern Entre Rios), the relief is much like that of the pampean plain, though the elevation is lower and the area is subject to frequent flooding. The flatness soon gives way toward the north to a gently rolling area, then to an undulating land interspersed with swamps, and finally to rugged hill country which represents the southern extension of the Brazilian Highlands (Fig. 102).

Mesopotamia is one of the less-developed regions of Argentina. The area supports only about 1 million people, many of whom are Indians. In fact, Corrientes is the most Indian province of the country. Much of the territory is unsettled and even unexplored, but there seems ample justification for considering it as potentially important. The whole area is well watered, receiving 40 inches of rain in the south to over 60 inches in the north. There is a marked summer maximum in the distribution, but the winters are seldom so dry as to interfere seriously with agricultural pursuits. In the northern, more tropical portions, high temperatures and high humidity on the lowlands are something of a handicap, but the highlands of Misiones and the lowlands of the south are attractive and healthful. Soils in general are fertile well-drained loams, except in the swampy areas of the extreme south and in Corrientes. The original vegetal cover, a grassland and open-forest vegetation, has provided the soil with ample supplies of humus. The natural forest vegetation of Misiones is an actual and potential source of forest products. Water-power sites, too, are present in the rugged and well-watered northern section.

Despite these regional assets, development of Mesopotamia has been slow. Grazing and tillage have been expanding in the south, but the northern portions remain largely unused. The reasons for the slow penetration of the region are to be found principally in a study of the leading economic activities of the area and in an analysis of the various handicaps that must be overcome before more rapid development is possible.

The Grazing Industry.—The raising of sheep and cattle is the chief economic activity in all of Mesopotamia, except Misiones; but a decline in the relative importance of the livestock industry seems likely, especially in the southern half of Entre Rios where crop production is expanding (Figs. 106 and 107). The grazing areas are favored by abundant, though not particularly nutritious, supplies of grass. Much of the territory is also well served by water transportation. Despite these regional assets, the livestock industry is faced with several difficult problems. Perhaps the most serious handicap to cattle production is the tick. As was mentioned in the chapter on The Pampa, cattle from this area are not allowed to move south of the Paraná River. Until the tick is brought under control, the cattle industry operates at a distinct disadvantage. A further handicap is the poor quality of the native stock, and little attention is paid to improving the breeds. The animals are large and bony and not good meat producers. Some difficulty is also encountered in the marketing of the animals. In the southern districts, they go to the packing plants of Rosario; but from the northern, more isolated areas the animals move to salting plants along the Uruguay River. Because of these handicaps and owing also to competition with other more favored regions of Argentina, cattle production in Mesopotamia is not likely to increase greatly in the future.

Sheep raising (for wool) is most important in the southeast, for much of the land in the north and west is too wet. Many of the same conditions (cheap transportation, grass, water supplies, etc.) that aided cattle production also favor sheep. As a result, this area has become one of the leading wool-producing sections of Argentina. As crop agriculture expands, however, it seems altogether likely that it will displace sheep from southern Mesopotamia.

The Crop-agriculture Pattern.—Although some commercial agriculture has developed along the southern margins of Mesopotamia, the region remains essentially one of subsistence production. Mandioca and peanuts are crops that enter into the daily diets of the inhabitants, the former being produced in the warmer and wetter regions of the north, the latter in the drier and cooler areas to the south. Corn is also a subsistence crop that is widely raised. Sugar cane and fruits attain some importance. Another product, primarily of commercial significance, which is peculiar to Mesopotamia is yerba maté. Yerba maté is both an agricultural crop and a forest product. Plantation production is expanding and will probably displace nearly all the wild crop. The area of greatest production is on the well-drained slopes of the hills of southern Misiones.

The most populous section of Mesopotamia is in the southern half of Entre Rios. Here wheat and flax are grown in large amounts. Colonists of Russian, German, and Jewish origin have settled in this section, and their crop agriculture has largely displaced the earlier pastoralists of the area.

Forest Industries.—The forests of Mesopotamia (principally in Misiones) have not been exploited sufficiently to bring about what might be called a forest industry, Yerba-maté leaves which were once gathered from the wild trees of the area are now obtained chiefly from cultivated trees (Fig. 154). The classification of yerba maté as a forest product, therefore, hardly seems justified. Aside from yerba-maté gathering, the forests are not utilized to any extent. They represent a potential rather than an actual resource of the Republic. Fairly good stands of pine and *cedro* are present, but inaccessibility to market is one of the chief difficulties in the way of exploitation (Fig. 120).

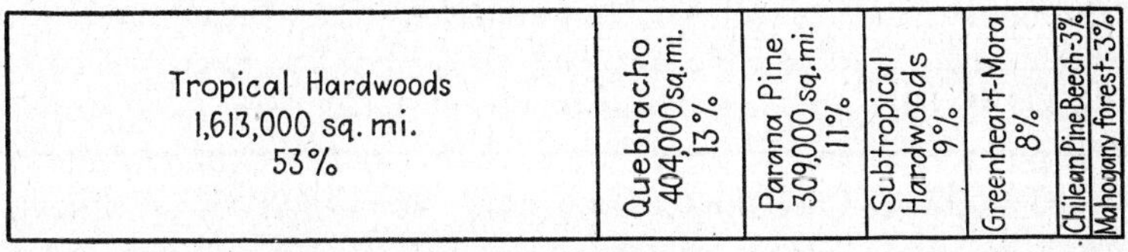

Tropical Hardwoods 1,613,000 sq. mi. 53%	Quebracho 404,000 sq.mi. 13%	Parana Pine 309,000 sq.mi. 11%	Subtropical Hardwoods 9%	Greenheart-Mora 8%	Chilean Pine Beech-3% Mahogany forest-3%

Fig. 120.—Forest areas of South America

THE CHACO

Although some specialized agricultural development is taking place along its southern margins, the 150,000 square miles that make up the Chaco are the least developed of the low plains of Argentina (Fig. 102). Economic penetration of the Chaco has been, and probably will continue to be, slow. The climate of the area is one of the greatest handicaps to development. Precipitation comes in the summer, and winters are excessively dry (Figs. 8 and 9). Summers are hot, humid, and enervating. Heavy rainfall, combined with low relief, produces swampy conditions throughout much of the Chaco during the summer. Winters are so dry that supplies of fresh water are frequently inadequate and alternative sources have not been located. In the west, only intermittent streams flow from the Andean region, and satisfactory underground-water sources have not been discovered.

Most wells, both deep and shallow, have encountered only saline water. In the east, near the Paraná River, wells are more likely to be fresh, but even here reliable supplies of fresh water are not always obtainable. Two rivers (the Pilcomayo and the Bermejo) do cross the north of the Chaco, but much of this area is swampy, seasonally inundated, and inhabited almost exclusively by Indians.

Colonization of the Chaco is delayed not only by climate and the closely related problem of the water supply but also by other serious conditions. Access to the region is difficult. Rail lines are largely lacking. Much of the territory is not reached by waterways, and the shallowness of many existing streams, even during the rainy season, closes them to navigation for all except small boats. Various tropical pests, particularly the tick and the locust, as well as tropical diseases are rampant in the area. Wild animals, which prey on the livestock, and poisonous snakes are present in large numbers. In addition, the Indians of the region are hostile.

With all these handicaps, it would seem that the Chaco is of little value to Argentina, and this statement, in general, is true. The region, though, does possess certain assets. From a commercial point of view, the area has two industries of regional importance and a third of minor significance. The quebracho tree from the forests of the Chaco provides the region's leading export (Fig. 121). Cotton, a relatively new product, has increased in importance in recent years. The cattle industry plays a minor part in the commercial economy. Crop agriculture, away from the cotton area, is confined almost entirely to subsistence farming, and there seems little likelihood of marked expansion. Poor transportation, lack of markets, locust plagues, and other unfavorable conditions delay agricultural development.

The Quebracho Industry.—The major quebracho-producing region of Argentina is located near the Paraná and Paraguay rivers in the north central part of the Chaco. This area provides both the bulk of the tannin extract and most of the quebracho logs exported from Argentina. Exports of logs amounted to 194,-000 pounds in 1937 and tannin to 438,000 pounds with a total value of $15,000,000 (Fig. 121).

Localization of the industry near the Paraná River is due in part to better stands of *quebracho chaqueno* here than elsewhere

in the Chaco. This tree yields 25 per cent tannin, much higher
than other types. Abundant supplies of water, needed in large
amounts by the tannin factories, help to locate the industry near
the rivers. Good trees, though, are being rapidly used up; and, at
the present rate of consumption, it is estimated that the resource
will have been completely utilized in about 35 years. Nothing is
being done to replant the quebracho forests, since it requires
100 years for the tree to mature.

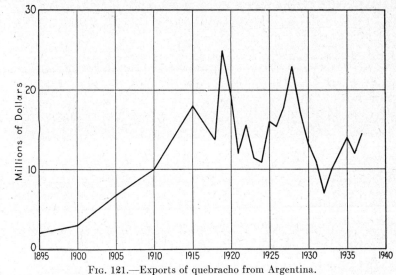

FIG. 121.—Exports of quebracho from Argentina.

Another and somewhat different type of exploitation of the
quebracho forest is pursued in the central part of the province
of Santiago del Estero. The tree of this area is of lower tannin
content (usually about 10 per cent) and is used primarily for
railroad ties and fence posts in the Pampa. Since sawmills have
less need for water than the tannin factories, exploitation of the
forests of Santiago del Estero is not seriously handicapped by a
scarcity of water. In the dry winter season, water wagons bring
additional supplies into the district.

The "Cotton Belt."—Cotton in the Chaco is confined to the
southern margins of the region where production first started
about the turn of the century. By 1928, cotton occupied some
210,000 acres; today (1938), it occupies about 1,000,000 acres.
The industry has been fostered by the government in many ways.

Rail transportation to the area has been developed. Free seed, financial aid, cheap land, and experts to give advice and aid have all been provided to stimulate production. Most of the cotton is a hybrid of American and Sea Island. Yields are in general high, but the fibers vary greatly in length. Baled cotton is likely to be dirty and discolored. Most of the crop is raised by small farmers, aided, at the picking season, by Indians of whom some twenty-five thousand come into the area during the harvest.

Although cotton is favored by climate and soil in the Chaco, there remain many problems to be solved. The ignorance of the farmers is a great handicap, though, of course, not an insurmountable difficulty. Perhaps more serious are the numerous insects and pests that attack the cotton plants. Locusts are particularly troublesome. The farms are protected somewhat by iron sheets and ditches. The sheets form barriers against the swarms of advancing locusts which strike the sheets, fall into the ditches, and are then covered with kerosene and burned. This method helps reduce the damage, but the locusts are so numerous that they exact a very high toll from the cotton planters. Other pests and diseases also attack the cotton plant. The pink boll weevil, ants, leaf worm, and cotton wilt all reduce the amount of cotton picked. As a result of these various handicaps, on the average only about 70 to 75 per cent of the total area planted is harvested.

The Cattle Industry.—Cattle are only of minor importance in the Chaco (Fig. 108). There is an abundant supply of native grasses which are highly nutritive during the summer rains but lose their feeding value as they grow tall, coarse, and hard with the approach of the winter drought. The problem of providing nourishing forage is overcome to some degree in the vicinity of Santa Fé where alfalfa is grown. Lack of water throughout much of the Chaco during the winter months increases the difficulty of caring for the stock. Diseases and insect pests also harass the cattle. The area is the heart of the tick zone, and the hoof-and-mouth disease is common in the region.

The cattle industry, unlike cotton, is an old activity of the Chaco. Its beginning goes back some 300 years. The present unimportant place it holds in the economic life of the region cannot, therefore, be attributed to recent development. Neither are the various unfavorable natural conditions, outlined above, entirely responsible for the backward condition in which the industry finds itself. A combination of economic factors also delays expansion. The area, as has been emphasized in other connections, is remote and lacking in transportation facilities. This makes access to market difficult and expensive, two serious handicaps to be overcome before the area can compete successfully with more favorably located stock-producing regions.

OASES, ARID PLAINS, AND MOUNTAINS OF THE WEST

The Oases.—The oases of western Argentina are relatively insignificant in size, but they achieve outstanding importance in the economy of the region as well as in that of the entire country, because of their great productive capacity. The principal oases are in the piedmont section of the Andes (Figs. 102 and 122). Once they functioned as way stations

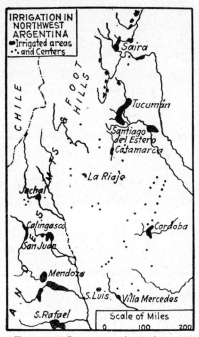

FIG. 122.—In western Argentina crops can be raised only where irrigation is possible. (*After Denis.*)

for soldiers and traders moving from the eastern regions across the arid plains to the Spanish centers in the Bolivian plateau (see Chap. IX). It was here that food and water were obtainable and a certain amount of way trade was possible. Mendoza, San Juan, and Tucumán (founded in 1561, 1562, and 1565, respectively) were among the first to become important settlements, and today they remain significant outposts of Argentina.

In western Argentina, almost none of the land can be cultivated without irrigation, and, unfortunately, only a relatively small portion of the region can be irrigated because water is not available. The irrigation works are of various sorts: (1) In several of the arid provinces lying at the base of the Andes and in the northern half of the country are small scattered areas that are irrigated from mountain streams (Fig. 122). Here individual farmers divert water from the rivers and irrigate such land as they can. The total area thus served is relatively small. (2) In a few places—notably in Mendoza and Tucumán—the mountain streams are large enough and numerous enough to supply water for larger areas. About 1 million acres are irrigated in Mendoza and a smaller number in Tucumán. Most of this irrigation is due to the initiative of the cultivators themselves and was carried on in a small way even in the colonial period. (3) In certain places, the government has assisted in financing large irrigation projects or has carried out the entire project, as in the valley of Rio Neuquén. Such projects have proved very costly, and not all of them are financially successful because of the heavy water charges against the irrigated land. The total area of irrigated land in Argentina is about 2 million acres, or about 8 per cent as much land as is under irrigation in the western part of the United States.

Owing to the fact that the oases of Argentina are located in a belt extending through some 15 degrees of latitude, there is considerable variety in products grown and a certain measure of local specialization. In the northern section in and around Tucumán, sugar cane is the chief crop; in the south, the oases of Mendoza and San Juan yield 95 per cent of the 150 million gallons of wine produced in Argentina; in the central zone, transitional between the sugar area of the north and the wine districts of the south, such oases as Catamarca and La Rioja produce wine and alfalfa as cash crops, but there is less specialization and a tendency toward greater variety and more diversity in crops raised than in the other centers. Products of the middle zone are sold in the mines of the near-by Andes. Alfalfa is also sold to feed cattle being driven over the mountains to Chile.

Tucumán and sugar are synonymous in Argentina, for the province produces 80 per cent of the country's total. Tucumán is one of the most densely peopled portions of the Republic (Figs. 98 and 101). Sugar accounts in large measure for this large population, for the crop occupies one-half of all the cultivated land of the province. The crop was first grown when a rail line was extended from Córdoba to Tucumán in 1874. From that time, production increased until it achieved its present importance of around 650 million pounds. Although sugar raising is favored by generally high temperatures and abundant sunshine, the yield varies greatly from year to year. In 1914, for example, the yield was 704,000,000 pounds. Two years later it dropped to 185,000,-000 pounds. This great variation is due primarily to two causes —drought and frost. Lack of sufficient irrigation water and occasional frosts are serious handicaps which limit the financial success of the industry.

Fig. 123.—Airplane view of Mendoza.

The cane is grown both on large plantations and on small farms. About one-half of it is refined locally, and the other half moves by rail to refineries in Rosario and Buenos Aires. Jujuy and Salta, two small oases to the north of Tucumán, have somewhat more favorable natural conditions for sugar; but their remote location, lack of capital, small labor supply, and small amount of irrigable land available all handicap expansion of the industry.

Just as Tucumán is noted for its sugar, Mendoza (Figs. 123 and 124) and San Juan attain prominence because of their grapes and wine. Some 80 to 85 per cent of all the acreage in grapes in Argentina is in these oases. In 1883, when Mendoza was joined with the coastal cities by rail, wine production first began to achieve significance and eventually led to the development of Mendoza as one of the richest sections of the country. Wine production was also stimulated by European-born immigrants, especially Italian and Spanish, who came to the area. Although some table grapes are raised and exported from these oases, the remoteness of the district from markets favors the production of wine, a commodity

Fig. 124.—Paseo de la Alameda in the city of Mendoza, at the foot of the Andes. The city is surrounded by grape vineyards and is the most important wine-making center in South America.

that is less perishable and better able to stand the cost of transportation to market. The relative remoteness of Mendoza has also helped to stimulate the development of some small-scale manufacturing. Although handicapped by lack of raw materials and fuel, the province manufactures building materials, wagons, and flour. The value of its manufactured products is higher than that in any of the neighboring provinces (Fig. 100).

Although the oases of Argentina are most noted for their sugar and wine, and justly so, many other crops are important. Alfalfa, for example, occupies more land than grapes. Corn and potatoes are raised in large amounts. Fruits, other than grapes, are increasing in importance. Oranges, lemons, limes, figs, apricots, prunes, and many other fruits are raised on a small scale. The fruit of

Argentina has one decided advantage. It enters the Northern Hemisphere markets during the "off season." The growth of the fruit industry is indicated by the increase in the value of Argentina's exports of the commodity. In 1916, exports of fruits amounted to $45,000, in 1921 to $204,000, and in 1937 to $2,046,000.

Arid Plains and Mountains.—The arid plains and mountains of western Argentina, except in the irrigated oases, are very sparsely populated. All the area has a density of less than 10 per square mile. Many sections have less than 5, and one portion, the Territory of Los Andes, has less than 1 person per square mile (Figs. 98 and 101). The map of population density in terms of political units, moreover, does not tell the complete story. Parts of some of these western provinces and territories are entirely lacking in population. A lowland section between Tucumán and Córdoba (the Salinas Grandes), for example, is a vast tract of some 7,000 square miles without inhabitants.

Xerophytic vegetation, expressive of the aridity of the area, is characteristic throughout the region. The heaviest rainfall comes in the northeast; but the 30 inches or so that fall here all come in the summer season, and the high evaporation rate and porosity of the soil greatly impair its effectiveness. Elsewhere, annual precipitation amounts to much less than 30 inches. At least one-third receives less than 10 inches (Figs. 8 and 9).

Largely because of this excessive aridity, crop raising is unimportant. Although this region includes much rugged country and the highest mountain (Fig. 6) in South America (Mt. Aconcagua, approximately 23,000 feet), there is considerable level land at low elevations that could be farmed if water were available. Extension of irrigation works beyond the present small areas seems unlikely, however, for the few small streams crossing the territory are already being utilized. As a result, agricultural activity centers primarily in the grazing industry. But, even in the grazing industry, there are expressions of the region's aridity. Goats and wool sheep, able to subsist on meager pastures and small amounts of water, are more important than cattle which require better pasture lands and more water. Lack of transportation facilities, as well as the paucity of forage, hampers the cattle industry. The animals raised are marketed as low-grade frozen beef or as draft animals.

Goats and wool sheep are well adapted to the arid environment and the relatively isolated conditions. Goats are the more important; for they can exist on exceedingly poor pastures, and the chief product they yield—skins—is a commodity that is relatively easy to market. In the mountainous sections around Córdoba, three-fourths of all the goats in Argentina are produced. Wool sheep (Merino) are also able to subsist in these arid plains and mountains and yield a product that presents few marketing problems.

Other animals, mules for the near-by Bolivian mines and llamas in Puna de Atacama, are also raised, but their importance in the region's economy is much less than that of goats, sheep, and cattle.

Aside from livestock grazing, the only other economic activity in the region is mining and this is relatively insignificant. On the slopes of the Andes, 14,000 feet above sea level, in the Province of La Rioja is the little town of Famatina. This is the center of the principal copper-producing section of Argentina, but total production is very insignificant. Small deposits of tungsten, lead, tin, salt, borax, and gypsum also are in the region but either are of such small size or are in such remote sections that they cannot be economically utilized at the present time.

The arid plains and mountains of western Argentina, then, should be thought of as sparsely populated grazing areas specializing in animal products (hides, skins, wool, and frozen meats) that are relatively nonperishable. Moreover, there seems little likelihood that the grazing industry will expand to any marked degree or that the economy of the region will witness any striking changes for a long time to come. The arid plains stand in contrast, both in activities carried on and in population densities, to the oases with their specialized irrigation agriculture and high productivity and their relatively dense populations.

PATAGONIA

Patagonia is that portion of Argentina south of approximately 38 or 39°S. latitude (Fig. 102). This area of some 300,000 square miles stands in marked contrast to the other regions of the country. Its much colder climate and plateau topography give it regional unity and separate it from the arid plains and mountains to the north and from the flat Pampa to the northeast.

The region is one of the least attractive of the Republic. Bitterly cold winters in the south and disagreeable ones everywhere characterize the area. Except in the mountains, little rain falls (Figs. 8 and 9), and the stony land of the plateau has only a scant vegetal cover of bunch grass and scrub (Fig. 125). Snow covers most of Patagonia in winter, and violent winds are common at all seasons. Largely because of Patagonia's unattractive environment, the population density is very low. In each of the territories included in the region, there is less than one per square mile (Fig. 101).

Fig. 125.—View of Patagonian plateau.

Settlement of Patagonia progressed slowly. Although by the end of the eighteenth century there were Spanish settlements exploiting the salt deposits and exporting hides and skins from Carmen de Patagones at the mouth of the Río Negro, active colonization did not progress rapidly until the latter part of the nineteenth century. In fact, Patagonia did not become definitely a part of Argentina until 1902, after the settlement of a boundary dispute with Chile. From the time of its earliest settlements to the present, the distinctive occupation of the region has been sheep raising and particularly sheep raising on a large scale. Most of the land that affords pasturage for sheep is used for that purpose. Cattle are relatively unimportant. Ranches covering hundreds of thousands of acres have been acquired, and Scotch,

Welsh, and English owners are common. Many of these came from the sheep-raising Falkland Islands (British) near by. So thin is the pasturage that ten times as much land must be allowed for each animal as is necessary on the Pampa. Despite this condition, Patagonia has about one-fourth of the country's sheep and produces one-half of all its wool. Ranch houses are miles apart, and a family may not see a neighbor for weeks at a time. Aside from sheep raising, there is little other use to which the bleak Patagonian steppe can be put, and it would seem that the region,

FIG. 126. Lake Nahuel Huapi, Argentina lake country.

like many parts of the arid West of the United States, holds little promise beyond this.

Not all the sheep of Patagonia are wool sheep. In the north, most of them are a merino type which yield a medium-grade wool. Dust and burrs, however, get into the wool, because of careless production methods, and reduce its value. In the south, mutton sheep are more common. Freezing plants have been established at several points along the coast of Santa Cruz, and the production of meat is more important than wool in this territory.

Throughout most of Patagonia, cultivated crops cannot be grown without irrigation. In the valley bottoms of Neuquén Territory, wheat, rye, and potatoes are raised under irrigation for local consumption, and to supply the shepherds of the plateau. Some crop agriculture is also carried on in the deep valleys of the Sub-Andean depression, the area south of Lake Nahuel Haupí

Fig. 127.—Cypress logs at lumber mill, Bariloche.

Fig. 128.—Laguna Frias.

(Fig. 126) and east of the Andes. Here some wheat, vegetables, and fruits are grown without irrigation for local needs. The Sub-Andean depression is important for both sheep and cattle production. A little grain is grown on the plateau, but crop raising is only for local use and is relatively unimportant.

Other economic activities in Patagonia, with the exception of oil exploitation at Comodoro Rivadavia (see Chap. IX), are largely nonexistent. Some medium- to high-grade coal deposits, the best in Argentina, are in Neuquén Territory in the extreme northwestern boundary of the region; but these deposits are 1,000 miles from industrial sections of the Pampa. They, consequently, have been only partly developed. Forests on the slopes of the Andes, pines in the northwest and beeches south of Lake Nahuel Huapí, cover a considerable area, but their isolated location retards exploitation[1] (Fig. 127). Owing in part to the beautiful scenery of lakes and mountains in southern and western Patagonia, many have hoped for a rapid expansion of the tourist trade (Fig. 128). The general remote location of the area, however, is a retarding influence. In fact, in view of the existing conditions of climate, relief, and general isolation of the area, it seems likely that the existing economic activities of present-day Patagonia will continue, and that the region will remain a sparsely populated territory devoted primarily to the raising of wool and mutton sheep.

[1] Only one rail line crosses Patagonia, and that lies well to the north and does not run completely across the country.

Chapter XII. Uruguay

Uruguay is the smallest of the South American republics (72,000 square miles). It is both a part of the River Plata lands, separated from Argentina by the Uruguay River, and also a southern prolongation of the Brazilian hills. It is less flat than Argentina and less hilly than the adjoining part of Brazil. There is almost no waste land. For the most part, it is a rolling, grassy plain with few forests and no mountains—an excellent grazing land. The sea and the estuary of the River Plata form half of its boundary and give to the country an essentially oceanic climate, perhaps the most agreeable possessed by any South American people. On this coast has grown up one of the most fashionable bathing resorts in the Southern Hemisphere, and to it flock the wealth and gaiety of Argentina and Brazil as well as of Uruguay. Snow almost never falls in any part of the country, and even frosts are infrequent. The rainfall averages over 40 inches a year, but occasionally serious droughts occur,[1] as they do in Argentina. On the coast, the summers are delightful; in the interior, they become hot, but not for a long period. So far as surface features and climate are concerned, Uruguay is a happily situated country.

The little country of Uruguay, formerly known as the Banda, has had a stormy career. On two occasions, it was for short periods annexed to the Argentine Confederation. At another time, it was claimed and held as part of Brazil. In the long, bitter war against the Paraguayan dictator López, it fought as an ally of both Brazil and Argentina; and, during more than half its period as an independent nation, two hostile factions within the country

---

[1] Unfavorable weather conditions led to the death of 600,000 cattle and 5 million sheep in 1914, and the drought of 1916 caused the death of 1½ million cattle (*U.S. Dept. of Commerce Report*, Dec. 10, 1918).

(the Colorados and the Blancos) fought each other more or less continuously. Yet the country has prospered and progressed. In 1800, it had only a scattering of people, not exceeding 30,000; but this nucleus grew to upward of 800,000 in 1900 and was estimated at over 2,000,000 in 1937.

Most of the Indians were exterminated, and persons with Negro blood were mainly confined to the region of the Brazilian border. Nearly the entire Uruguayan population are of European stock and are an upstanding and forward-looking people, a small nation, but one of the most progressive in South America.

THE ECONOMIC PATTERN

Uruguay is a country of one main resource and one main industry. The natural wealth of the country lies in its soil and in its wide, rolling pastures, clad in nutritious grasses, somewhat richer than the native grasses of Argentina, but less rich than the Argentine alfalfa fields. Uruguay has made little headway with alfalfa, partly because its native pastures are good.

Only 7 per cent of the land is devoted to crop farms. About 60 per cent is used for stock raising and 20 per cent for mixed stock and crop ranches. The typical Uruguayan is first, last, and always a ranchman. He loves the saddle and the green and billowy pasture lands with their herds of grazing cattle and flocks of sheep. Even less than his Argentine neighbor does he take to the plow and the cultivator. He knows an easier and pleasanter way to obtain wealth from his lands, and he takes little interest in the laborious life of a farmer. Less than 8 per cent of the population is engaged in agriculture. In no other country of the Western Hemisphere do the economic interests of a whole nation so completely center in the single industry of stock raising as they do in Uruguay. Practically every other phase of industry depends upon the raising of sheep and cattle, and 65 to 75 per cent of the land is devoted to pastures. This specialization is the consequence of (1) favoring geographical conditions, (2) the sparse population and large landholdings, (3) the traditional preference of the people for the free, open-air life of the ranchman, and (4) the profitableness of the industry. Undoubtedly in Uruguay, as in its larger sister republic of Argentina, stock raising has been the most logical way of utilizing the great holdings of grassland; for such land is abundant, laborers are few, and the mildness of the winters makes unnecessary the building of shelters for the animals. Where people are very numerous and land is scarce, as in Japan, the land must be intensively cultivated in order to feed the people. The securing of food for an overpopulation is the controlling motive. In a land like Uruguay, the problem is reversed and becomes: How can a small population utilize much land in a way to get satisfactory returns? In 1908, Uruguay had more than 35 million head of livestock, mainly sheep and cattle, or thirty-five times the human population of the country. The number of animals is now about one-half as great, but the quality is higher. The purebred and crossbred sheep yield more than twice the weight of wool that the native breeds yielded; and improved breeds of cattle yield more and better meat than the old Spanish Longhorns. In spite, then, of the declining number of sheep and cattle in the country, the value of the animal products exported is now double what it was in 1908 or in previous years.

The Sheep-raising Industry.—Before the perfecting of refrigerating methods and refrigerator ships, about the only commercial products of Uruguay were wool and hides and skins. As a rule, sheep are raised on the poorer lands of the earth and especially on the drier lands, for they are able to subsist on scanty pasturage where cattle cannot thrive. Moreover, wool is a good commodity to produce in places remote from the world's great markets, because it can be shipped long distances. It is valuable in proportion to its weight and can stand the freight charges for a long sea journey. The latter was formerly the chief reason for specializing in sheep raising in the River Plata lands; it was not the poor quality of the land or the dry climate, for Uruguay has good land and usually has ample rainfall. As recently as 1928, Uruguay exported 120 million pounds of wool valued at $30,-000,000. This was an average year's shipment; in some past years, it has been much greater. This product still ranks first in the list of Uruguayan exports, amounting to 85 million pounds with a value of $23,000,000 in 1937. The annual wool clip of the country averages $10 per capita of the population. In proportion to area and population, Uruguay has been the foremost sheep-raising country of the world, although, on account of its small area, its absolute rank has usually been seventh or eighth. On the whole, the relative importance of sheep in Uruguay is slowly declining, and that of cattle is increasing.

Cattle Raising.—A half century or more ago, cattle in Uruguay were killed mainly for their hides and for the making of jerked beef. At one time, 20 *saladeros*, or salting plants, devoted themselves to slaughtering the lean cattle, drying and salting the beef, and exporting it to Cuba and Brazil. This method of preparing meat for shipment was the principal one for several decades and is still employed on a considerable scale. In the 5-year period, 1904–1908, $2\frac{3}{4}$ million cattle were slaughtered in the *saladeros* and an average of some 100 million pounds of the dried meat (*tasajo*) was exported annually. Of late, the production of this type of meat has become relatively small for three reasons: (1) the declining importations into Brazil, which now supplies most of its own meat; (2) the higher price of cattle; and (3) the increasing practice of chilling and freezing meat. The rise of refrigeration and the decline of drying and salting beef and of making beef extract may be seen in the changes between 1913, 1921, and 1932.

	1913	1921	1932
Cattle slaughtered for chilling or freezing....	132,650	275,667	496,992
Cattle slaughtered for drying and salting....	253,600	87,707	
Cattle slaughtered for beef-extract factories..	81,100	15,959	4,687

Since native cattle were cheap, thousands of them were slaughtered each year, and their meat was used in making beef extract. The most famous of the five beef-extract factories is the great Liebig establishment at Fray Bentos on the Uruguay River, where 75,000 to 100,000 cattle a year were formerly slaughtered. But this large industry has declined with the rise in meat prices, for it can prosper only on cheap cattle.

There are four modern packing plants in Uruguay, three belonging to the Chicago packers and one to an English company (Fig. 129). The largest plant belongs to Swift & Co. These packers are called trusts in South America and became unpopular there as they did in the United States. In both Argentina and Uruguay, there has been a demand for government-owned packing plants which should free the public from the trusts.

A large part of the beef prepared in the Uruguayan packing plants in the past has been frozen rather than chilled. This is due partly to the lower grade of many of the cattle, the better meat being chilled rather than frozen (Fig. 130). Large quantities

FIG. 129.—View of the slaughtering and meat-packing plant of Swift and Co. near Montevideo, Uruguay. (*Courtesy of Swift & Co.*)

FIG. 130.—Cattle show at Montevideo. Like Argentina, Uruguay is also a land of high-grade cattle.

of meat are also canned. The foremost of the animal products (by weight) exported from Uruguay is frozen beef. Meat and wool account for about two-thirds of the value of all exports from Uruguay (Fig. 131). The demand of the packers for good cattle not only has caused an increase in cattle raising in Uruguay but is leading to an improvement in the quality. In addition to the large exportations of beef products, Uruguay is a very large supplier of hides and skins—some 55 to 60 million pounds per year.

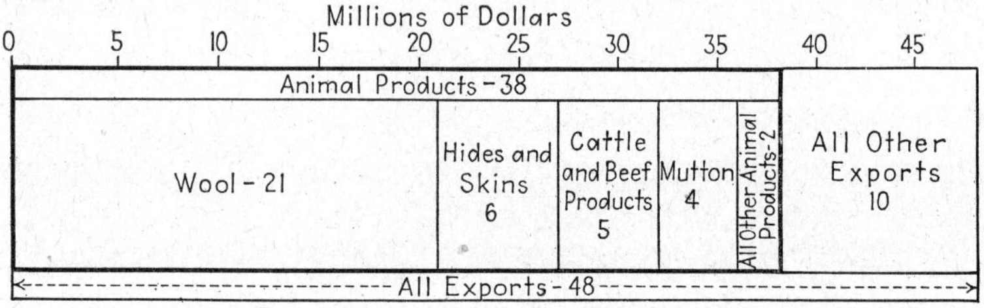

FIG. 131.—Exports of Uruguay by classes, 3-year average, 1935–1937.

The Minor Importance of Agriculture.—It has already been pointed out that the people of Uruguay do not take to agriculture, partly because they are not fond of agricultural work and partly because of the small population of the country. Only 1 acre in 20 of the land is under cultivation. Three crops occupy 90 per cent of the cultivated land; wheat is raised on half of this area, and corn and flax together occupy as much more land. Owing to the small production of cereals and other vegetable foods, the people of Uruguay eat a great deal of meat and also import agricultural products. Moderate quantities of fruits are grown, especially wine grapes. The government has a 1,000-acre experimental farm and is seeking to stimulate interest in agriculture and to increase the agricultural output of the country, but only slow progress is being made. Immigrants come into the country slowly, partly because of the high cost of living in Uruguay and partly because they find it difficult to secure land.

The locust pest is a menace to the growing crops, and considerable damage is done nearly every year. The government maintains an organized force of men, known as the *Defensa Agricola*, trained in combating the locusts. Soldiers of the regular army cooperate in times of need, and thus the ravages of the pest are held in check.

Transportation Facilities.—Because of the rolling topography and good drainage, the country roads in Uruguay are somewhat

better than those in Argentina. Not infrequently, they are
extremely wide (100 feet or more) and include strips of grassland
upon which flocks and herds may feed while being driven long
distances. There are about 1,500 miles of good paved roads and
several hundred miles of unimproved highways. The many
streams in the country require an unusually large number of
bridges which in that country are expensive. Poor roads are less

FIG. 132.—The railway system of Uruguay converges on the port of Montevideo.

of a handicap in a pastoral country than in an agricultural
country, for sheep and cattle can be driven to markets and to
railway stations. There is, nevertheless, a sustained interest in
good roads, stimulated by 36,000 motor vehicles in Montevideo
alone (1935) and 14,000 in country districts.

The railway system (dating from 1865) consists of a main
system of over 1,000 miles, the Central Uruguay, and several
lesser systems which act as feeders (a total of 1,900 miles). The

whole system converges upon Montevideo, the chief city and port (Fig. 132). It is nearly all standard gauge. In proportion to area, Uruguay has more miles of railway than any other country in South America and is exceeded only by Cuba in all Latin America. Nearly all the lines are owned by British capital and are under efficient British management. A short mileage of state railways has been built.

For various reasons, the railways have been somewhat costly to build; and since fuel, materials, and equipment are largely imported, the cost of operation is high and freight rates are high, at least in comparison with average rates in the United States. An important reason for the high rates is the unbalanced movement of traffic. Most of the tonnage is moving toward the ports, especially Montevideo, and little is moving in the opposite direction.

By 1911, various railways in Brazil and the main railway in Uruguay had been linked up for a distance of 2,000 miles, from Montevideo to Rio de Janeiro. It is a long and somewhat uninteresting journey requiring 4 days; the service is not yet good, and there is relatively little through traffic. The ocean route is still preferred.

Commercial Foci.—One city and its suburbs dominate the urban life of Uruguay. Montevideo, the capital, chief city, and leading port of Uruguay, has approximately 700,000 people, over one-fourth of the population of the country (Fig. 133). It dates from 1726 and is, therefore, a much younger city than Buenos Aires. The city owes its location to a small peninsula and a partly protected bay which make a natural harbor possible at this point on the coast (Fig. 134). The site is also favorable for ocean commerce in that it is virtually at the outer end of the River Plata estuary, a half-day's sailing below Buenos Aires. By nature, Montevideo is a better port than Buenos Aires; however, the latter has been improved and equipped in a superior manner but at great cost. Over $40,000,000 have been expended on Montevideo harbor and its port facilities, which include 36 warehouses.

The railway system of Uruguay has been developed with Montevideo as its focus, and nearly all the ocean commerce of the country passes through that port. It is a fine, attractive city with modern improvements but is much less hustling and extravagant than Buenos Aires (Fig. 135). The small development of manu-

facturing that has taken place in Uruguay is mainly confined to
Montevideo and is most largely connected with the preparation

FIG. 133.—View of Federal Building, Montevideo. (*Courtesy of F. G. Matheson.*)

FIG. 134.—Airplane view of Montevideo and its harbor.

of meat products. There are about one hundred flour mills, large
and small, in the country.

Montevideo is fourteen times the size of its next nearest rival, Paysandú (50,000), a river port, railway center, and meat-packing center on the Uruguay River about 300 miles from the capital.

Fig. 135.—One of the fine bathing beaches of Montevideo, frequented by both Uruguayans and Argentinians. (*Courtesy of F. G. Matheson.*)

Most urban centers of Uruguay are focal points for their immediate hinterland. They function as collection and distribution centers for the territory in which they are located, and few achieve more than local importance.

External Relations and the Trade Pattern.—In proportion to its population, Uruguay is a wealthy country. Poverty is little

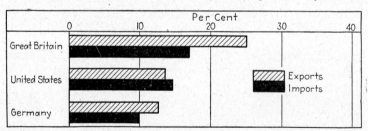

Fig. 136.—Per cent of total trade of Uruguay with selected countries, 3-year average, 1935–1937.

known, and the per capita exports of the country frequently reach $50 annually, though in recent years the value has averaged between $20 and $25; 95 per cent of these exports are animal products. Usually 10 or 15 per cent go to the United States, but a much larger proportion (about 25 per cent) goes to the United Kingdom (Fig. 136). A country that sells much abroad has a large purchasing power and, hence, may support a large import trade. The import trade is very diversified. Coal, petroleum and petroleum products, textile yarns and fabrics, sugar, yerba maté, lumber, and a great variety of manufactured and semimanufactured goods are the outstanding commodities moving into Uruguay. Total import trade amounts to about $35,000,000 to

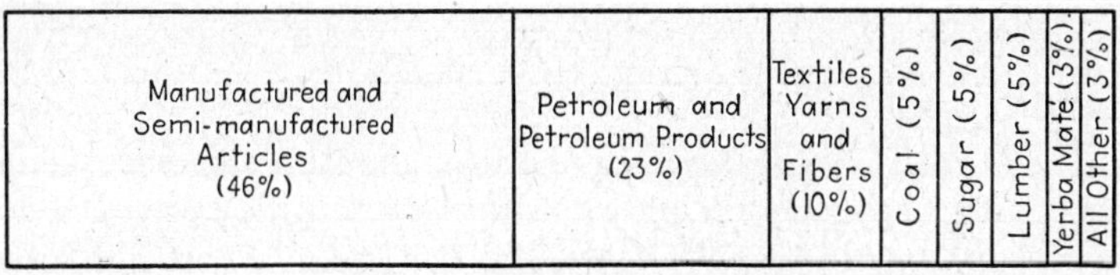

Manufactured and Semi-manufactured Articles (46%)	Petroleum and Petroleum Products (23%)	Textiles Yarns and Fibers (10%)	Coal (5%)	Sugar (5%)	Lumber (5%)	Yerba Maté (3%)	All Other (3%)

Fig. 137.—Per cent of various commodities in the import trade of Uruguay, 2-year average, 1936–1937.

$45,000,000 per year (Fig. 137). The annual value of exports— $45,000,000 to $55,000,000—is usually greater than that of imports, giving an export balance of trade. This is essential to the financial stability of the nation, which has a large foreign debt; 40 per cent of the revenues of the country is required for interest on the national debt. The credit of the country and its financial record are, however, among the best in Latin America. Its imports are mainly manufactured products bought from Europe and the United States. Trade between the United States and Uruguay is now much larger than it was before the World War.

Chapter XIII. Paraguay

There seems to be little justification for the existence of an independent country in the 176,000 square miles occupied by Paraguay. Its territory should have been part of the adjoining countries which touch the sea. It was a case of historical accident that led to the establishment of a separate country where none should have been. After a country has been established and a sense of nationality has been developed in its people, the country's right to exist as an independent nation is generally accepted, however badly it may be handicapped by its unfavorable situation and boundaries.

The navigator Sebastian Cabot sailed up the Paraná-Paraguay in 1527, nearly a century before the landing of the Pilgrims in Massachusetts; and a later explorer founded the city of Asunción in 1535. Thus did this city, 1,000 miles up the river from the Atlantic, begin its existence ahead of Buenos Aires, Rio de Janeiro, or Montevideo, the outstanding port cities of South America.

An important reason for navigating this waterway so far inland and for locating settlements there was the desire of the Spaniards to establish a route to the famous silver mines of Potosí in the present Bolivia. To reach these mines by the route that led across the Isthmus of Panama, down the west coast of South America, and across the lofty Andes in their widest and most difficult part required an exceedingly long journey. Moreover, that route led through the Caribbean Sea, which was infested by buccaneers. The eastern and southern route from Spain to the River Plata, up the Paraná-Paraguay, and overland to Potosí was somewhat easier and less dangerous. Thus was the nucleus of the future Paraguay planted in the interior of South America on the route to the silver mines of Upper Peru (Bolivia).

In 1811, the Paraguayans revolted against Spanish rule and set up an independent nation as the other Spanish colonies in America were doing. Three dictators in succession ruled the country until 1870. During the last 5 years of this period, the last dictator Francisco López involved his country in the most terrible war South America has ever had. In this struggle, López and the Paraguayans fought Argentina, Brazil, and Uruguay until almost every male who was able to bear arms in Paraguay had been killed. Of the Paraguayan population of 1,300,000 in 1864, only 220,000 remained in 1870, and of these only 28,700 were men. The losses of men and land reduced Paraguay to the present position of impotency that it occupies.

During the long and bitter war against the triple alliance composed of Argentina, Brazil, and Uruguay, the Paraguayans displayed a perseverance and hardihood seldom exceeded; but the war left the country depleted of men, and that depletion has scarcely yet been made good.

The Guarani Indians, a group of agricultural tribes that occupied this part of South America, form a large element in the racial stock of Paraguay. Only a minor fraction of the people are pure Indians, but an even smaller fraction are pure whites. It is essentially a mestizo race, formed by the fusion of Spaniards and Indians, together with a small but influential element of pure Spanish and other European immigrants entering since 1870. Although the official and literary language of the country is Spanish, the language of the common people is Guarani, and this is one of the factors that holds the nation back. Another factor is the isolation of the country and its lack of immediate contact with the more advanced parts of neighboring nations. A somewhat enervating climate and a too free use of native rum are further retarding factors in the backwardness of the nation. Only a minor fraction of the children have the opportunity of attending school, and at least two-thirds of the population cannot read or write. The National University at Asunción has a few hundred students. Almost the entire population lives by crude agriculture, stock raising, and the forest industries. The plane of living is low, except among the leading families in a few cities. It is estimated that the 900,000 people (more or less) have the purchasing power of an American city of 150,000.

THE AGRICULTURAL PATTERN

Paraguay consists of two well-defined regions. "The River Paraguay divides the country into two quite distinct areas. In

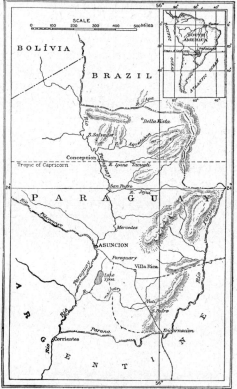

fact, it is doubtful if any river in the world forms the boundary line between two regions so different in almost every respect— topography, soil, plants, people, and industries."[1]

Most of the people and towns, including Asunción, the capital, and most of the economic development are found in a narrow belt parallel to the river on the eastern bank (Fig. 138). The part of eastern Paraguay that slopes toward the Paraguay River is a region of low plains, in part poorly drained and less than half forest-covered. It includes most of the cultivated lands of the Republic, but

Fig. 138.—Sketch map of Paraguay. (*Courtesy of Pan-American Union.*)

less than one-half of 1 per cent is under cultivation. The soil is a fertile red type common in this part of South America. A variety of crops is grown, but few are of commercial importance. A large part of the production is consumed locally, and

---

[1] Schurz, W. L. Paraguay: A Commercial Handbook, *Special Agents Series* 199, U.S Dept. of Commerce, Washington, D.C., 1920.

only two or three agricultural products are exported. The leading crops of commercial importance include: cotton, tobacco, oranges, and petit-grain oil.[1] Rice, sugar cane, manioc (or mandioca), corn (maize), and beans are grown for local use.

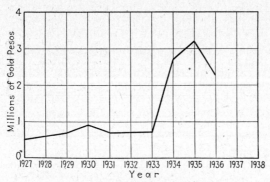

Fig. 139.—Cotton exports from Paraguay.

Cotton yields well and in recent years has become the chief money crop and principal export commodity of Paraguay (Fig. 139). In the last few years, cotton has accounted for one-fourth to over one-third of the total value of all exports; it has displaced tobacco as the principal commercial crop. Production could be

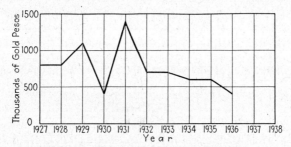

Fig. 140.—Tobacco exports from Paraguay.

increased greatly if less primitive methods were employed. *Tobacco*, once the chief export crop, occupies a secondary position in the agricultural economy of the country today (1937). Its ex-

---

[1] Petit-grain oil is obtained from bitter-orange leaves. It is used in the manufacture of perfume. Export varies between 75 and 100 metric tons. In 1937, the export value was approximately $250,000.

port value is only about one-tenth that of cotton. Production methods are primitive, but the quality is fairly high. The tobacco is carefully graded, and some seven varieties are shipped into foreign markets, much of it to Argentina (Fig. 140). Annual production amounts to between 15 and 20 million pounds per year. *Oranges* are the characteristic fruit of Paraguay, growing without attention and spreading even into the forests. It is doubtful whether any other part of the world is so perfectly suited to the growth of this fruit. So cheap and common are oranges that little value is placed upon them, and about the only external markets to which they can be sent are Argentina and Uruguay. The industry is poorly managed, and the crop yields little profit

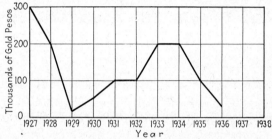

Fig. 141.—Exports of oranges from Paraguay.

to the grower because of high freight rates and high marketing costs. In recent years, there has been more careful attention paid to sorting and grading. As a result, prices have increased, and oranges may become a more important export commodity of Paraguay (Fig. 141).

Two crops, *corn* and *manioc*, are staple items in the diet of the Paraguayans. These crops, produced wherever people live, require little care. Yields are sufficient for the local needs. *Rice*, grown in the swampy areas and on the flood plain of the Paraguay and Parana rivers, is one of the chief foods used in the country. It is produced under very primitive methods and is threshed by driving oxen or mules over the straw. The quantity grown is much below the requirements of the country. *Sugar cane* is one of the more promising crops. Acreage is small, and the industry is dominated by a few producers, one of whom grinds more than half the cane of the country. Total production would be about 1 month's work for a large Cuban sugar mill. The large variety of crops raised is indicative of the fertility of the country; that production is no greater indicates the general backward condition of agriculture and the primitive methods used in most farming activity.

A commentary on the backwardness of agriculture in Paraguay is seen in the fact that this warm, fertile country does not produce enough food for its own people and needs to import considerable quantities from the outside. In order to develop more fully her agricultural resources, Paraguay needs immigrants; but its geographical remoteness and general unattractiveness when compared with Argentina, Uruguay, or southern Brazil have prevented its securing any considerable number of immigrants. Considering its poverty of national revenues, Paraguay cannot compete with these more favored lands in the inducements offered to settlers. If, therefore, it is to secure immigrants, some exceptional device has to be adopted. One of these devices is the agricultural colony of which there are two types: (1) the national colony, and (2) the private colony. Both government lands and private lands are subdivided into small farms; and, by means of agents, propaganda, and advertising, an effort is made to induce colonies of immigrants to settle on these lands and improve them. Unfortunately, promises held out are usually too optimistic, and the colonists find realities far below their expectations and become dissatisfied. Most of the colonies either have failed or are maintaining a precarious existence. A small minority of the people have attained reasonable success.

Efforts of this general sort are being made in other parts of South America—efforts of land companies or other private interests to induce people to go into out-of-the-way lands and subject themselves to deprivations and hardships in an effort to develop a remote region before the time for doing so is ripe. Efforts to establish colonies in the montaña of Peru and Bolivia, efforts to get people to develop Alaska, and even some of the irrigation projects in the United States, Canada, and Brazil represent this misguided effort to develop, at heavy cost of labor, privation, or money, certain parts of the world that are not yet needed—not needed because better located and more fertile lands are lying unused or half used. These forced and premature efforts of development companies have brought hardships and disappointments to large numbers of people.

THE GRAZING INDUSTRY

It is estimated that there are over four times as many cattle as people in Paraguay (Fig. 142). The native cattle, descended from Spanish stock introduced long ago, have degenerated. Some of the Indian zebu type from Brazil have been brought in; but although they are more disease-resistant than other cattle, they make poor beef, for their meat is tough and lacking in fat. The more progressive cattle companies have introduced foreign purebred cattle, especially Herefords, and have improved the stock on their *estancias*. One of the largest of these companies owns a tract of 1¼ million acres and keeps 150,000 cattle. In certain respects, this section of South America, including adjacent

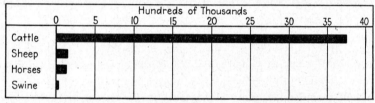

Fig. 142.—Principal domestic animals of Paraguay, 1936.

parts of Brazil, holds out considerable promise of providing increasingly for the world's future supply of meat, for the following reasons: (1) The land is very cheap. (2) The climate is mild, and no shelter or winter feeding need be provided, for the cattle graze the year round. (3) Taxation is so low that it is nearly negligible. (4) The civilized Indians and half-breeds take readily to cattle herding. The chief difficulties are the pests and diseases, which are more troublesome in a warm climate than in a cool one, and the remoteness and isolation of the country. The three American meat-packing plants that were erected in Paraguay during the World War have closed. A few of the large cattle-raising companies have made excellent profits and have shown that, under enlightened business management, cattle raising in Paraguay may be profitable.

OTHER LAND-USE PATTERNS

North and south through eastern Paraguay runs the low divide which separates the drainage of the upper Paraná from that of the Paraguay (Fig. 138). The lands sloping toward the Paraná are more than 80 per cent forested, including the principal yerba forests and yerba estates of the country. This eastward slope is a wilderness, subtropical in climate, uncrossed by any railway, and possessed of no city or town of any size. Its main outlet is by way of the rivers of the Paraná system by which the yerba and a few minor products ultimately reach Buenos Aires.

The portion of the Republic lying west of the Paraguay River belongs to the wide sweep of undulating plains known as the Chaco, which also include parts of Argentina and Bolivia. The Paraguay Chaco is only partly explored. It is of very little economic importance except for cattle raising and limited quantities of quebracho taken from the scattered forests (Fig. 143). It is

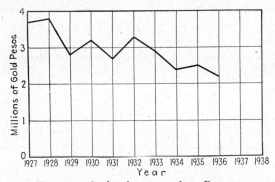

Fig. 143.—Quebracho exports from Paraguay.

believed, however, that it may have future possibilities for cattle raising.

The rainfall ranges from 35 inches in the Chaco, where damaging droughts sometimes occur, to 60 inches in the forest region of the east. The temperatures are tropical and semitropical but are subject to the wide variations that characterize the interiors of continents. It is by no means the sort of country that can offer many attractions to European immigrants. Much more attractive lands lying nearer the sea are still available in South America.

THE COMMERCIAL PATTERN

Commerce in Paraguay, both internal and external, is in a very low stage of development. Transportation lines are largely lacking, and commercial centers are few and unimportant. Only one railway reaches into the country and connects Asunción with

Buenos Aires in Argentina, 938 miles distant. With only one rail line and practically no good roads, much dependence is placed on the rivers for transportation (Fig. 138). Fast mail boats run between Buenos Aires and Asunción. Small boats on the Upper Paraguay and Paraná give connection with northern and eastern sections of the country. An air line from Rio de Janeiro to Buenos Aires via Asunción links the Paraguayan capital with both Brazil and Argentina.

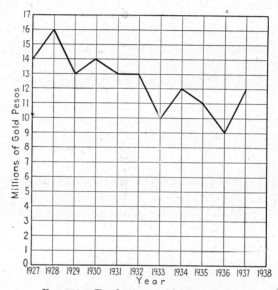

FIG. 144.—Total export trade of Paraguay.

Asunción (95,000) is the leading commercial center of Paraguay and one of the oldest cities in South America. It is the only important city of Paraguay. Some local manufacturing has developed here, most of it having to do with the processing of agricultural and forest products, in flour and textile mills, cotton gins, distilleries, tanneries, cigarette factories, and other minor industries.

The foreign trade of Paraguay is the smallest of any of the South American countries (Fig. 144). The export products fall into three major groups (Fig. 145) which account for 99 per cent of the total: (1) agricultural products, among which cotton accounts for at least three-fourths of the total; (2) animal products; and (3) forest products—yerba maté, quebracho, and some timber (Fig. 146). Imports are more diversified, but foodstuffs

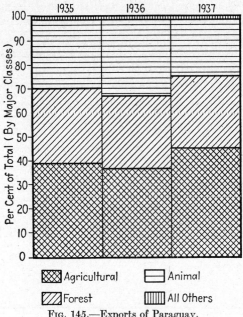

FIG. 145.—Exports of Paraguay.

FIG. 146.—Moving timber in Paraguay.

and textiles form 60 per cent of the total. Manufactured goods, of course, constitute most of the imports, for Paraguay has almost no general manufacturing except, as described above, the simple articles for local use.

Paraguay's principal trade relations in the past have been with Argentina. Much of this trade was in goods sent to Argentina for transshipment. Since 1937, Paraguayan importers and exporters have tended to buy and sell directly rather than through neighboring countries. In 1936, for example, 58 per cent of the country's exports passed through Argentina. In 1937, the percentage had dropped to about 23. Aside from this indirect trade, Paraguay buys most (40 to 50 per cent) and sells most (19 to 34 per cent) to Argentina. Next in importance in imports come Germany, Japan, the United Kingdom, and the United States. Exports go chiefly to Germany, the United Kingdom, and the United States.

Chapter XIV. Brazil:
General Description, Interior
Tablelands, and Southern States

GENERAL DESCRIPTION

Brazil is generally known as a producer of coffee, as a rising source of cotton, or because of its immense size. Whatever else people know concerning Brazil, most of them know that it is big (Fig. 147). It is not only the largest country in South America; it constitutes 45 per cent of the area of the continent. It is larger than the United States and almost as large as Canada. From the standpoint of area, it is one of the five great countries of the world and the only one of these that lies almost wholly in the tropics. It has, outside of polar areas, probably the largest unexplored region in the world. Relative to its size, it has a very sparse population. Yet some experts say that it can support 800 million people, and many Brazilians believe their country will have 240 million by the end of the twentieth century. Unlike the Spanish colonies, which split up into many nations, this Portuguese colony remained intact after it separated from the mother country, and it now holds nearly half the population of the continent under one government.

The first outstanding geographical fact concerning Brazil, then, is its territorial bigness.

The second geographical fact of importance is the location of most of the country within the tropics (Fig. 5). Tropical climates have both advantages and disadvantages; but, so far as white people are concerned, the disadvantages predominate. The greater part of Brazil is still undeveloped and very sparsely peopled, in part because of the direct and indirect consequences of the climate.

The third significant geographical fact is the presence in eastern Brazil of an extensive highland. This provides an area larger than the British Isles, France, and Germany combined, where the elevation of the land reduces the tropical heat (Fig. 148). The plateau occupies nearly one-quarter of Brazil and lies near the sea. Its surface is hilly and in places mountainous, but most of it can be used for crops or pasturage. It is, by all odds, the most important feature of the country.

Fig. 147.—Map of comparative areas of Brazil and European countries, excluding U.S.S.R. except Ukraine. (*From "Brazil of Today," National Dept. of Commerce of Brazil*, 1931.)

1. Albania	9. Luxembourg	17. Jugoslavia	25. Germany
2. Bulgaria	10. Greece	18. Finland	26. Rumania
3. Estonia	11. Denmark	19. France	27. Sweden
4. Ireland	12. Hungary	20. Italy	28. Switzerland
5. Austria	13. Ukraine I	21. Poland	29. Turkey
6. Danzig	14. Lithuania	22. Great Britain	30. Czechoslovakia
7. Spain	15. Holland	23. Ukraine II	31. Portugal
8. Ukraine III	16. Latvia	24. Norway	32. Belgium

Physical Regions.—Brazil divides naturally into three main physical regions: (1) the Eastern Plateau and associated Lowlands; the Amazon Lowlands which are low in elevation, but at all seasons, deluged with tropical downpours, and partly covered with dense forest; (3) the Interior Lowlands and Plateau, an area consisting more of grasslands than of forests and a very large part of which lies in the drainage basin of the Paraná-Paraguay River system (Fig. 148).

The Eastern Highland, or Brazilian Plateau, is one of the major upland masses of the world with an extent of approximately 1 million square miles. With the exception of a relatively small area in the northeast, the region slopes toward the interior and consequently is mostly drained by the tributaries of the Amazon and the Paraná rivers. Along the sea for over 1,000 miles, the eastern escarpment of this plateau rises almost from the shore. Its seaward edge appears like a range of mountains, and part of it has

Fig. 148.—Natural regions of Brazil.

been named the Serra do Mar. So steep is this escarpment that it is with great difficulty that two standard-gauge railways have surmounted the grades, and one of these is able to make the ascent only by the use of cables. The railroad that runs north from Rio de Janeiro through Petropolis uses rack and pinion to ascend the steep slopes. A coastal plain of considerable width is found north of the seventeenth parallel, and on this plain are the two large cities of Bahia and Pernambuco.

The highland of eastern Brazil is the redeeming physical feature of the country. Its surface averages about 2,500 feet in elevation and is surmounted by ranges rising to 8,000 feet (Fig. 148). Since every thousand feet of elevation reduces the average temperature about 3°F., the surface of this highland is 7 or 8 degrees cooler than it would be if the region were a low plain. The southern half of the highland is fairly cool much of the year, and the white people who live there are energetic and enterprising.

On the basis of climate and products, the eastern plateau may be divided into northern, central, and southern sections (Fig. 148). The former is distinctly tropical in character, and a majority of the people have Negro blood. The farther south one goes, the fewer Negroes he finds. This northern section is agricultural. Four staple crops are produced, sugar, cacao, cotton, and tobacco, although these crops are not all confined to this section. The central section is somewhat milder in temperature and is the most advanced part of Brazil. It includes three of the leading states: São Paulo, the great coffee-producing state; Minas Geraes, the mineral-bearing state; and Rio de Janeiro, in which the capital is located. The southern section lies south of the Tropic of Capricorn and has a warm temperate climate. It is only partly developed but contains the progressive states of Rio Grande do Sul and Santa Catharina, with their many cattle, swine, and sheep, and the state of Paraná with its pine forests and yerba groves.

In this eastern highland and on its coast live over 90 per cent of the people of the country (Fig. 1). The only large city of Brazil that is not thus located is Pará, the ocean gate for the Amazon valley. Between the eastern plateau and the great lowland interior, there is very little intercommunication. Most of the navigable rivers flow, not toward the coast, but toward the Amazon, and only one railway entirely crosses the plateau and the southern interior. Roads are being constructed, but long distances and sparse population make highway development difficult. It is to be noted that the highland section of eastern Brazil is as large as Argentina and that the part of this highland well suited to agriculture is larger than the Argentine Pampa. With all Brazil's waste land, it still has a very large area of well-located farm land where whites may live. Yet it is a significant fact that two-thirds of the area of Brazil is unoccupied except by Indian tribes and occasional small settlements which contain a few whites. Vast areas are virtually unknown even to the Brazilians themselves. The great extent of undeveloped country is one of the most impressive facts in the geography of Brazil.

Land Utilization.—Throughout most of Brazil, rainfall is ample for crops except in the northeast, where sheltered valleys between ridges are shut off from the rain-bearing winds and frequently suffer from serious droughts (Figs. 8 and 9). Costly irrigation works have been started, and principles of dry-farming methods have been introduced; but the area is large, and the expense is great. Brazil has somewhat more than 2 billion acres of land, about 80 per cent of which is not occupied as farm lands. The 20 per cent that is included in the 650,000 farms would make 10 states the size of Illinois or 10 countries the size of England. Of this area, fully 75 per cent is pasture and brushland, and 6 per cent is covered with forest. Thus, the land actually cultivated is less than the area of 2 states like Illinois. There are many large estates, but the average size of farms is 660 acres, or nearly five times the average size in the United States. On the whole, farm land is relatively cheap in Brazil, though it doubled in value between 1910 and 1920. In the latter year, the official census placed the value of the 400 million acres of farm land at about $3,000,000,000, or $7.50 per acre. Nearly all the cultivated land lies relatively near the coast, usually within 400 miles.

The agricultural lands may be divided into (1) the hot lands of the north, including such important states as Bahia and Pernambuco; (2) the mild tropical, including the two leading states of Minas Geraes and São Paulo; and (3) the warm temperate, composed of Paraná, Santa Catharina, and Rio Grande do Sul (Fig. 149). Even São Paulo and southern Minas Geraes might be considered as warm temperate because of the altitude of most of their land. The two large interior states of Matto Grosso and Goyaz contain extensive grasslands but very little cultivated land. There is practically no cultivation north of the Amazon and not much anywhere in the vast Amazon Lowland, which is deluged with rains, partly flooded in the rainy season, and too sultry in temperature to attract settlers.

An outstanding characteristic of Brazil is its enormous area of land capable of growing the products of commerce in almost unlimited quantities and the exceedingly small area of the country (about $1\frac{1}{2}$ per cent) that is actually cultivated (Fig. 150). It is also worthy of note that 64 per cent of the value of all agricultural property is found in three states, São Paulo (27 per cent), Rio Grande do Sul (19 per cent), and Minas Geraes (18 per cent).

Fig. 149.—States and territories of Brazil. (*Brazil, Ministry of Foreign Affairs.*)

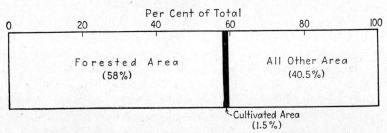

Fig. 150.—Proportion of cultivated and uncultivated land in Brazil.

The great producing capacity of the best of this land may be judged from the fact that all the coffee of Brazil, which is two-thirds of the world's supply, is grown on one-fourth of the area of a state like Indiana, or one-fourteenth of the area of São Paulo.

The comments of Lord Bryce,[1] one of the most competent and kindly of observers, are of interest in this connection:

"Taking Brazil as a whole, no great country in the world, owned by a European race, possesses so large a proportion of land available for the support of human life and productive industry. In the United States there are deserts, and of the gigantic Russian Empire much is desert and much is frozen waste. But on the Portuguese of Brazil nature has bestowed nothing for which man cannot find a use. . . . The material prosperity of a country, however, depends less on its natural resources than on the quality of the labor applied to its development and on the intelligence that directs that labor. In these respects Brazil has been less fortunate."

The People of Brazil.—For three centuries, Brazil was a Portuguese colony, and its eastern portion was settled by immigrants from Portugal. Many of the distinguished families of the present are descended from the Brazilian nobility and gentry of the days when Brazil was an empire, ruled by a royal family of Portuguese origin. In fact, the king and court of Portugal resided in Brazil during a part of the Napoleonic period. The language of the country is Portuguese; the traditions, ideals, and social and political standards are inherited from Portugal, as those of the United States are inherited from Great Britain. Both peoples, of course, have been steadily modified in the New World.

The same demand for plantation labor that brought Negro slavery into the southern United States brought it into Brazil, and slavery was finally abolished in Brazil only in 1888. Many slaves had been freed, however, before this. The Brazilians have no such race feeling toward colored people as the North Americans have. They pride themselves upon the fact that there is no color line in Brazil. So far as color is concerned, whites, mulattoes, and blacks may attend the same schools, ride in the same cars, and attend the same social gatherings. In actual practice, very few colored people become sufficiently wealthy to move in the upper circles of Brazilian society. However, a man having Negro blood in his veins may rise to the higher political offices if he is otherwise acceptable.

In Brazil, as in all Latin America, there is a very strong feeling that a gentleman must not do manual work, even of the

[1] "South America, Observations and Impressions," p. 404, New York, 1912.

lightest kind. This caste attitude is breaking down somewhat in those sections into which have come white immigrants who do manual labor. But, when these immigrants rise in the economic scale and become well-to-do, as is frequently the case, they tend to adopt the traditions of the country and to look down upon the man who works. In any country where colored people do most of the manual labor, this attitude of mind on the part of the upper class is sure to develop.

There are no reliable statistics on the proportion of whites, mulattoes, and Negroes in Brazil. Probably not over one-third of the population is white; perhaps 5 per cent is Indian and 10 per cent pure Negro. In the north, people who have Negro and Indian blood are greatly in the majority. In the states from Rio de Janeiro southward, people who are wholly white or nearly white predominate. In the interior, the sparse population is mainly Indian or a mixture of Indian and white, with a possible further mixture of Negro blood. The Brazilian census figures are inaccurate and undiscriminating with respect to the make-up of the population, and they cast little light on the true racial composition. The absence of a social color line facilitates the intermarriage of all types and mixtures, and the trend must inevitably be in the direction of a fusion of racial elements into a Brazilian people of mixed ancestry.

The vast majority of the colored people are poor, illiterate, unambitious, and inefficient as laborers. Eighty per cent of the total population is said to be unable to read and write. In the northern states, where Negroes predominate, their unsanitary mode of life makes them easy victims of tropical diseases, which still further reduce their vitality and cause a high death rate. A close observer and cautious writer thus describes the Negroes of Brazil:

"The negro is indolent; work inspires him with a profound horror; he will allow himself to be driven to it only by hunger or by thirst; when all other resources fail him, then only he presents himself at the morning roll call and offers his services. . . . Taking them all in all, the negroes in the sugar-producing regions like Minas form a type of laborer of very indifferent economic value. . . . To sum up: the moral and economic inferiority of the negro populations of Brazil is incontestable. The puerility of the negroes is extreme. They have no foresight, and are innocent of any form of ambition, the sole motive power of progress.

. . . Alcoholism is not the only plague of the negro population. It is the prey of other maladies which are bred by the utter lack of hygiene."[1]

In the southern half of the highland area and conspicuously in the region of São Paulo, European immigrants are numerous, and a much higher degree of energy is evident. The future progress of Brazil depends much upon the spread of these European peoples over the highland states and the gradual domination of the economic life of the country by them. The immigrants are mainly Italians, Portuguese, and Spaniards; but Germans, Slavs, and other Europeans and some Asiatics (particularly Japanese) are included. An earlier German immigration into the south has given rise to several distinctly German sections where the German language and German customs still prevail. The Italians are most numerous in the State of São Paulo where many are employed on the coffee estates. Although several Brazilian states have assisted immigrants to enter, the arrivals have averaged about 85,000 a year for several years, as compared with 100,000 a year before the World War. European immigrants are slow to enter countries where there are large numbers of colored laborers with whom they must compete. Very low wages and a very low plane of living exist among the laborers of Brazil, and the whole economic life of the nation consequently suffers.

The upper class of Brazilians are refined, accomplished, and socially charming. They travel extensively, send their sons to universities, and maintain brilliant social circles in the chief cities. They are fond of political office, love oratory, and patronize art, and many of them succeed in business undertakings, especially in coffee growing. As a people, however, the Brazilians do not take to business, industrial enterprises, and practical occupations with any such keen relish as do the people of the United States, Canada, Great Britain, or Germany. This is due partly to differences in climate and partly to differences in inherited attitudes of mind. The educated Brazilians lean more toward the fine arts than toward the mechanical arts and more toward genteel leisure than toward engrossment in business. The vast expenditures on the beautifying of the water front of Rio de Janeiro, on the magnificent opera houses of São Paulo and Rio de Janeiro, and on the made-to-order capital city of Bello Horizonte in

[1] Denis, Pierre. "Brazil," pp. 319, 322, 325, New York, 1911.

Minas Geraes are examples of the ways in which Brazilian leaders love to spend public money. At the same time, there are not schools for half the children, and there is little interest in the education of the lower three-fourths of the people. Extravagance and looseness in public expenditures have burdened Brazil with a public debt that has steadily increased in times of peace and has threatened the financial stability of the Republic. Lack of cohesiveness acts as a deterrent to national unity; often, there is more pride in being the citizen of a state than there is in being a citizen of the Republic.

INTERIOR TABLELANDS

Character of the Region.—The southern interior of Brazil is partly a tropical lowland plain but includes also the low plateau of Matto Grosso (Fig. 148). So far as natural vegetation goes, upward of two-thirds of the region is grassland with patches of scrub scattered through it. Less than one-third is forest land. The rainfall is fairly abundant (50 to 60 inches) with a distinct dry season from May to September (Figs. 8 and 9). There is much swampland, and the chief use that is made of the region is for the pasturing of cattle. Cattle ranches of great extent exist; even the average size of *fazendas* (farms or estates) in this region is over 5,000 acres.

The greater part of this southern interior is included in the State of Matto Grosso, which is 5½ times the size of England but has only 375,000 people. This great interior state has no convenient outlet to the sea. The Paraná River southward to Buenos Aires is of some use, but it has many limitations. The poorly maintained single-track railroad to São Paulo serves only a small section in the extreme south. Both these routes are slow, the rates are high, and most of Matto Grosso is not within hundreds of miles of either. The cattle that reach outer markets are driven long distances—hundreds of miles—and many of them are later pastured in the fattening grounds of São Paulo and Minas Geraes.

The greater part of the State of Goyaz (255,000 square miles) also belongs to this region. This state, too, has made little progress in economic development and has only about three-fourths of 1 million people, or less than the single city of São Paulo. In Goyaz, the Brazilian Government has set aside an area for a

Federal District and future capital. At present, this area is part
of a wilderness into which no railroad penetrates (Fig. 151).

Owing to the remoteness of this interior section and to its
tropical climate, population has been slow in entering, and the

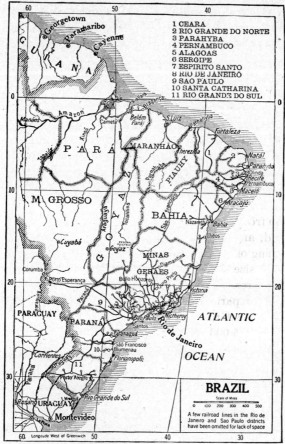

FIG. 151.—Railways of Brazil. The principal railway not shown is the Madeira-
Mamoré, in the western interior. (*Courtesy of W. H. Haas and the Journal of
Geography.*)

density is only one person to the square mile. Agricultural crops,
if raised, cannot be shipped to the distant markets of the east or
south, for the cost is nearly prohibitive. Only 3 per cent of the
farms of Brazil are in this interior region. The manganese deposits

are of potential value but cannot pay the high cost of shipment except at times of great demand, such as the World War. The forests of pine and the included groves of yerba maté are mainly in states that border on the ocean and are treated in the section dealing with southeastern Brazil.

Almost the only product of this remote section that can be raised and marketed at a profit is cattle. They can be driven to market at relatively low cost. They are not high-grade animals, for the better European cattle easily become victims of the fever-carrying tick which abounds in this warm climate. There is reason for believing, however, that Matto Grosso and Goyaz will some day be great cattle-producing states. There are at present many millions of cattle in the area; with increased control of pests and with the development of breeds better adapted to the climate, many more cattle can be raised and the quality much improved.

An American geographer[1] who is especially familiar with Brazil thus writes of this region:

"It is very striking that in this age of mobilization of resources such a large area should be so little known, and even in large part under the control of the Indian, with almost no expanding frontier encroaching. The reason is not a lack of available resources or extremely adverse climatic and physiographic conditions as might be presumed, but it is due, chiefly if not wholly, to the fact that there is no good natural outlet for the products of the region to reach a world market. This fact has kept its resources locked up and this part almost completely isolated from the other more favored sections. The size and latent possibilities of this great undeveloped region have had, therefore, little part in the economic development of Brazil. Its very bigness has been a handicap, and to bring this great region with its rich but undeveloped resources in touch with other sections and with the outside world is the great problem for the country as a whole."

THE SOUTHERN STATES

Physical Features and Agricultural Development of the Region. The Tropic of Capricorn passes through the southern part of the State of São Paulo, close to the city of São Paulo. Hence, only a small corner of this state is in the temperate, or intermediate, zone (Fig. 5). The states of Rio Grande do Sul and Santa Catharina and nearly all of the State of Paraná are in this zone; they

[1] Haas, William H. *Jour. of Geog.*, vol. 24, p. 84, March, 1925.

correspond in latitude to our states of Florida and Georgia. The
plateau of eastern Brazil extends through Paraná, Santa Catharina, and part of Rio Grande do Sul, and its elevation somewhat
reduces their average temperature (Fig. 148). The former two
of these states originally were 80 per cent forest-covered, and the
larger part of their land is still in forests or in recently cut-over
land. The State of Rio Grande do Sul represents a transition between the forest section of the north, with its heavier summer
rainfall, and the grasslands of Uruguay, where the summer rains
are uncertain. A well-drained rolling plateau makes up most of
the region with elevations somewhat less than the highlands
farther north. In general, the region has a healthful climate due to
its elevation and latitude. Summer temperatures are high in the
lowlands, but the plateau areas have cool nights. On the higher
elevations, snow is not infrequent. Throughout the area, there is
notably uniform, ample, but not excessive, precipitation (Figs.
8 and 9). Although the area is attractive for settlement, it is still
sparsely settled and has only recently attracted attention. This
condition is largely due to the fact that early Brazil centered in
Pernambuco and Bahia, and this area was earlier neglected.
However, this southward-protruding tongue of Brazil is a land of
achievement and of promise. Already Rio Grande do Sul is one of
the leading states of the Republic in energy, wealth, manufacturing, and general development. In the middle of the last century,
large numbers of German farmers entered the region and have
prospered. In many communities, German is the language in
common use. In this region are the pine forests and the yerba
groves which give rise to two of the most important forest industries of Brazil. Two of the states are important for corn and
swine. Rio Grande do Sul is the only Brazilian state that makes
a business of wheat raising. It vies with Bahia for first place in
the production of tobacco, is one of the leaders in rice production,
and grows 90 per cent of the grapes. Important also on many
of the farms of the area are beans, cassava (mandioca), and
potatoes. In this single state with its moderate temperatures and
extensive grasslands are found one-fourth of the cattle and three-
fifths of the sheep of Brazil. The population of these three states
is almost entirely of European descent. Rio Grande do Sul has
more people than the Republic of Uruguay and twice as many as
Paraguay. In the states of Rio Grande do Sul and Santa Cath-

arina are the only coal mines operating in Brazil. The extreme southeastern section is second only to the eastern section of Brazil in economic importance.

Rice is a common food among the working people of Brazil. Formerly, a large part of the rice was imported; but an import tax was imposed, and the country now produces about 60 million bushels a year, or about 1 bushel per capita. This is more than enough for the home requirements, and a small surplus is exported. The crop is raised in every state in the Republic, but the regions of most intensive cultivation are the coastal lowlands of the states of São Paulo and especially of Rio Grande do Sul where water for flooding is abundant. A great deal of upland rice is grown, especially in São Paulo and Minas Geraes. These three states produce 75 per cent of the total rice crop of the nation, which is several times as great as its wheat crop. The rice is raised in small fields by crude methods. The yield is usually below 35 bushels an acre, contrasted with about 60 bushels in California. The quantity of rice grown in Brazil is only a fraction of what could be grown; for, in the lowlands of the Amazon system of rivers, there are millions of acres of land suited to rice production. For purposes of comparison, it may be pointed out that Brazil produces almost twice as much rice as the United States, but only one-fortieth as much as India and Burma.

Livestock and Meat Industries.—Up to the present, most of the products of southern Brazil come from animals, particularly cattle. Here is found the most important livestock area of the country, and these states have conditions that indicate an increase in the future development of the livestock industry. Almost one-third of the cattle, about two-thirds of the sheep, and about one-third of the swine of Brazil are found in these three southern states.

Cattle.—Since the three southern states and their neighbors—Minas Geraes, Goyaz, and São Paulo—raise most of the cattle of Brazil the industry as a whole is treated here. In these sections, the heat is moderate, grasslands are abundant and relatively cheap, and railway transportation is good (Fig. 152). In the interior are grasslands where cattle are cheaply raised. As already indicated, cattle raising is the most suitable industry for this remote region. The cattle from the interior are driven long distances, reach the fattening grounds of São Paulo and Minas

Geraes in a lean condition, and are here pastured for 8 to 12 months to bring them into fit condition for slaughter. About 40 million cattle are raised in Brazil. Of these, about 25 per cent are raised in Rio Grande do Sul and 22 per cent in Minas Geraes.

THREE PERIODS OF CATTLE RAISING IN BRAZIL.—In almost any country where grasslands are abundant and population is relatively sparse, cattle and sheep raising are an economic adaptation. During the early colonial days, the Portuguese brought European

FIG. 152.—Distribution of cattle in Brazil. (*Brazil, Ministry of Foreign Affairs.*)

cattle into Brazil. Little attention was paid to improving the breeds, and the animals deteriorated to a lank, bony type. With the development of the tropical plantations worked by great numbers of slaves, the second period of the cattle and meat industry followed. In this period, large numbers of lean cattle were killed, and the meat was dried and salted as *xarque*, or jerked beef. The industry began in southern Brazil as early as 1798. This cheap meat has always found its chief market among the colored laborers of the northeast, and only a small proportion has been exported. During the latter part of this period, which extends down to 1914, an effort was made to improve the native cattle by importing the East Indian humped cow known as the zebu. This animal, accustomed to warm climates, proved adaptable to Brazil; and, at present, a very large proportion of the cattle in the warmer parts of the country have zebu blood. They are not, however, good beef cattle, as judged by European standards, and their meat does not sell well in north European markets.

The marked success of Argentina in improving its cattle by the importation of purebred animals and the subsequent development of the exportation of high-grade beef have initiated similar movements on a smaller scale in Brazil. During the World War, modern slaughtering and meat-packing plants were established in southern and eastern Brazil. This step brought in the third period in the cattle industry, namely, the present period of improved breeds of cattle and refrigerated beef. In this evolution of the beef industry, it is a matter of interest that the present development has been brought about by a group of influences originating wholly outside Brazil: (1) The stimulus to the improvement of the beef cattle came through the demand for good beef in European markets. (2) The improvement of the beef is being achieved by importing cattle that have been brought to high perfection in old and advanced countries. (3) The final step was taken when foreign meat-packing companies that had acquired experience and wealth, mainly in the United States, brought that experience and capital to South America and employed it in developing an export meat industry. This development had been made possible by the perfecting of the refrigeration process and the equipment of refrigerator ships.

PRESENT CONDITIONS OF THE BEEF INDUSTRY.—There is still a large demand for jerked beef in tropical Brazil, and several hundred thousand cattle are annually slaughtered in many plants devoted to the salting and drying of this meat; most of these plants are in Rio Grande do Sul, Minas Geraes, and Matto Grosso. They now prepare upward of 100 million pounds annually, a decline from the high point of 175 million pounds in 1912. Modern slaughtering and meat-packing plants have been established in Brazil, including several large ones in the State of São Paulo, and in Rio Grande do Sul. The majority of the plants belong to the great packing companies of Chicago. Others are British. An impetus was given to this industry by the war demands for meat at high prices; and, in one of the war years, 150 million pounds were exported. After the war, Brazilian exports fell off greatly, but, by 1928, they had risen to the highest figure ever attained by Brazil. In 1937, about 200 million pounds of chilled, frozen, and canned meat were exported.

Cattle raising in a warm country like Brazil has both advantages and disadvantages arising from the climate. The chief

SWINE
One dot = 10,000 pigs

FIG. 153.—Swine raising and corn growing go together in Brazil as they do in the United States. (*Map by Hunnicutt.*)

advantage is the fact that cattle can graze all the year round without shelter. The great disadvantage arises from the numerous insect pests and diseases. The cattle tick, which carries the Texas fever, and the berny fly are among the chief pests. If, in the future, pests can be controlled, breeds improved, and railway transportation provided, Brazil, with her vast grazing area, can supply enormous quantities of beef. Perhaps it is to this huge country that the meat-importing countries must next look to supply their ever-growing needs, when cooler lands like Argentina, Uruguay, the United States, Australia, and New Zealand have reached their limits of exportation, as the United States already seems to have done.

Hog Raising.—Only two countries, China and the United States, raise more hogs than Brazil. Most of the 25 million hogs in Brazil are found in the more temperate eastern and south-eastern states (Fig. 153). Rio Grande do Sul is one of the most important hog-raising states. Here the hogs are fattened on corn or, in these pioneer areas, are able to find food in the forests and wood lots. They are generally of a poor type, thin, and hard to fatten; but they provide a cheap food for the small farmer. Only small quantities of frozen or chilled pork are exported by the large packers, but large amounts of lard are exported.

Sheep Raising.—Brazil is, on the whole, too warm to be an important sheep-raising country. Even little Uruguay has more sheep than Brazil, and more than half of the latter's 13 million are in the coolest state of the Republic, Rio Grande do Sul. The sheep are raised primarily to satisfy the local growing demand for wool, and constant importation of sheep from other areas is necessary to maintain the quality of the fleece due to the high temperatures of the area.

The Forest Industries.—There are at least three distinct forest areas in Brazil: (1) The vast tropical forests of the Amazon basin. (2) A strip of originally heavy forest from 30 to 200 miles wide extending along the rainy eastern coast from Cape São Roque to Rio Grande do Sul, a distance of 1,700 miles; because of nearness to the centers of population, this forest strip has supplied a large part of the lumber, timber, posts, poles, railway ties, etc., cut in Brazil. (3) The pine forests of the southeast.

The Paraná Pine.—The Paraná pine forests cover approximately 100 million acres. Frequently, there are large stands of nearly unmixed pine, with mature trees averaging 80 to 120 feet in height and reaching 4 to 6 feet in diameter. This is the largest and best softwood forest in South America. It is estimated that there are 50 billion board feet within reach of present means of transportation and about 800 billion board feet in reserve. About two-thirds of the lumber output is used in Brazil and the remainder exported. About 40 per cent of all the lumber exported from Brazil is shipped from the single port of Paranaguá, the ocean terminal of a railway that reaches into the Pine Belt. A railway from these forests also reaches the populous state of

São Paulo. Large modern sawmills equipped with machinery from the United States have been built. An enormous tract of land tributary to these mills has been acquired, and the most important lumbering industry in South America is likely to develop here. From 100 to 125 million feet of Paraná pine are exported annually, about nine-tenths of it going to Argentina and the balance to Uruguay.[1]

Yerba Maté.—The forest region where Brazil, Paraguay, and Argentina meet is the native home of the tree that yields yerba[2] maté, or Paraguay tea. Substantially, the entire commercial supply of about 230,000 tons a year comes from southern Brazil, eastern Paraguay, and northeastern Argentina. The Brazilian State of Paraná produces about 65 per cent of the supply. This stimulating beverage, made by pouring boiling water over the dried and pulverized yerba-maté leaves, is the favorite drink of several million people, many of whom

Fig. 154.—Yerba-maté tree in open planting. (*Photograph by Alfred Hasbrouck.*)

regard it as one of the necessary items of their diet. It is believed to possess remarkable qualities. It is said that, without even the slight injury arising from the continued use of tea or coffee, this drink refreshes, nourishes, and stimulates. The tea is usually sucked from a gourd through a special tube called a *bombilla* and is taken as many times daily as is convenient. Laborers drink it in large quantities to supply a vegetable element in their meat diet and would resent the deprivation if the drink were not abundantly supplied by their employers.

The tree grows wild in the forest in the same general habitat as the Paraná pine; it attains a height of 30 to 40 feet (Fig. 154).

[1] See Kircher, Joseph C., Paraná Pine Lumber Industry of Brazil, *Trade Information Bull.* 92, U.S. Dept. of Commerce, April, 1923.

[2] In Brazil, the tea is called *herva matte.*

It does not grow in solid stands or groves but is mixed with other forest trees, often in dense thickets in which it is difficult

Fig. 155.—Drying the leaves of yerba maté. (*Copyright by Ewing Galloway*.)

Fig. 156.—Chute for carrying bags of yerba maté from river banks to boats. (*Photograph by Alfred Hasbrouck*.)

to work. The increasing demand for yerba maté and the substantial profits derived from producing it have led to the planting of groves, some of them covering tens of thousands of acres and numbering millions of trees. One British corporation in Paraguay owns land whose area equals that of the State of New Jersey, only a portion of which, however, is suited to the growing of yerba.

For the artificial *yerbales*, the trees are started in carefully prepared beds and are transplanted in orderly plantations much the same as coffee trees. At 4 years of age, cutting begins, and

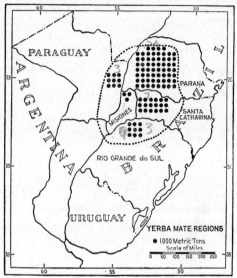

Fig. 157.—Regions of yerba-maté production. The Brazilian state of Paraná is the leading producer.

such are the recuperative powers of the tree that 70 to 80 per cent of the branches may be cut off without injury. In the case of the wild trees, cutting is permitted by law only once in 4 years. After removing the branches (Fig. 155), they are passed over a fire partly to dry the leaves which are later fully dried, packed, and shipped to centers where they are ground and prepared for market (Fig. 156).

The country in which the yerba is produced has few railroads, and much of the product is shipped by the rivers of the Paraná and Paraguay systems (Fig. 157). Small boats collect the bags along the small streams and transport them to points on the main rivers whence the regular river steamers carry them downstream, mainly to Uruguay and Argentina, where most of the exported yerba is consumed. All efforts to create a demand for the beverage in Europe and North America have failed. It would seem, however, that a drink of such merit ought eventually to find extensive use in the Northern Hemisphere.

Southern Brazil is, by far, the chief producer of yerba, but the best quality comes from Paraguay. It is one of the least expensive of drinks, the dried leaves selling in quantities at less than 10 cents a pound. Unlike tea and coffee which are so largely consumed in distant lands, yerba is practically all produced and consumed in the basin of the River Plata and its branches.

Fuel.[1]—Brazil has very limited quantities of low-grade coal in the southeastern states of Rio Grande do Sul and Santa Catharina. Before the World War, Brazil imported nearly all its coal, three-fourths of it from Great Britain. Ocean freights were low, and good British coal sold in the ports of Brazil at $8 a ton or lower in 1913. In 1917, the same quality of coal sold for four times this figure, a price that was virtually prohibitive. Even at this price, sufficient quantities were not obtainable, and government agencies undertook to aid the development of the low-grade mines in the extreme south. Not only is this coal high in ash (20 to 55 per cent) and in volatile matter, but it is remote from the chief markets and expensive to mine and transport. When delivered at Santos or Rio de Janeiro, it costs as much as British coal or even more. By crushing, washing, and making into briquettes, a good quality of fuel is made, but it is expensive. Brazilian authorities are hopeful that a successful process for coking this coal on a commercial scale may be discovered, but such a hope does not seem likely to be realized because of the quality of the coal. Only a few mines are operating. The chief one is in Rio Grande do Sul, which at times yields half of the 400,000 tons of coal mined in Brazil.

Wood is generally used in locomotives in the interior, and increasing quantities of fuel oil are imported. As a rule, coal power is more expensive in Brazil than is hydroelectric power, and the latter is commonly employed in manufacturing. On the railways of Rio Grande do Sul, some twenty American locomotives designed especially to burn native coal are in use more or less successfully.

[1] See The Fuel Problem in Brazil, *U.S. Commerce Reports*, Nov. 23, 1918.

Manufacturing and Cities of the Southern States.—Aside from meat packing, lumber milling, yerba-maté preparation, manufactures of some farm equipment, and making of leather goods and furniture, there has been little industrial activity in these southern states. With increase in population and consequent greater market, industrial activity will increase with a probable dependence, for the most part, on easily developed hydroelectric power rather than coal.

The southern part of Brazil is relatively new and therefore has but few large cities. There are but two south of São Paulo with more than 100,000 inhabitants—Porto Alegre and Curitiba.

Porto Alegre with about 350,000 inhabitants is the capital of Rio Grande do Sul and an important, growing port on the Quahyba River about 10 miles from the northern end of the Lagoa dos Patos. Large ocean steamers cannot reach the port, but it has a lively trade and is becoming one of the most modern and up-to-date cities in Brazil.

Curitiba is the largest center in Paraná having a population of nearly 125,000. It enjoys a pleasant climate, as it is situated at an elevation of 3,000 feet. Commercially, it is important as a center for the yerba-maté trade and to a lesser extent for coffee and Paraná pine.

Smaller cities are of local importance, particularly the ports of Paranaguá, Pelotas, and Rio Grande. The last, at the entrance of Lagoa dos Patos, ranks fifth in importance of the ports of Brazil and is the most southerly port in the Republic available to ocean-going steamers.

Chapter XV. The Heart of Brazil

GEOGRAPHICAL CHARACTER OF EAST CENTRAL BRAZIL

This region, consisting of the two large states of Minas Geraes and São Paulo and the two small coastal states of Rio de Janeiro and Espirito Santo, is the most important section of Brazil.

FIG. 158.—View of Brazilian Highlands north of Rio de Janeiro.

Topographically, it is almost wholly included within the eastern plateau, whose seaward, dissected edge rises steeply from the coastal plain and appears like a mountain range (Fig. 148). The water parting from which the main rivers flow toward the Paraná

346

basin is so near the sea that it is within sight of the Atlantic. After passing this escarpment from the ocean side, the rolling, moun-

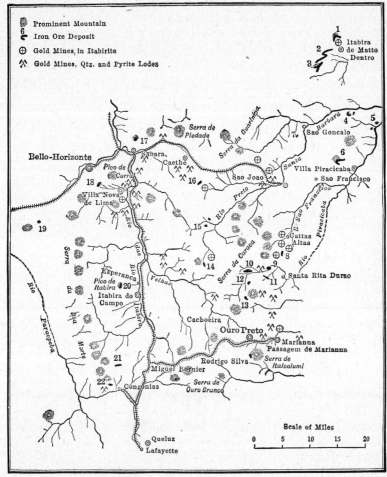

FIG. 159.—Map showing the location of the principal iron-ore deposits and gold mines of Minas Geraes. 1. Caue. 2. Esmeril. 3. Conceicao. 4. Andrade. 5. Monlevade. 6. Morro Agudo. 7. Cocaes. 8. Bananal. 9. Morro da Mina. 10. Alegria. 11. Fabrica Nova. 12. Germano. 13. Timpopeba. 14. Capanema. 15. Mutuca. 16. Gongo Soco. 17. Gaya. 18. Aguas Claras. 19. Jangada. 20. Catta Branca. 21. Fabrica 22. Casa de Pedra. (*After Harder.*)

tain-studded plateau slopes gradually off to the west and merges into the vast plains of the Paraná Lowland. Its relief is similar to that of New England, but the mountain ranges are somewhat higher (Fig. 158). Most of the virgin forest has been cut, but much brushland exists. Only a minor part of the soil is actually under cultivation, except in favored sections such as the Coffee Belt of São Paulo. Extensive, rolling pasture lands, fair country homes, and frequent cities and towns along the railways characterize the region. It is a land of coffee, cotton, fruit, and cattle, of considerable manufacturing, and of large mineral wealth but small mineral production (Fig. 159). The minerals are mainly in the State of Minas Geraes.[1] In these four states, constituting only 11 per cent of the area of the country, live over 40 per cent of the people. The capital and metropolis Rio de Janeiro; the most rapidly growing city São Paulo; the chief coffee port Santos; the best system of railways and highways; and the chief industrial development are found in this region. Rainfall is usually ample for crops, frosts are rare, summers are hot, and winters are particularly delightful. The elevation of 2,000 to 4,000 feet is an important factor in the temperature and the health of the region. A desirable class of European immigrants flows in gradually and helps to swell the white population which here equals and probably exceeds the colored. On account of its economic, political, and educational preeminence, this region is truly the heart of Brazil.

MINERAL RESOURCES

Output of Gold Now Small.—During the colonial period, the Portuguese, like the Spaniards, were mainly interested in obtaining gold and silver. The eighteenth century was a very productive period in Brazil; during this time, $540,000,000 worth of gold was estimated to have been mined, and Villa Rica, now called Ouro Preto, was one of the richest cities in all South America. Both placer and vein deposits are widely distributed in the highlands of Brazil, but very few of these can now be worked at a profit. A large part of the gold comes from two very deep British-owned mines near Bello Horizonte, the capital of Minas Geraes. The mine at St. John del Rey is one of the deepest in the world (over 8,000 feet). At this depth, the mine temperature is well above 100°F., and ventilation is a problem. The second mine, not far

---

[1] Minas Geraes means *general mines*.

away, is not so deep and not so productive. Coal is so expensive that the mining companies have installed hydroelectric plants to supply power for the mines. The great number of mines and of small workings that have been attempted have mostly failed.[1] The recent gold output from Brazil averages $2,000,000 or $3,000,000 a year, or about equal to that of Colombia. In no country of South America is gold mining now important, and the entire continent yields only $12,000,000 a year as compared with ten or twelve times that value from North America.

Past and Present Production of Diamonds.—Diamonds have been produced in Brazil for 200 years, but the present importance of this industry is small, owing in part to the great output from South Africa. For nearly 150 years, however, Brazil was the world's chief source of diamonds; even yet, several thousand persons are engaged intermittently in hunting them. Diamonds are found in many of the states of Brazil, but from river gravels in Minas Geraes and Bahia come most of the stones. Diamantina has been the chief of several producing districts in Minas Geraes. Most of the gem diamonds are of small size, seldom exceeding 7 or 8 carats. Occasionally, large stones are found, valued at hundreds of thousands of dollars. Most of the workings are conducted by natives in a primitive way.

Among the most valuable stones found in Bahia are the carbonados, or black diamonds, which formerly were ignored. The carbonados are used mainly for cutting purposes, especially in rock drills and glass-cutters' tools. The average output is unknown, but it probably falls below $2,000,000 a year, as contrasted with $40,000,000 or $50,000,000 worth of rough diamonds annually exported from South Africa.

Brazil as a Source of Manganese.—Manganese is used in the making of steel. About 14 pounds are employed in making each ton of steel, by either the Bessemer or the open-hearth process. It is, therefore, one of the key metals. The largest known deposits are (1) in the Caucasus mountains in south Russia, (2) in India, and (3) in Brazil. The last-mentioned country has valuable deposits in several places, but the most accessible mines are in Minas Geraes, 300 miles north of Rio de Janeiro and near the active gold workings. During the World War, when supplies from

[1] There has been a recent revival of placer mining, in 1935; it is estimated that at least 50 per cent of the gold was produced from alluvial deposits.

Russia and India were hard to get, the output of manganese from Brazil rose to over $\frac{1}{2}$ million tons a year, valued at $7,000-000. In postwar years, the production has been 200,000 to 300,-000 tons. The largest of the steel companies in the United States is the leading producer of manganese in Brazil. Very large deposits also exist in the interior of the country near the city of Corumbá, at the head of navigation of the Paraguay River. At times, manganese has been the most valuable of the mineral exports of Brazil, although it forms less than 1 per cent of the value of all exports. The metal is not used within the country, for Brazil has practically no steelmaking industry. Brazil normally supplies 3 or 4 per cent of the world's requirements of manganese, and most of this is shipped to the United States.

The Largest Undeveloped Iron-ore Deposits in the World.—In the state of Minas Geraes are iron-ore deposits of fabulous richness and extent. They contain upward of 12 billion tons of the highest grade ore and huge additional quantities of lower grade ore. Most of the ore lies at the surface of the ground and forms actual mountains of hematite. More than 50 outcroppings have been located. Nearly all the ore bodies have passed into foreign ownership, mainly British and American. The most valuable deposits are in the vicinity of Itabira de Matto Dentro, about 300 miles inland from the coast (Fig. 159). No railway actually reaches them, but a line from the port of Victoria is nearly completed.

It is an unfortunate fact that nowhere in all Brazil is there the coking coal necessary for iron-smelting operations; total annual production is less than 1 million tons. A little ore is smelted with charcoal. Electric smelting is expensive, although the mineral region can supply cheap hydroelectric power. It is believed that the only way in which these ores can be utilized is as follows: (1) to build a heavy railway line to the coast; (2) there to construct great ore docks like those at the head of Lake Superior; (3) to create a fleet of specially designed ore-carrying steamships to ply between this port and steelmaking centers on the coast of the United States or of Western Europe where the ores will be smelted; and (4) to carry back to Brazil the necessary coke to smelt the iron needed for eastern South America. If a very large volume of business could thus be built up, there is a possibility that the enormous investment might eventually pay. Only a very wealthy corporation, one that is able to wait years for its profits, could undertake such a costly and uncertain project.

In Brazil, each individual state imposes export taxes upon products that are shipped out of the state. This is one of the chief means of securing revenues. Quite naturally, the Government of Minas Geraes does not wish to see one of its greatest resources shipped away by foreign corporations without some satisfactory returns to the state. It desires to have at least part of the ore smelted within the state and as much steel as possible made there. Also, the Brazilian Government wishes Brazilian coal to be used if there is any process by which this low-grade coal can be utilized. All these conflicting interests will make the mining and utilizing of the Brazilian ores exceptionally difficult, but such rich deposits must eventually come into use.

The Brazilian Government reports that about 130,000 tons of iron and steel are being produced within the country yearly. Most of the pig iron comes from small plants in the State of Minas Geraes. A little progress in steelmaking has been made, but the industry is in its infancy and can exist only because of a high protective tariff.

Monazite Sand.—The peculiarly brilliant light given by the Welsbach gas mantles is due to thorium nitrate in which they are dipped. A leading source of the thorium is the monazite sands formed by the disintegration of certain rocks on and near the coast of central Brazil, which is one of the two chief sources of this substance. Production is now small, and the industry is more interesting than important.

Minerals: Conclusion.—There can be little doubt that the vast area of Brazil contains much undiscovered mineral wealth. It is strange that the value of the mineral output of the country should have actually declined during the past century when the world's demand for minerals has been advancing at a tremendous rate; yet such is the case. The known sources of gold and diamonds seem to have been pretty well worked out. Only small quantities of coal exist, and those are of low grade and are found in the far south; hence, the huge quantities of high-grade iron ore cannot be utilized within the country except as imported coke or coking coal is employed. Electric smelting with hydroelectric power is not practicable on a large scale. If smelting with the use of hydroelectric power should later become feasible, Brazil has a large amount of potential water power. No petroleum of importance has been found, and the oil shales reported to be abundant in Bahia cannot yet be profitably used. Workable deposits of such useful metals as copper, lead, zinc, tin, and nickel have not been discovered, if they exist. Brazil, one of the largest countries in the world, is yielding a smaller value of minerals than some single mines in Peru and Chile yield.

AGRICULTURE

Coffee in the Economic Life of Brazil.—Brazil is in no sense a one-crop country; yet one industry—coffee growing—means more to the international trade of the country than all other branches of agriculture combined. The area of the corn crop, for example, is greater than that of the coffee crop; yet it has far less economic importance (page 372). The explanation lies in the fact that coffee is the great money crop and the one great export crop upon which the nation has come to depend. It is the flow of money into Brazil from the coffee-buying peoples of the world that enables the country to buy the imported things that it must have in order to grow. The earnings of its more than 3 billion coffee trees long enabled Brazil to pay interest on a heavy foreign debt and to buy the foreign-made locomotives, machinery, structural steel, chemicals, and other products needed for its own development.

It is the demands of the enormous coffee crop that have given this region the best railroad system in any part of Brazil (Fig. 151). In the millions of acres of coffee plantations and their equipment lies the largest single source of Brazilian wealth, and the wealthy coffee planters constitute the aristocracy of the nation. No other one of the large countries of the world is so dependent upon a single product as Brazil is upon coffee. Cuba is no less dependent upon sugar, and Chile upon nitrate; but these are countries of small populations. A considerable part of the national interest of Brazil is directly concerned with the preservation, control, and promotion of this dominant industry. The statesmen of Brazil, however, are among the first to recognize that any country so dependent upon the oversea sale of a single commodity is peculiarly vulnerable and sensitive to adverse influence in other parts of the world. Consequently, Brazil is seeking to diversify its agricultural production and to secure the highest possible degree of self-sufficiency.

Evolution of the Coffee Industry.—When the bloodless revolution of 1889 overthrew the Empire of Brazil and instituted the Republic, the country was supplying to the world's trade less than 4 million sacks[1] of coffee yearly (Fig. 160). In the period following, and more especially from 1895 to 1905, an enormous expansion of coffee plantations occurred, and the production about doubled. This precipitated a coffee crisis which was slowly

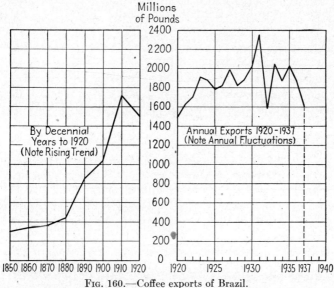

Fig. 160.—Coffee exports of Brazil.

relieved by the valorization methods described in a later paragraph. From 1910 to 1920, there was practically no increase in the quantity of coffee grown in Brazil; but, a little later, new planting was resumed, and an additional 4 million sacks a year, or 12 million in all, were placed on the market. One year (1907), the production reached nearly 18 million bags, or $4\frac{1}{2}$ times that at the beginning of the Republic in 1889. The disastrous frost of June, 1918, did such damage to the trees that for several years the crop varied around 14 million sacks but rose to the unprecedented figure of 28 million sacks in 1928, and a crash in prices followed.

[1] A standard sack of coffee in Brazil weighs 60 kilos, or 132 pounds.

Location of the Chief Coffee Districts.—A century of experimentation has taught coffee planters that a small portion of Brazil is ideally suited to large-scale coffee growing. About 70 per cent of the crop is grown in portions of two states—the northern part of São Paulo and the southern part of Minas Geraes (Fig. 161). Here, on a total area not exceeding one-quarter of Indiana, is grown nearly two-thirds of the world's coffee. The region of most concentrated production is 250 miles

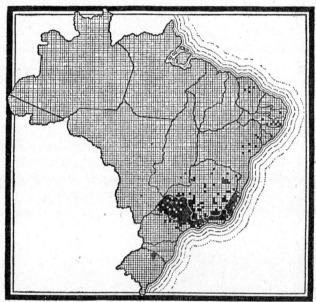

Fig. 161.—Principal coffee-producing areas of Brazil. (*Brazil, Ministry of Foreign Affairs.*)

northwest of the port of Santos, through which the greater part of the coffee is shipped. Contrary to the usual belief, little coffee is grown close to the city of São Paulo, but the coffee-carrying railroads converge upon this city and feed a steady stream of coffee to the single British-owned railroad which takes it to Santos and thereby is made the busiest and most profitable railroad in South America. The São Paulo portion of the Coffee Belt produces 40 to 50 per cent of the Brazilian crop; 25 to 30 per cent comes from Minas Geraes, and 10 per cent from the State of Rio de Janeiro. A more recent development of coffee plantations is in progress in the northern part of the State of

Paraná. The success of coffee growing in this restricted area, a success that has completely eclipsed all other coffee regions, suggests that here are combined an unusual number of natural advantages for the production of this particular crop. These advantages are: (1) the peculiar character of the soil; (2) the tropical but not excessively hot temperature; (3) the rolling and well-drained land; (4) the ample but not heavy rainfall, with a dry season for picking and curing the coffee; (5) nearness to exporting ports; and (6) a more recently acquired advantage, inexpensive electric power for operating machinery on the *fazendas*.

The Ideal Climate, Soil, and Surface.[1]—At an earlier period, the center of the Coffee Belt of Brazil was immediately inland from Rio de Janeiro, in a region slightly more tropical than the present center in northern São Paulo. Gradually, the coffee planters found that the hilly country lying further inland and at somewhat higher elevations is better suited to the crop than the region nearer Rio de Janeiro. In this São Paulo district, the rainfall averages between 45 and 60 inches a year, but there is a dry season in the winter (June, July, August) when the precipitation is only about 1 inch each month, as contrasted with 8 or 10 inches a month during December, January, and February (Figs. 8 and 9). Thus there is provided a hot and wet growing season and a cooler and drier harvest season. The traveler in the São Paulo coffee district notes that the coffee trees are mostly on the broad tops and slopes of the hills, the bottom lands being commonly devoted to other crops or to pasturage (Fig. 162). Experience has shown the planter the wisdom of this practice. For, on occasional cool nights, the air falls below the frost temperature; thus becoming slightly heavier, it flows down the slopes and gathers in the valleys, where freezing may occur. On rare occasions, freezing temperatures occur even on the higher ground, and serious damage is done. The most successful coffee lands of Brazil are those on the outer edge of the tropics between latitudes 21 and 23½°S.

The best soil for coffee is the dark-red loam derived mainly from the decay of intrusive (igneous) rocks, which, in great

[1] See Ward, R. DeC., The Economic Climatology of the Coffee District of São Paulo, Brazil, *Bull. Am. Geog. Soc.*, Vol. 43, pp. 428–455, June, 1910; also, by the same author, A Visit to the Brazilian Coffee Country, *Nat. Geog. Mag.*, Vol. 22, p. 908, October, 1911.

FIG. 162.—Scene in the coffee region of São Paulo. (*Photograph by Gaersly.*)

masses, penetrate the red shales and sandstones of the interior of São Paulo. Red soils are common in Brazil, but the particular *terra roxa* is rich in iron and potash, which are peculiarly in demand by the coffee trees. Coffee is raised on other soils in Brazil, but nowhere else so successfully as on the *terra roxa*.

Equipment and Activities of a Great Coffee Fazenda.—One of the largest of coffee *fazendas*[1] lies in the northern part of the State of São Paulo, the most intensive of the coffee-growing districts. The activities of this *fazenda* of over 30,000 acres, with five million trees, reveal the magnitude that the largest of these enterprises have attained. Twenty miles of private railway traverse the plantation and connect it with the main railroad. From 7 to 10 million pounds of coffee are marketed yearly. Coffee growing is the principal activity of the *fazenda*, but not the only important one, for there are kept 2,500 to 3,000 cattle; several hundred acres of cotton are grown, and over 5,000 people employed on the place are housed and fed. In its high degree of self-sufficiency, the great *fazenda* resembles the English manor of the fourteenth century. A large part of the necessary food is produced on the place. The owners operate an almost completely integrated economic unit. Corn is ground in their own mill, bakery products are made in their own ovens, and meat is slaughtered and sold by their own butcher shop. A general store sells the needed supplies, schools are maintained for the children, a church holds services, and moving pictures are provided. Lumber is cut in their own sawmill from trees grown on the estate, and this lumber is made into their own wagons, cars, and implements. In their harness shop are made the harness and saddlery needed on the plantation; and they have their own shoemakers and tailors. Their own foundry and machine shop casts and tools even the complex parts of their machinery. Almost everything required can be produced, made, or repaired within the *fazenda*. Of course, it is the large establishment only that attains this degree of self-sufficiency.

Method of Growing Coffee.—The best coffee land is that from which forests have just been cleared. The small coffee trees are started in the nurseries; when about 1 foot high, they are transplanted to their permanent places in rows some 10 or 12 feet

---

[1] The famous Dumont *fazenda*, now owned by a British company. *Fazenda* has various meanings but commonly applies to a landed estate of considerable size.

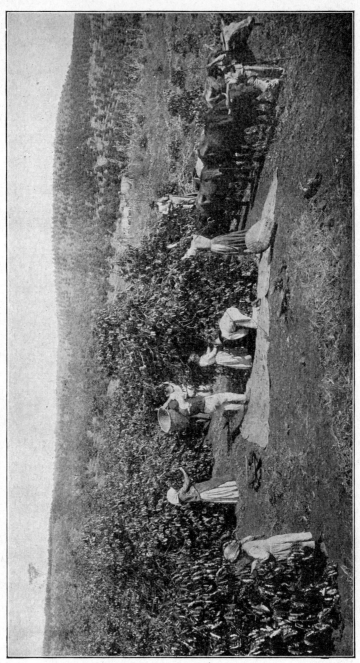

FIG. 163:—Picking coffee in São Paulo. (*Photograph by Gaensly.*)

apart each way. The tree takes on a bushy growth, within 5 or 6 years is bearing coffee berries, and continues to do so for 30 or 40 years longer. Its productivity declines in its later years, and a point is reached at which it is economy to replant or discontinue growing coffee on a particular ground; for, like other crops, coffee exhausts the land upon which it grows. One element of superiority of the red soil of this region is its ability to maintain a vigorous production of coffee for a long period of years.

Cultivation of the coffee land must go on steadily to keep down weeds and keep the soil loose. This is almost invariably done on the large plantations by "colonists," who with their families— and the larger the better—live in villages on the plantations and contract to care for a definite number of trees. An adult can care for 2,000 to 3,000. A family with a number of children may care for 8,000 or more. Some kind of fertilization is desirable, and imported chemical fertilizers are used to a limited extent if the price of coffee justifies the outlay.

Harvesting and Preparing for Market.—About the first of May, the trees are loaded with red berries the size of cranberries, and picking begins (Fig. 163). The berries are stripped from the branches and fall upon cloth spread under the trees or upon the ground to be raked up later. Occasionally, broad, shallow baskets are used to catch the berries as they are stripped from the branches. Wagons or cars haul the berries to the washing tanks and canals where a sorting out of the inferior berries is accomplished, and pebbles, leaves, and twigs, etc., are removed. Running water carries the washed berries to the mill where the fleshy pulp is removed; then the seeds move on to the drying floors. These are extensive brick- , tile- , or cement-floored areas upon which the coffee seeds, still enclosed in a thin husk, are spread for 12 to 25 days to dry in the sun. Later, the coffee is raked into heaps to cure for several days more. During this drying and curing process, the coffee is injured if it is wet by rain. After this process, the dry coffee goes to another mill which removes the remaining coatings, screens the coffee, and delivers it sorted into several types into jute bags holding 132 pounds. On the large *fazendas*, all this is done on the place (Fig. 164); but much coffee is grown by small planters who take their coffee to central plants that do the work for them (Fig. 165).

Fig. 164.— Buildings of the coffee *fazenda* Nova Louzã, São Paulo, Brazil. (*Photograph by Gaensly.*)

Handling Coffee at the Port of Santos.—Each year through the port of Santos pass 7 to 10 million bags of coffee. Under the restrictive control of shipments in force for several years, 35,000 bags a day were allowed to be shipped from the interior to Santos, and 12,000 to Rio de Janeiro. At Santos are scores of warehouses used by the coffee dealers for storing, inspecting, and mixing the coffee which is afterward carted to the great shipping warehouses that line the water front. By means of modern belt-conveyer and

FIG. 165.—*Fazenda* Chapadoa, near Campinas.

chute systems, the bags are delivered into the holds of many ships at once, rapidly and cheaply. The Santos docks are models of efficiency (Fig. 166).

At the port are located the offices of the coffee brokers, shippers, and buyers, by whom the coffee is graded into nine types according to quality, tasted by expert tasters, and classified according to flavor. Most of the coffee passes through the hands of some one of 40 or 50 established firms by whom it is shipped. The largest of these handle as high as 500,000 to 800,000 bags a year. They usually advance money to coffee growers, an important service in a country lacking in liquid capital. Santos is a city of practically a single industry. Nowhere else is a great port so fully devoted to the handling of a single commodity as is the case in Santos, second port of Brazil, but first in value of exports.

Fig. 166.—Loading coffee, Santos.

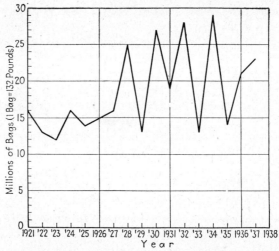

Fig. 167.—Coffee production in Brazil fluctuates widely from year to year due to both economic and climatic conditions.

Efforts to Control Prices.—The geographical conditions under which coffee is grown in Brazil are so favorable and profits at times have been so large that overproduction has occurred, and the consequent fall in prices endangered the whole industry (Fig. 167). In 1902, a law forbidding further planting of coffee trees for a period of years was enacted, but this could not bring immediate relief to the planters. About 1905, the prices were so low and discontent among the coffee growers was so clamorous that the government found itself forced to go to their aid. After much discussion and prolonged efforts, a foreign loan was secured; with the proceeds, millions of bags of coffee were purchased, stored in the United States and Europe, and later placed upon the market somewhat slowly. Thus the price was pushed upward, and, in the course of 2 or 3 years, the various restrictive measures that were adopted brought demand and supply into accord; the stored coffee was disposed of, the loan was paid back, and a profit was realized by the government. The first valorization plan had been successful, and the coffee industry was rescued for the time being.

Again in 1917, the State of São Paulo felt it necessary to attempt a valorization scheme. It bought up and stored great quantities of coffee for the purpose of maintaining prices and also of getting into the hands of the planters the much-needed money for their crop. The severe frost of the following year so curtailed the coffee crop that the stored coffee sold at a good profit, and again the industry was rescued. The third attempt in 1921, involving the purchase and storing by the government of $4\frac{1}{2}$ million sacks, proved successful. Thus have three valorization efforts succeeded; but there is well-grounded opposition to frequent repetitions of government financing of the coffee crop, and other methods of stabilizing prices are being worked out. The plan employed in the year 1924 and immediately following involved the construction by the São Paulo State Government of nine large storehouses in the interior of the state. These are capable of storing at one time about half the usual crop. By law, all coffee of the state had to be shipped to these public warehouses, where it was stored and warehouse receipts were issued to the owners of the coffee. These receipts could be sold or used as security for loans, and thus the planter could secure money promptly without a seasonal flooding of the market with coffee and the attendant depression of prices. By an arrangement with the railroads, the coffee from the public warehouses could be shipped to Santos only at the rate of a certain number of sacks a day. Thus it was hoped to maintain prices and protect the industry. Clearly, it was an artificial process. In that it tended to raise prices, it has encouraged the extension of coffee planting not only in Brazil but also in other coffee-growing countries, and an oversupply of coffee was sure to follow. The crop of 28 million sacks that was produced in 1928 brought the scheme to ruin. In São Paulo, an organization known as the "Institute for the Permanent Defense of Coffee" was set up that makes loans to planters and plans for the purchase and retention of coffee. It regulates deliveries, collects taxes, and directs propaganda for increased consumption of coffee. The government has, in recent years, taken further precautionary measures for the defense of coffee by methodically eliminating excess of crops. Up to the end of 1938, over 60 million bags of coffee were destroyed, largely by burning.

Coffee Exports.—Coffee formed more than half the value of the exports of Brazil until recent years. In 1929, it accounted for 69 per cent in value of Brazil's exports but only 45 per cent in 1938. This was due to the decline in price of coffee and the rise of other items (notably cotton and oranges), not to the falling off in the quantity of coffee. There is considerable annual variation in the amount of coffee exported, but it fluctuates around 15 million bags (Fig. 160). About 60 per cent is shipped from Santos, and about one-half the balance from Rio de Janeiro.

The National Government of Brazil is not allowed by the constitution to collect export taxes, a privilege reserved for the individual states. The greater part of the revenues of the important state of São Paulo comes from the export tax on coffee, amounting to about 6 per cent of its value. So great are the volume and value of the coffee trade that complete facilities for grading, blending, storing, transporting, selling, loading, shipping, insuring, and financing have been perfected, and the major part of these facilities centers in the port of Santos.

The greater part of the coffee is shipped in line steamers to North America and Europe. It is a common practice for these liners to take such cargo as is obtainable at Buenos Aires and complete their cargoes at Santos or Rio de Janeiro by taking as much coffee as they can carry or obtain. The United States takes more of the Brazilian coffee than all the rest of the world. As a rule, the greater part of this enters the port of New York; New Orleans is second. In all the principal coffee-importing countries, one port, or, at the most, two ports receive most of the coffee.

In France, it is Havre; in England, London; in Germany, Bremen; in Italy, Genoa; and in Holland, Amsterdam and Rotterdam. This specialization of certain ports and of a certain section of the port in special products is common throughout the commercial world. It makes for efficiency of handling and centralizes in a convenient way the shipping, importing, and financing companies devoted to that particular product.

Summary of Coffee in Brazil.—The native home of the coffee plant was in the Old World, but it was brought to America where it so prospered that about 90 per cent of the total production now comes from America and 60 to 70 per cent from the single country of Brazil. Java, Arabia, Ceylon, and other coffee-growing regions of the East have declined to relative insignificance in this industry. Why has Brazil, of all possible countries, become so preeminently the country of coffee? In this, and in all similar cases, the answer is essentially the same. It must be the same when the complete adjustment of a crop to all the factors involved in its production and marketing is attained. Brazil supplies the greater part of the world's coffee because it is able to produce and deliver an acceptable article in sufficient quantity more cheaply than any other country. In general, the great products of world trade are produced where they are because of geographical and other advantages that the particular regions possess—advantages that enable them to produce and market the product more cheaply than their competitors. In Brazil, there is a large area of ancient rock whose decay yields a particular soil that proves to be ideally suited to coffee. Furthermore, this region of ideal soil lies just where the tropical and subtropical belts meet, giving a climate neither too hot nor too cool. It lies in a hilly upland some 2,500 feet above the sea, and the planter may select just the altitude that gives him relative freedom from frosts and yet avoids the scalding heat of the tropics, which is unfavorable to coffee. Moreover, the rolling topography ensures good drainage, but the slopes are not so steep that soil wash is a menace. Added to these favoring features is a type of rainfall that gives ample water for the crop, and yet also a relatively dry season of several months for harvesting the crop. This regimen is found on the southern side of the tropical zone in Brazil. Coffee does not thrive in the heart of the tropics except at high altitudes, and there the marketing becomes expensive (Fig. 168). Finally, the Brazilian

Coffee Belt is near the sea. Because of this unusual combination of favoring geographical conditions, Brazil has outdistanced all competitors in coffee growing and dominates the world market in one of the great commercial products.

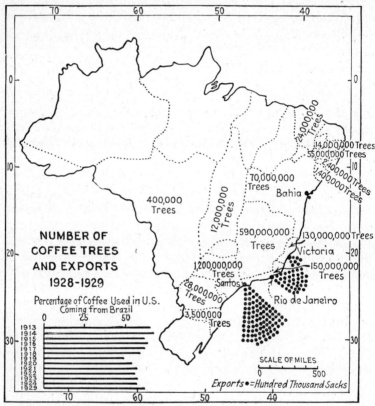

Fig. 168.—Coffee trees by states. Nearly all of the coffee is exported from two ports—Santos and Rio de Janeiro. Although some change in the production of certain areas has occurred since 1928–1929, the relative importance of the various districts is much the same at present as it was a decade ago.

But these favorable factors easily lead to overproduction. To prevent this or avoid its economic consequences, the country resorted to artificial expedients of valorization or control. Brazil's experience is an excellent illustration of the interaction of geographical, economic, and political forces. One group, the geographical, arises out of the natural conditions; a second, the economic, grows out of the cheapness of production and the consequent tendency for supply to exceed demand; and the third, the political, is the effort of government to maintain prices that the two other sets of forces are tending to depress. Seldom can man by thus invoking political or other artificial expedients set at naught for very long the operation of fundamental economic influences. A purely artificial bolstering up of prices cannot permanently succeed.

Cotton.—Although coffee is still the dominant product for Brazilian export, cotton in Brazil has made the headlines in numerous publications in recent years. From a production of slightly over 450,000 bales in 1928, raw cotton rose to approximately 2 million bales in 1937. From exports of 80,000 bales in 1929, it exceeded 1 million bales in 1938, thus becoming Brazil's most important export after coffee. Cotton is almost 19 per cent in value of the Republic's exports and in the last 4 years (to 1938) has averaged about 20 per cent in quantity of the cotton export from the United States. Brazil now ranks fourth in acreage given over to cotton and fifth or sixth in production.

Favorable and Unfavorable Factors.—From the State of São Paulo northward for nearly 1,000 miles, eastern Brazil has large sections whose climate and soil are well suited to cotton. The total area of such land is said to equal that in the United States. The International Cotton Commission (British) which made a detailed study of eight eastern states in 1921 and 1923 reached the conclusion that Brazil has superior natural advantages for the raising of cotton. The soil, over large areas, resulting from the decay of the ancient rocks of this region, is exceedingly rich in the plant foods required by the cotton plant, and the yield of fiber in some sections is large. In the United States, a good yield is a half bale to the acre; in parts of eastern Brazil, a bale (500 pounds) of lint cotton to the acre is not unusual, and the commission found lands producing 800 pounds per acre. Land is cheaper in Brazil than in the United States, and the cost of producing cotton is lower, probably not over one-half so much. But the labor is less intelligent, and the methods of picking are careless. In the southern zone, especially in the State of São Paulo, the ordinary American upland cotton, with a staple (fiber) about 1 inch in length, yields nearly twice as much as in the United States (Fig. 169). In the north, a perennial cotton tree produces long-staple cotton for 5 to 15 years without replanting. The British commission says:

"When one compares the yields of these two zones with those of any other cotton-growing country of the world, one cannot come to any other conclusion but that, in view of the general shortage of cotton in the world under normal conditions, cotton is bound to assert itself there."

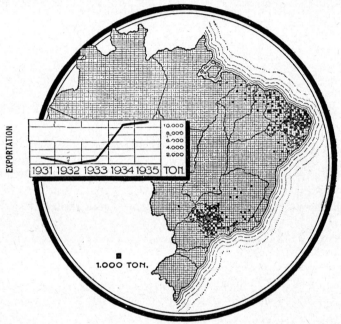

Fig. 169.—Cotton-producing zones in Brazil. (*Brazil, Ministry of Foreign Affairs.*)

Why, then, has cotton production been erratic and, until very recently, relatively small in Brazil? The answer lies partly in the competition of two other crops—sugar in the north and coffee in the south—and partly in the unscientific methods of production. Coffee and sugar have proved, on the whole, more profitable than cotton under the conditions that have prevailed in Brazil. So superior are the geographical advantages for growing coffee in São Paulo and adjacent states that other parts of the world have not been able to produce it so cheaply. As a result of this favored situation, the planters of one part of Brazil have gradually concentrated their efforts on coffee, have developed skill in

growing, picking, and marketing coffee, and have built up the
facilities for transporting, grading, storing, financing, and exporting coffee—in short, have become specialists in coffee. In
the same way, the planters of the southern part of the United
States have perfected facilities for growing, grading, storing, and
marketing cotton. It is usually true that specialization on a
certain product in a given region tends more and more to absorb
the interests and energies of the people to the exclusion of other
products. The industry grows by its own momentum.

Fig. 170.—Cultivating cotton fields in São Paulo. (*Photograph by F. Heyer.*)

In a similar but less intensified way, sugar has been the preferred crop of a part of northeastern Brazil. Moreover, the
Government of Brazil has done little, until recently, in the way
of investigation and encouragement of cotton growing. Now that
cotton spinning and weaving have become the leading manufacturing industries in Brazil, interest in cotton growing is
increasing. Investigations are in progress, and more careful selec-
tion of seed and better methods of growing and marketing are
developing. When cotton prices are high, cotton acreage rises;
when prices fall, the acreage drops. Cotton growing has thus
been treated as a side issue and not as a permanent year-in-and-
out industry.

The recent impetus in the cotton growing in Brazil comes largely from the increased prices due in most part to governmental restriction on cotton production in the United States

FIG. 171.—Cotton field in São Paulo. Cotton produces heavily in Brazil if intelligently cultivated. (*Photograph by F. Heyer.*)

(page 372). Most of the expansion in cotton acreage has taken place in São Paulo and neighboring areas (Fig. 169). Here, American upland cotton is raised which produces a shorter fiber

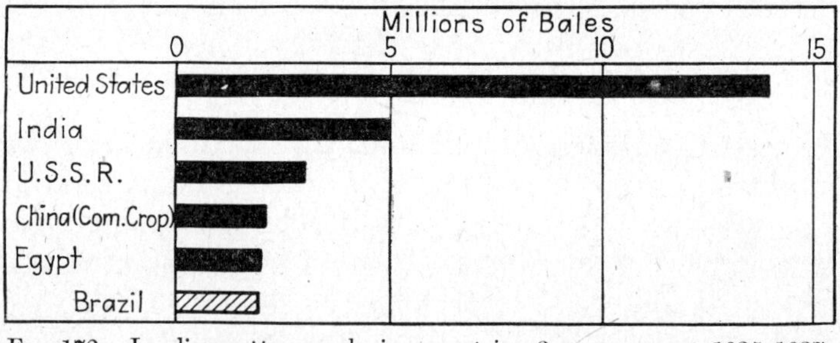

FIG. 172.—Leading cotton-producing countries, 3-year average, 1935–1937.

than does that of the northeastern part of Brazil, but under much better conditions of labor and management. Methods that have developed in the cotton-growing region of the United States have been copied, often under the direction of experts from the latter country (Fig. 170).

"Cotton from São Paulo, where the major part of the crop is grown, is of an excellent quality, maintained by the state's own Agronomical Institute, which controls the sale and supervises the growing of all seed (Fig. 171). Yield per acre is rising but has not yet reached the United States average, chiefly because Brazil cannot afford fertilizer."[1]

The expansion seems to have reached a temporary plateau in production, but this status will probably not be permanent (Fig. 172).

Future Prospects of Cotton.—When the world's demand for cotton is again normal, there is likely to be a shortage in cheap cotton. The United States, having to fight the ravages of the boll weevil, with greater labor costs, and with restricted production, may find in Brazil an important competitor. Brazil is the logical place to which the cotton mills of Europe may turn for increasing supplies of cotton. In the last few years, large amounts have been exported to Germany, Japan, and Great Britain. Whether or not the people and the Government of Brazil pursue the apparent opportunity remains to be seen. They have shown marked ability in growing coffee and in handling difficult problems that have arisen in connection with controlling coffee exports and prices. If Brazil devoted a part of its energies to cotton with the same intelligence that it has shown in respect to the coffee industry, the country will become one of the great cotton producers of the world.

Exportation and Domestic Manufacture.—Europe was able to get comparatively little cotton from the United States during its Civil War. The price soared to an unheard-of height, and cotton production in Brazil and elsewhere was greatly stimulated. During this period, Brazil in 1 year exported 355,000 bales; but, with the postwar fall of prices, planters went back to sugar and coffee, and Brazilian cotton exports declined to unimportance. The good prices of 1923 and 1924 and the demand created by the increasing textile industry of the country stimulated cotton planting; exports exceeded 150,000 bales a year,[2] and consumption in the mills of the country at the same time was several times as much. With some 40 million of its own people to clothe, Brazil,

[1] *Fortune Magazine*, Brazil, June, 1939.
[2] The United States normally exports around 8 million bales.

for some time to come, will use at home the greater part of its cotton.

The making of cotton goods is the foremost manufacturing industry of Brazil; it is chiefly centered in São Paulo and Rio de Janeiro. The industry trebled between 1905 and 1917 and is steadily growing. Modern machinery is in use, dyeing and printing are developed, and nearly all the common fabrics are made. Only the finer goods are imported. Between 300 and 400 cotton mills, employing upward of 125,000 workers, are in operation. The Italians of São Paulo, many of whom were cotton-mill operatives in northern Italy, are the leaders in this industry. Like all manufactures in Brazil, cotton goods are protected by a high import tariff. On the other hand, every yard of goods is taxed. Cotton manufacturing is, however, a very profitable industry, and manufacturers are becoming wealthy. Should markets be expanded to take care of a greater output, power could be easily obtained, for Brazil has 36 million potential horsepower based on ordinary minimum flow with only 1 million horsepower developed.

Food Crops.—In quantity annually raised, corn leads all other food crops by a wide margin, as the following table of approximate acreage indicates. About 75 per cent of the corn is grown in three states, Minas Geraes, São Paulo, and Rio Grande do Sul, the great food-producing states of the Republic.

Crop	Acres	Crop	Acres
Coffee...............	8,500,000	Cotton..............	6,000,000
Corn................	10,000,000	Sugar..............	1,250,000
Beans...............	2,250,000	Mandioca..........	875,000
Rice................	2,250,000	Wheat.............	375,000
		Tobacco............	250,000

Corn combines with rice, beans, and mandioca to form the food of the common people. It is also the chief feed for swine, and most of the 16 to 18 million swine in Brazil are raised in the Corn Belt of that country. Although Brazil ranks next to the United States as a corn-producing country, it raises only about one-twelfth as much. Mandioca[1] is a native of Brazil; it grows

[1] Also called manioc and cassava.

vigorously in poor soil, yields very heavily with little labor, may
be prepared for eating in a variety of ways, and is one of the
greatest of all starch producers (Fig. 173). Only the fleshy roots,
larger than potatoes, are used for food. One of the important
products is manioc flour, used much as wheat flour is. Owing to
the large quantity that 1 acre produces and the small amount of
labor required to raise the crop, it fits ideally into the agriculture

Fig. 173.—Mandioca, the most important starch food raised in Brazil. Tapioca
is one of the products made from mandioca. (*Map by Hunnicutt.*)

of a country where hard work is avoided. The tapioca of commerce is made from mandioca starch. Of corn and mandioca, as
of many other crops, the vast area of Brazil is capable of producing almost unlimited quantities.

Beans form one of the important foods in Brazil, and their
per capita consumption is very high. The ordinary cereals,
wheat, barley, rye, and oats, are raised but little in Brazil,
mainly because they are primarily the products of a cooler climate and do not yield well except in the far south. Nearly all the
wheat grown in Brazil is raised in Rio Grande do Sul, the most
southerly state.

OTHER ECONOMIC ACTIVITIES OF THE
EAST CENTRAL REGION

The predominance of this part of Brazil in wealth, manufacturing, means of transportation, and general progressiveness has already been noted and is further developed in a later chapter. It contains the three most populous and important cities of the country—Rio de Janeiro, São Paulo, and Santos. The economic leadership of the State of São Paulo is outstanding, and the rapid growth of the city of São Paulo leads many to believe that .it will soon be the largest city of the Republic. Unfortunately, there is a lack of strong cohesion among the states of Brazil. This is evidenced in a number of revolutions that have broken out in several states. They were crushed out by federal troops, but this spirit of revolution, which has appeared in the southern states and in São Paulo, is disquieting. These are leading states of the nation, and their loyal adherence to the federal government is essential to the maintenance of the nation.

Chapter XVI. Brazil: The Tropical Northeast and the Amazon Valley

THE NORTHEAST

General Characteristics of the Region.—Nine states are included in this section of Brazil (Fig. 149). Bahia and Pernambuco are the most important. Most of the others are small, and much of their area is coastal lowland. Both Bahia and Pernambuco, however, have large areas that belong to the eastern plateau and hence are somewhat elevated. Each of the nine states has one or more ports from which short railroads lead inland, and the only cities of importance are on the coast. Two of these cities, Bahia and Pernambuco, rank, respectively, third and fourth among Brazilian ports.

A portion of the Northeast has the lightest rainfall in all Brazil, a fact that is reflected in the large number of goats in the livestock population (Figs. 8 and 9). Two-thirds of the 6 million goats of Brazil are found in four of these states. The goat is able to thrive in dry, hot lands better than sheep and cattle. The light rainfall is also reflected in the relatively small proportion of forest land. Less than half of the region originally carried forests, and much of that has been cleared.

The six small states clustered at the "nose" of Brazil all together have about half the area of Bahia, but they are thickly populated, averaging over 50 persons to the square mile (Fig. 1). A majority of the people are Negroes or have Negro blood. Tropical agriculture is the dominant industry and, as a rule, is crudely and inefficiently carried on. The yields of cacao, sugar, and tobacco are relatively low, and the average quality of the products themselves is not high. The large state of Bahia produces the greater part of the cacao that is grown in Brazil and

375

usually leads all of the states in the production of tobacco. Pernambuco and Alagôas are among the leading sugar producers. This region also raises much of the cotton of Brazil, including a species of tree cotton already mentioned.

The general economic condition of this region may be judged from the fact that although it has 35 per cent of the people of Brazil, it supplies less than 20 per cent of the exports and takes only 10 per cent of the imports. In other words, its participation in the foreign trade of the country is less than half as much per capita as the average of Brazil as a whole. By way of comparison, it may be stated that the 12½ million people of Argentina send abroad an average of more than ten times as much as the 15 million of northeastern Brazil. It is clear that this part of Brazil, like many other parts, is yielding only a small fraction of its capabilities. The region furnishes an example of a tropical people living the easygoing life that their climate permits.

Irrigation in Northeastern Brazil.—In four of the northeastern states, the rainfall is exceedingly erratic.[1] During some years, there is a succession of terrific downpours followed by violent floods (Figs. 8 and 9). In other years, disastrous droughts occur, crops fail, animals die of starvation, and thousands of people are compelled to leave the drought-stricken land and seek a livelihood elsewhere. The great drought of 1877 to 1880 continued 2½ years. Twenty-nine of these droughts were recorded during two centuries. Irrigation of an inexpensive kind has long been attempted, but with indifferent success. In 1919, a very costly series of irrigation projects was authorized by the government. Eleven large dams costing millions of dollars each and many smaller ones were planned, and work was begun. Many of these are not being completed because of great cost and the deficiency of funds. The work that will be completed may or may not materially relieve the situation. With the vast area of unused agricultural land in Brazil, there seems to be little defense for the expenditure of tens of millions of dollars on uncertain irrigation projects.

Agricultural Production of the Northeast.—The northeast province was the most important area in the early agricultural development of Brazil. Although agriculture is still the chief

[1] See Jefferson, Mark, New Rainfall Maps of Brazil, *Geog. Rev.*, Vol. 14, pp. 127–135, January, 1924.

source of livelihood in this region, the section has lost first place in the agricultural production of the country.

Brazil a Leading Producer of Cacao Beans.—A phenomenal increase in the production of cacao beans has taken place in the British colony of the Gold Coast on the shore of the Gulf of Guinea in Africa. Ecuador, once the leading producer, has fallen to a relatively minor position because of the rapid increase in production in the Gold Coast. The average annual export of cacao beans from Brazil, now holding second rank in cacao production, is upward of 250 million pounds a year, over 90 per cent of which comes from the State of Bahia. The Cacao Belt, lying not far from the sea, is 360 miles long by 90 miles wide and contains approximately 70 million trees. Along the southern coast of Bahia are 10 or 12 small ports, and, in the immediate hinterland of these ports and of the larger port of Bahia, most of the cacao of Brazil is grown. It is shipped in small coasting vessels from these ports to Bahia, where the beans are graded, resacked, and exported (Fig. 174). Of the cacao thus shipped, about 50 per cent is grown near the single port of Ilhéos, which is connected by a railway with feeders extending back into a region especially adapted to cacao growing.

As a rule, the new cacao groves are planted on recently cleared forest land and are cared for by natives who do the work in a desultory fashion. They prefer this sort of independent occupation to working for wages; hence, small cacao plantations are the rule. The product is only fair in quality, and the beans usually command a low or medium price as compared with the sweeter cacao of Venezuela, for example. The native planters have little capital and must be financed by local merchants or brokers who charge well for the service. There are a number of pests that attack the tree or the fruit; the worst is an ant called the *quem-quem* which kills the young trees in the badly infested regions.

Ordinarily, the United States takes more than one-half the cacao exported from Brazil and pays an average price of 10 cents a pound in New York. Of this, the native cacao grower gets little more than half. An acre of well-cared-for trees yields in Bahia 300 to 400 pounds of cacao beans, which at 5 cents a pound gives the planter $15 or $20 an acre after the trees begin to bear at 5 or 6 years of age. This is a lower return than coffee, sugar, or cotton yields; but less labor and capital are required, and this fact

suits the industry to the unambitious natives who are quite
satisfied with a living.

FIG. 174.—Cacao-producing areas of Brazil. (*Brazil, Ministry of Foreign Affairs.*)

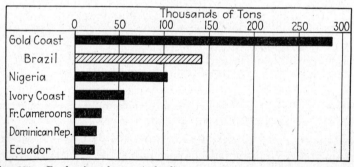

FIG. 175.—Production of cacao in leading countries, 3-year average, 1935–1937.

The annual value of the cacao exported from Brazil fluctuates
widely because of the rise and fall of prices, but a fair average
of recent years is $18,000,000, which is 6 or 7 per cent of that of
coffee (Fig. 175). Bahia is more favorably located for growing and

marketing cacao than is the Gold Coast of Africa and could easily produce as large a crop; but the lax methods employed, the general backwardness of the region, and the absence of constructive help from government sources have permitted even the Guinea Coast of Africa to make greater progress in this industry than Brazil or any other region in America. The Cacao Institute of Brazil was created in 1931 and was later converted into a cooperative society. The production has greatly increased in the last few years.

Sugar Production.—Six outstanding facts about sugar production in Brazil are:

1. The almost limitless *potential* production of the country. Lands in Brazil that are suited to sugar growing total hundreds of millions of acres.

2. The small annual production (800,000 metric tons) contrasted with the possible yield of Brazil or with Cuba's 4 or 5 million metric tons.

3. The prolonged decline of the sugar industry from 1880 until the World War, when high prices again stimulated cane growing. The exportation in 1912 was only one-ninth as large as it had been 30 years earlier, and even now the exportation is scarcely back to that of 1880.

4. The wide diffusion of cane growing in every state of the Republic, and the great number of little, crude, local mills that produce brown sugar for local use.

5. The lack of business organization, the unscientific methods of production, and the poor and expensive means of transportation.

6. The existence of a considerable number of strictly modern sugar mills and of a few modern refineries. There are said to be about one hundred mills with modern or semimodern machinery.

THE FORMER IMPORTANCE OF SUGAR IN BRAZIL.—The colony of Brazil was exporting a little sugar to the mother country Portugal when the Pilgrims were settling in Massachusetts. Throughout the seventeenth, eighteenth, and most of the nineteenth centuries, sugar was the foremost of tropical crops and the one that made tropical colonies more coveted by European monarchs than were colonies in higher latitudes. The sugar planters of the West Indies and Brazil were the millionaires of the New World. Two events during the nineteenth century brought the sugar plantations almost to ruin: (1) the abolition of

slavery with its consequent shortage of labor, for the liberated
slaves objected to regular work; and (2) the rise of the bounty-fed
beet-sugar industry of Europe. By 1900, sugar prices had dropped
so low that the inefficient methods prevailing in Brazil could not
produce sugar of a quality and at a price that permitted exportation at a profit. In the years 1910 to 1913, only about 27,000 tons
of sugar a year were exported from Brazil, though at one time that

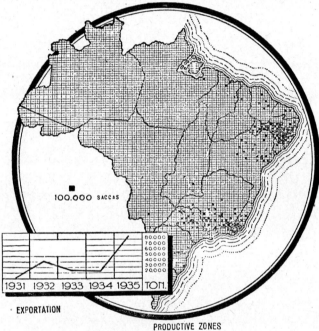

Fig. 176.—Sugar-producing areas of Brazil. (*Brazil, Ministry of Foreign Affairs.*)

country was the foremost exporter of sugar in the world. In recent
years, the production and the exportation have increased, and
Brazil now ranks sixth among the cane-sugar countries (Cuba,
India, Java, Hawaii, Formosa, Brazil).

PRINCIPAL SUGAR-GROWING REGIONS OF BRAZIL.—Pernambuco is the premier sugar-growing state, yielding about 30 per
cent of the total of the country. Sugar is also the chief product of
that state, which some years ago had 1,300 primitive sugar mills,
many of which have given place to mills with modern or semimodern equipment.

Another sugar area of importance is the Campos district along the Parahiba River in the State of Rio de Janeiro. Here, the cultivation is intensive, and methods are somewhat scientific. In this relatively small area, between 75,000 and 100,000 tons of sugar are annually produced. The nearness of this valley to the chief city Rio de Janeiro is its main advantage.

The great and populous states of Minas Geraes and São Paulo are second and third, respectively, in yield of sugar; but the sugar lands are widely scattered, and most of the sugar is con-

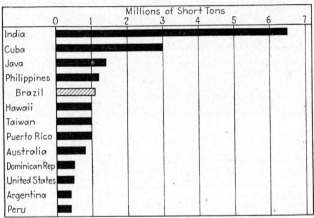

FIG. 177.—Production of cane sugar in leading countries, 3-year average, 1935–1937.

sumed locally. Two little states on the extreme northeastern coast, Alagôas and Sergipe, are also important producers, and these two, together with their neighbor Pernambuco, supply nearly half of the sugar grown in Brazil (Fig. 176).

FUTURE PROSPECTS OF SUGAR.—Since its return to prominence in Brazil, sugar ranks among the secondary exports of the country; yet the value of these exports is less than 10 cents per capita of the population. In Peru, the annual exports of sugar average $1.25 per capita of its population, and in Cuba about $25 (Fig. 177).

In Brazil, the production and exportation of sugar suffer under the same handicaps that restrict all agricultural industries, with the possible exception of coffee. These handicaps are the inefficiency of the colored laborer, the general backwardness of the methods employed, the export taxes, and the insufficiency of capital and of transportation. Brazil is a country of prodigious producing ability, but deficiencies of various kinds in the greater part of the country prevent satisfactory progress in those regions. In the states of São Paulo, Rio de Janeiro, Rio Grande do Sul, and Minas Geraes, conditions are far more favorable, partly because a better climate has attracted European immigrants and their energy and ability have aided greatly in developing the vast potentialities of these sections.

The sugar industry of Brazil, like several other industries, needs men of energy, experience, and capital to do for it what such men have done in Cuba, Puerto Rico, and Hawaii and what they have done for coffee in São Paulo. Realizing the gravity of the sugar situation, the Brazilian Government created the Institute of Sugar and Alcohol which is to study and solve, as far as possible, the problems of sugar production. Brazil can greatly increase its sugar acreage, but planting and production must be considered in relation to the amount produced in other areas.

Brazil High in Rank in Tobacco Production.—Among the farm crops of Brazil, tobacco ranks about eighth; yet the country is one of the four leaders in tobacco production. The total quantity grown annually somewhat exceeds a good crop in Virginia, or one-eighth of the United States crop. The states of Bahia and Rio Grande do Sul produce about two-thirds of the total of Brazil. Methods of cultivation and preparing for market are unscientific, and the quality and export price are relatively low. Among the country's exports, tobacco usually ranks eighth or ninth, with an annual value of about $6,000,000.

Other Crops.—It has already been mentioned that northeastern Brazil is an important source of cotton, although São Paulo, as a single state, is the leading producer. This region also raises great quantities of mandioca, the generally used starch food of Brazil (Fig. 173). Bananas grow almost anywhere in the tropics; oranges of most delicious flavor and surprising size and cheapness are abundant, notably in Bahia, but in many other states, also. The fruit-growing possibilities of Brazil are practically unlimited. The production of rice and corn in the northeast is very small. On the whole, the region falls far below its reasonable production of crops.

THE AMAZON BASIN

Character of the Region.—The Amazon drains nearly 2 million square miles of Brazil in addition to parts of five neighboring countries (Fig. 148). The size of Brazil is directly related to the size of the Amazon system. The Pope's Line of Demarcation gave to Portugal only a small part of the area now included in Brazil. The massive barrier of the Andes prevented the Spanish colonists from penetrating far into tropical South America from the west, but the navigable Amazon system readily led the Portuguese and later the Brazilians into the continent from the east. Moreover, the country tributary to the Amazon has its natural outlet eastward. The geographical factors favored the spread of the people of Brazil over the Amazon basin and up to the very base of the Andes, and they have come into possession of almost all the Amazon country.

In the Amazon Lowland, the rainfall is heavy, although there is a wide variation as the sun moves north and then south in its apparent seasonal migration (Figs. 8 and 9). This phenomenon is due to the same causes that give us our change of seasons in the temperate zones. The belt of heaviest rainfall migrates with the sun northward in our summer and southward in our winter, and gives to the Amazon valley very heavy rains from December to April and lighter rains from May to November. The great heat and abundant moisture give rise to the tropical forests, or *selvas*, of the Amazon, whose chief product has been rubber.

The Amazon is a river of amazing size. For example, only by constant dredging can a depth of 9 feet be maintained on the Mississippi between New Orleans and the mouth of the Ohio; and $100,000,000 have been expended on the Ohio River to secure a minimum depth of 9 feet at all times of the year. Contrast this with the Amazon, which has an average depth of more than 100 feet for a distance equal to the length of the Mississippi and, in its lower course, exceeds 200 feet in depth. Ocean-going steamships may ascend the Amazon to Iquitos in Peru, a distance of 2,300 miles; and smaller steamers ascend each of the main tributaries 500 to 1,000 miles. The depth of the rivers varies greatly from low water in September to high water in March. During high water, some of the rivers rise 40 or 50 feet, overflowing their banks and spreading out to a width that not infrequently reaches 150 to 200 miles. As a rule, the riverbanks are low, and the land is flat throughout the vast flood plain; even at medium height of water, great stretches of swamp fringe the rivers. No other large river has such a gentle gradient; in the final 2,000 miles of its flow, the Amazon descends only 35 feet, or an average of 0.2 inch to the mile. It has been said that the Amazon basin, with its great area of swamplands, the enormous volume of the main river, and the intricate maze of tributaries, is as much a reservoir as a drainage system.

In spite of the large food-producing power of which this basin is potentially capable, it actually does not produce enough food for its few scattered people, and food is imported. Many steamships navigate the rivers. The Brazilian Government maintains several lines which are usually run at a financial loss that is made up from the Brazilian treasury. The rivers provide ways into the interior; but the climate, the jungle, and its diseases keep the population small.

The Population.—More people live on the little island of Manhattan in New York, N.Y., than live in the Amazon basin. The great majority of the residents are Indians and half-castes who eke out a scanty subsistence by collecting forest products and possibly carrying on a little crude agriculture.

Manáos is the only important city in the interior of the Amazon valley, with a population of about 90,000. The city is about 1,000 miles inland on the Rio Negro, near the junction with the Amazon. It was a busy city in former days, handling a large part of the upriver rubber and acting as the chief mercantile and financial center of a vast region.

The estimated population of the Amazon region of Brazil is approximately as follows:

Pará (partly in the Amazon basin)...........	1,540,000
Matto Grosso (partly in the Amazon basin)...	370,000
Amazonas.................................	440,000
Acre Territory............................	115,000
Average of 1 person to about ⅖ square mile.	2,465,000

The Madeira-Mamoré Railroad.—By a treaty entered into in 1903, Bolivia ceded to Brazil her claim to a large area known as the Territory of Acre at the headwaters of the Amazon. The agreement bound Brazil to provide for the building of a railroad around the rapids of the Madeira River, one of the navigable affluents of the Amazon, heading in Bolivia. Such a railroad had previously been attempted in 1872 and again in 1877, but the difficulties were so great that both attempts had failed. The 19 falls and rapids of the Madeira extend over a stretch of river 211 miles long. They have always been a most serious obstacle to the navigation of this great river, which, with its branch the Mamoré, forms the chief outlet for eastern Bolivia. In the years between 1900 and 1910, large quantities of rubber were carried down the river, and it was believed that a railway around the rapids would pay. After tremendous difficulties, entailing the death of many hundreds of workmen and involving a much greater cost than was expected, the railroad was completed under the direction of American engineers. Soon after the opening of the railroad came the decline in the output of Amazon rubber, and the railroad found itself with little traffic. It has proved a financial failure and is now doing only a small fraction of the predicted business. This is the only railroad in the upper Amazon valley.

Forests and Forest Products.—It is estimated that 58 per cent of the area of Brazil was originally forest-covered and that 40 to 45 per cent still is forested. The greater part of the Amazon basin has the heavy rains and high temperature characteristic of the belt of equatorial calms, conditions that make for a dense growth of trees, vines, and underbrush. In this river basin are forests covering 1 million square miles or more, "probably the most extensive solid body of forest in the world."

Much of the Amazon basin has a Tropical Rain Forest type of vegetation. There are a great variety of species, a tangled undergrowth, and a maze of vines looping from tree to tree. In places, one can make his way readily under a canopy of overhanging tree tops; in others, he can penetrate these forests only by the watercourses or by slowly and laboriously cutting a path. The majority of the trees are hardwood of many kinds, including such valuable woods as the mahogany, ebony, rosewood, and Spanish cedar. These trees are found not in large groups or solid stands but widely scattered, one here and one there. So intense is the struggle for space and so dense is the undergrowth that relatively few trees have an opportunity to grow large and stately.

Trees exceeding 3 feet in diameter are not common, and an acre of ground that would yield 8,000 board feet of lumber is counted good. The average yield of lumber in the forests of western Washington and Oregon is over 20,000 board feet per acre. The extreme difficulty and cost of getting the timber out of the Amazon region to the world's markets must long retard the exploitation of these forests. The impression sometimes given that tropical forests abound in costly woods and are more valuable than the pine or fir forests of middle latitudes is erroneous. Acre for acre, the tropics have no large forests of such value as the original white-pine forests or the Pacific-coast forests of North America.

For a country possessing such extensive forests, Brazil exports very little timber. The value of such exports amounts to only a few million dollars a year. This small exportation is due to two principal causes: (1) the fact that hardwoods predominate, and hardwoods are little used for construction purposes; (2) the high cost of getting the wood out of the forests and delivering it to foreign markets. It is a paradoxical fact that Brazil's enormous forests, one of her greatest natural resources, are at present of minor importance in the country's external trade. For example, only 4 per cent of the wood imported into the United States comes from Brazil.

The Rubber Forests.—In the tropical portion of various countries are found species of trees, vines, and shrubs that secrete a rubber-bearing latex. Over 500 species of such plants are known to exist. In the Amazon basin are 1 million square miles of forests through which rubber trees are scattered. Of the four groups of species from which most of the Amazon rubber has been obtained, the *Hevea* group of 10 species is much the most important; and, in this group, the *Hevea brasiliensis* supplies the greater part of the commercial rubber. The tree grows only in regions where the average annual temperature is as high as 70°F. and where the annual rainfall is above 80 inches. It is at its best in low, periodically flooded lands. Here, it attains a height of 100 feet or more and a girth of 3 or 4 feet. The finest specimens of these trees, those yielding the best rubber, grow far up toward the headwaters of the Amazon and its tributaries. The rubber trees are not found in dense stands but are distributed at considerable intervals. Since the rubber gatherers must cut paths through the jungle from tree to tree, this habit of growth of the tree adds to the difficulties and costs of collecting the rubber. During the rainy season (November to May), the lowlands are flooded, and rubber collecting ceases. All the rubber must be shipped out by way of the rivers. There are no roads in this part of Brazil; hence, only those rubber trees that stand within carrying distance of the rivers are reached. This means that large areas of rubber forest remain untouched.

METHODS OF COLLECTING AND CURING THE RUBBER.—Relatively little rubber is now collected in the Amazon forests. The methods here described are still employed, but on a much smaller scale than formerly.

Most of the rubber is collected on estates of large size, operated by men or companies having considerable capital. These estates may be 25 to 75 miles long and a few miles wide on one or both sides of the river. At the opening of the collecting season, the estate owner makes contracts with such Indians or other workers as he can secure. The rubber collector, called a *seringueiro*, obtains his necessary equipment and supplies at the store of his employer and pledges the season's rubber harvest in payment. For these supplies, mainly foodstuffs, he pays five to ten times their value in the markets of the outer world. He then enters the part of the forest allotted to him, builds a rude hut on the bank of the river, and enters upon the season's work. He can take care of about one hundred trees.

Tapping the trees is done in the morning and consists in cutting a gash through the bark, for the latex is in ducts in the inner bark. At the lower end of the gash, a little cup is hung to catch the white milk that oozes out and trickles down for a short time after tapping. In the afternoon, the collector makes the round of his trees, gathers the fluid from the cups, and returns with his bucket of latex to his hut. Here, over a smoky fire of palm nuts, he cures the rubber by dipping a paddle into the latex, smoking the layer of rubber on the paddle, dipping it again, smoking this layer, and so on, until a large biscuit or ball of rubber has been built up. This process of tapping and collecting is repeated day after day, perhaps not every day, but several times a week, a fresh gash being made each time. Because of rain, ill health, or disinclination, the worker seldom works more than 4 days a week, collecting a few pounds of latex each day. At the end of the season, he is fortunate indeed if he has collected enough rubber to pay his account at the employer's store. The biscuits of rubber are collected from the camps by canoes or launches, are taken to central stations, and later are sent in larger shipments to Manáos or Pará.

RISE AND DECLINE OF THE RUBBER INDUSTRY.—As early as 1825, 30 tons of crude rubber were exported from Brazil. The growth of this industry was slow, and during the next 75 years (1825–1900), the exportation rose to 27,000 tons. The development of rubber tires for bicycles and later for automobiles gave a tremendous stimulus to crude-rubber production, and the exportation from Brazil reached its high point in 1912, when it attained 43,000 tons, valued at $85,000,000 and ranked second in value only to coffee among Brazilian exports. At one time, the price of crude rubber rose to $3 a pound, yielding fabulous profits to the producers. Manáos, the chief interior center of the Brazilian rubber interests, and Pará, the chief seaport for rubber shipments, decided that the flow of wealth would continue indefinitely, built great private and public buildings, and for a time rode on the crest of a wave of prosperity.

In the meantime, the growth of rubber plantations in the Far East, which began about 1880, was going steadily forward. In 1900, 4 tons of plantation rubber were marketed; in 1910, 8,000 tons; and in 1913, the output from British and Dutch colonies in the Malay States, Ceylon, and the East Indies exceeded the output from Brazil. For nearly a decade, the Brazilian production continued at nearly the same level of about 38,000 tons a year; for "upriver fine pará" rubber is a very high-grade product and was not equaled in quality by plantation rubber until after the World War. Following this war, prices of raw rubber declined below 20 cents a pound, and the Brazilian industry was nearly ruined. The $78,000,000 exportation from Brazil in 1912 dropped to $6,000,000 in 1929. Most of the rubber gatherers were forced out of the forests by impending starvation. The wonderful boom days were over, and the only important industry in the Amazon valley was nearly killed by the competition of rubber produced elsewhere more scientifically and much more cheaply. It is estimated that the Amazon rubber costs fully twice as much to place on the market as does plantation rubber. The plantations now furnish about 97 per cent of the world's supply (Fig. 178).

Plantations have been attempted in various places in tropical America, but generally with little success. The expensive experiment made by Henry Ford in Brazil shows promise, but the trees are yet too young to predict ultimate success. If labor and managers of the same quality that are available in the Far East can be supplied in the Amazon basin, plantation rubber can be produced there just as well as in the East.

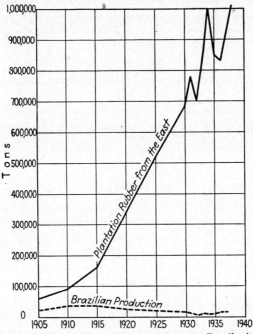

FIG. 178.—Comparison of crude-rubber production in Brazil with plantation rubber of the Far East—by 5-year periods, 1905–1930 and by 1-year periods, 1931–1937.

The rapid rise in rubber prices in 1925, apparently caused by a British enactment which sought to limit rubber production in the British Far Eastern possessions, temporarily revived rubber collecting in the Amazon basin. The high prices did not continue, and it is probable that rubber plantations will not be profitable in the American tropics, at least for some time to come.[1]

[1] The production in the last few years is considerably more than in 1929 but is still of relatively small importance.

Nuts, Wax, and Minor Forest Products.—The forests of Brazil yield a long list of products. Brazil nuts are exported to the value of $2,000,000 or $3,000,000 a year. The valuable carnauba wax, resembling beeswax, obtained from the leaves of the carnauba palm, is one of the important waxes of commerce and is exported to the value of $3,000,000 or $4,000,000 yearly. Many other forest products—gums, oils, waxes, dyewoods, and tanning extracts—are exported in small quantities. The total annual value of forest exports, including rubber and exports of maté, reaches only $25,000,000 or $30,000,000 a year, a very small sum for a country of such great forest resources.

Chapter XVII. Brazil:
Transportation, Manufacturing, and Commerce

TRANSPORTATION

Great Extent of Navigable Rivers.—The Amazon system surpasses all other river systems of the world in extent of navigable waters. It is officially stated that there are in Brazil 10,000 miles of rivers navigable by large steamers, and 20,000 to 30,000 miles additional that, at least during a part of the year, can be used by light-draft steamers. During the period when most of the world's supply of rubber was being shipped from the Amazon basin, the rivers were absolutely essential to the industry, for there was no other way of reaching the rubber forests.

In 1912, for example, there were 12 lines of steamers operated by the Amazon River Steam Navigation Company. Every important branch of the river was reached by more or less regular steamships, carrying in supplies to the rubber camps and bringing out rubber and limited quantities of other forest products. All this traffic has greatly declined with the falling off of the rubber exports; some of the steamship lines have been withdrawn and most of those remaining earn little if any profit, for the population of this region is very small. At times, a small line of Brazilian steamers has operated on the Paraná-Paraguay, connecting interior river towns with Buenos Aires, a distance of about 1,500 miles. Useful as many of the rivers are in enabling people and goods to reach the remote interior of Brazil, Peru, and Bolivia, the cost of transportation is very high. For example, an article that sells for $10 in New York will sell for about $40 in the river port of Riberalta in eastern Bolivia. Goods shipped from a European or United States port may be transferred eight to twelve times in reaching such upriver ports as Riberalta. Wood is the fuel mainly used by the steamboats, and much time is consumed in the frequent loading of this fuel.[1] The sultry heat is intense, the insect pests are numerous and baffling, progress is slow, and delays are exasperating. Yet, without these riverways, fully half Brazil could scarcely be penetrated at all and would remain practically unknown.

Roads.—A country of such vast extent, mountainous surface, heavy rainfall, and small revenues cannot be generally served by modern roads. The cost of building and maintaining a system of roads such as that found in France or in many states of the United States would overtax the federal and state budgets of Brazil. However, Brazil has been extending her highways rapidly in recent years. Roads extend for short distances from all ports, but there are but few highway nets. In the state of São Paulo and bordering areas, there is a good road system which serves the coffee district as well as being an outlet for the ever-increasing expansion in other products. Several roads are now being extended into the interior—one to Cuyabá in Matto Grosso. It is estimated that there are about 78,000 miles of highways in Brazil. Of these, about 13,500 miles may be considered good roads. Many more miles of roads are passable part of the year, but in many parts of Brazil transport is on the backs of mules or horses which follow tracks or trails rather than highways.

Railways of Brazil.—Somewhat more than half the railway mileage of Brazil is owned by the federal government, about one-third by private companies (mainly British), and the balance by the various state governments. The total mileage is approximately 20,500 as compared with 25,000 in Argentina (Fig. 151). More or less continuous railway building is in progress. Among the 140 railroads, there are seven different gauges, ranging from 0.6 to 1.6 meters. About 90 per cent of the mileage is 1 meter. Most of the early roads were built simply to connect seaports with their immediate hinterlands. The original lines have been extended, but many of these remain wholly unconnected with other lines. This is notably true in northeastern Brazil where no actual railway system yet exists. In the region extending from Rio de Janeiro southward, the various railroads have been connected, and a serviceable system exists. A long arm of this system

---

[1] A vivid account of a journey up the Amazon, through the 200 miles of the Madeira rapids, up the Mamoré and Guaporé and down the Paraguay-Paraná to Buenos Aires is given by Alex. P. Rogers, *World's Work*, vol. 23, pp. 625–640.

extends southward and connects with lines that reach Montevideo and Buenos Aires. Another line extends westward to the
Paraguay River on the boundary of Bolivia. Three adjacent
states—São Paulo, Minas Geraes, and Rio de Janeiro—contain

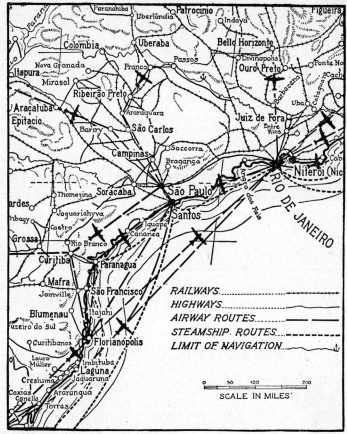

FIG. 179.—Transportation routes of southeastern Brazil. (*From "Commercial
Travelers' Guide to Latin America," Part II, East Coast of South America.*)

half of all the railway mileage of Brazil. The progressive southern
state of Rio Grande do Sul is also well equipped with railways.
The best railroad system is in the Coffee Belt. Excellent service
is maintained between Santos, São Paulo, Rio de Janeiro, and
several interior cities. Nearly all the railways are within 300 to
400 miles of the coast (Fig. 179).

Financial Condition of the Railroads.—The British-owned São Paulo Railway earns approximately $50,000 gross a mile annually; but the British-controlled Leopoldina Railway, a very important line, has never paid satisfactory dividends and is in financial difficulties. Its gross earnings are only about $4,000 a mile. The most important government railroad, the Central of Brazil, earns $10,000 a mile but is not profitable. The majority of the present lines are operated at a loss, which, in most cases, is made up from the public treasury. The deficits are due to the partly developed condition of many sections of the republic,

Fig. 180.—Section of the São Paulo Railway between Santos and São Paulo. The busiest and most profitable railroad in South America.

to the evils of political control, and to the leasehold system, under which certain government roads are leased to private operating companies. How to make the railways pay is one of Brazil's unsolved financial problems. Large areas, if they are to be developed, need additional railways; yet the government is not able financially to continue building the roads and paying the deficits that are inevitable.

The Famous São Paulo Railway.—Most profitable of all South American railroads is the British-owned São Paulo line. It is the only direct railway outlet to the sea from the great State of São Paulo (Fig. 180). Over this excellent double-track line is carried more than half of the world's coffee. The engineering difficulties involved in constructing a railway up the steep face of the Serra do Mar were tremendous. In a distance of 7 miles, the railroad ascends 2,600 feet to the plateau. Originally, the route included four inclined planes with gradients of 10 per cent, up which trains were hauled by cables. A relocating of the line has reduced the maximum gradient to 8 per cent; but cables must still be employed, and only short trains are taken up or down these inclines. The main line extends from the port of Santos, through the city of São Paulo, and somewhat beyond, a total of 86.5 miles. The 3 million tons of freight annually carried on this line make its revenues per mile very high. After exceptionally generous expenditures upon the line, its equipment, and its stations, the company still has been able to pay up to 14 per cent on its ordinary stock, which has sold at nearly three times its par value. The great prosperity of the road is due mainly to its virtual control of the huge coffee shipments to Santos.

Air Service.—Travel by air partly compensates for lack of other means of transportation. Commercial travelers and tourists frequently make use of the available air transportation which covers most of the important cities and many of the smaller centers in the interior.

WATER POWER AND MANUFACTURING

Great Potential Water Power.—On account of (1) its large size, (2) the great volume of its rivers due to heavy rainfall, and (3) the steep and irregular gradients of many of its rivers, Brazil has enormous potential water power. The total is estimated at 36 million horsepower, equal to or greater than that of the United States. However, the United States has about 18 million horsepower already developed, whereas Brazil has only about 1 million. Brazil has practically half the potential water power and more than half the developed water power of South America. Much of Brazil's potential power is in out-of-the-way parts of the country and will not be used for a long time to come. More than half this vast potential energy is located at the hundreds of falls and rapids in the eastern highlands, within reach of the most populous states. Many branches of the Paraná reach into São Paulo and Minas Geraes, and the Brazilian portion of this river system is estimated to offer forty times as much water power as the total actual development of such power in all Brazil. The Rio São Francisco has at least 2 million potential horsepower. The most important developments of water power are near the great cities of São Paulo and Rio de Janeiro, where hydroelectric power is used for the factories, for the street railways, for lighting, and to a small extent for railways.

The abundance of water power in the wealthiest and most progressive parts of Brazil is of unusual significance; for Brazil has very little coal, and even that is poor and is located in the far south. There are already about one hundred light and power companies in the State of São Paulo alone. Every city of any size in that state has electric light, and many villages and thousands of farms and plantations also have it. In the coffee district—that around Ribeirão Preto—80 per cent of the electric power that is developed is used on the coffee plantations for light and power. In the State of São Paulo alone, 250 cities, towns, and villages have hydroelectric-power stations controlled by about one hundred power companies. If Brazil continues to develop its manufacturing industries as it has done recently, there will be a steadily increasing demand for hydroelectric power. The shortage of native coal and the high cost of imported fuel make electric power in Brazil a matter of national significance.

Recent Rapid Growth of Manufacturing.—Up to the time of the World War, Brazil had made slow progress in the development of its manufactures. The country has been essentially a producer and exporter of raw or partly processed commodities. It mines very little coal and iron, and most of its people have had little training or experience in the complexities of modern manufacturing. Had not the World War cut Brazil off from the free importation of manufactured goods, the growth of manufacturing in the country doubtless would have continued slow. In addition to the war, three other factors have greatly stimulated manufacturing: (1) the great potential water power of eastern Brazil, (2) the high protective tariff, and (3) the depreciation of Brazilian currency to about one-fourth its par value. This depreciation was felt most in the purchase of imported goods, for the currency had only a fraction of its normal purchasing power when it came to buying imported goods. This was much less true, however, in buying Brazilian products that had been produced by labor paid in this same currency. During the years from 1915 on, for a decade, the profits on Brazilian-made manufactures were large, and rapid industrial progress was made. Between $500,000,000 and $1,000,000,000 were invested in upward of 10,000 manufacturing establishments, large and small. By 1929, the value of the output had risen well toward $1,000,000,000, with textiles easily in the lead. This was more than double the value in 1915. The rapid development of hydroelectric power in eastern Brazil has already been mentioned. This power is an essential element in promoting Brazilian industries and partly compensates for the shortage and high price of coal.

More than two-thirds of the manufacturing establishments are engaged in making five groups of product: (1) foods; (2) textiles, mainly cotton, but also silk, wool, and jute; (3) clothing, including shoes and hats; (4) clay products; and (5) wood products. In 20 or more lines of manufacturing, Brazil is virtually independent of imports. These include shoes, hats, tobacco, and matches. Little progress has been made, however, in the working of metals, and nearly all iron and steel products are imported. In all Brazil, there are about 10 small smelting plants.

The city of São Paulo has many large modern mills, notably textile mills. One silk mill employs 3,000 persons. The second manufacturing city is Rio de Janeiro, the capital. The southern State of Rio Grande do Sul is the third industrial state of the Republic. In no other part of South America is the growth of manufacturing so vigorous as it is in São Paulo with its stimulating climate, great water power, good railway systems, and capable population, many of whom came from the industrial cities of north Italy. Since 1931, industrialization has made rapid progress and promises a continued development. Brazil has certain advantages over Argentina in the upbuilding of industries: a much larger population and, hence, a larger home market; a larger variety of raw materials; and cheaper power. By way of comparison, it may be pointed out that all the manufactured goods made in Brazil have an annual value about equal to those made in Milwaukee, Wis., or in Leeds, England.

There is no little discontent among consumers in Brazil because of the large profits made by Brazilian manufacturers under the protection of the high tariff, and the consequent high prices. In this respect, conditions are similar to those in the United States in the past.

FOREIGN COMMERCE AND CITIES

The Foreign Trade of Brazil.—Certain facts relating to the international trade of Brazil stand out conspicuously: (1) The total trade is relatively small, owing partly to the high degree of self-sufficiency of the country. So large is Brazil that it can produce the greater part of the things that its people need; conversely, the population of over 40 million consumes the larger part of the commodities that are produced. The notable increase in manufacturing since 1915 has materially affected the importations. Although the per capita foreign trade of Argentina reaches

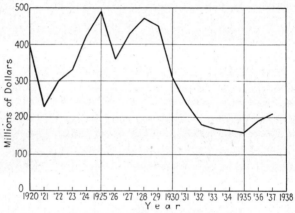

Fig. 181.—Export trade of Brazil.

$50 to $100, that of Brazil is about $15. (2) Five or six agricultural products form 80 per cent of the exports, and coffee alone forms about two-fifths. Other exports are fruits (especially oranges), hides, cacao, maté, and beef. (3) The country sells abroad many millions of dollars' worth of products in excess of its purchases abroad. This condition is highly favorable but is more than counteracted by the yearly payments of interest on foreign loans. (4) The United States is the largest buyer of the products of Brazil. Americans are coffee drinkers, as distinguished from the British who are tea drinkers. The United States takes a large percentage of Brazil's exports but supplies less than that proportion of its imports. In recent years, Germany has played an important role in Brazil's foreign trade. Coffee forms a large percentage of the value of all exports from Brazil to the United States. (5)

Rubber, once the second export in value from Brazil, has fallen to a place of minor importance and is now outranked by several other products. (6) Two-thirds to three-fourths of the foreign trade of Brazil passes through the two ports of Rio de Janeiro and Santos, the former leading in imports and the latter in exports because of the enormous coffee shipments.

All things considered, the international trade of Brazil is smaller than it ought to be for such a populous country and one so richly endowed by nature (Fig. 181). One important reason for this is to be found in the large proportion of colored people who are content to produce little and whose wants are few and simple. The people of southern and eastern Brazil, living in about one-eighth of the total area, are responsible for over four-fifths of the overseas commerce of the country. Although Argentina has less than one-third as many people as Brazil, its international commerce is almost twice as great. If all the people of Brazil produced and consumed as much per capita as do those of São Paulo, the foreign trade of Brazil would be quadrupled.

The Principal Cities.—Rio de Janeiro, the capital and metropolis of Brazil, owes its location and growth primarily to the superb harbor and its beautiful setting. Evidently, this section of the coast has been depressed in past geologic time, and the ocean has backed up into a deep, broad coastal basin, fringed with mountains of unique shape and of great beauty (Fig. 182). Enormous sums of money have been expended upon the beautifying of this ocean front (Fig. 183). For miles, a magnificent boulevard, shaded with trees, brilliantly illuminated at night by multiple rows of ornamental lights, extends along this curving, mountain-studded shore. Unlike most port cities, Rio reveals to the visitor nothing of docks or warehouses or anything unsightly as he enters the harbor. Everything is beautiful. Even the steamer landing is in a parklike section (Fig. 184). The city's claim to first place among the beautiful harbors of the world is probably justified (Fig. 185). "More extravagant prose has been written about Rio and Naples than about any other cities in the world (Fig. 186). And Rio more nearly deserves it (Fig. 187)."[1] Across the bay is the city of Nictheroy, capital of the State of Rio de Janeiro. The city of Rio de Janeiro constitutes the Federal District, corresponding to our District of Columbia, and is

[1] *Fortune Magazine*, June, 1939.

politically separate from the state of the same name. The city is an important industrial center with textiles the leading product.

Rio has a population of about 1,800,000 but is growing less rapidly than São Paulo. Rio and Santos are the two leading com-

Fig. 182.—General view of city of Rio de Janeiro and outer harbor. In the middle ground is the famous Sugar Loaf.

Fig. 183.—View of Gloria Park showing part of downtown Rio de Janeiro.

mercial cities, between them handling upward of two-thirds of the exports and imports of the country.

Though Rio de Janeiro is the present capital of the Republic, a Federal District of the future has been legally established in the State of Goyaz, 600 miles inland, in a practically uninhabited region.

Fig. 184.—Part of the port works of Rio de Janeiro, capital and metropolis of Brazil. Population almost 2,000,000.

Fig. 185.—Residence street in Rio de Janeiro.

Fig. 186.—Avenida Rio Branco, principal street of Rio de Janeiro. (*Courtesy of F. G. Matheson.*)

Fig. 187.—Close-up view of Sugar Loaf, Rio de Janeiro.

Fig. 188.—Plaza and section of city of São Paulo.

São Paulo is the capital of the state of the same name and is the second largest city of Brazil. It has a population of about 1,200,000, most of whom are white. Although located at the edge of the tropics, it stands at an elevation generally above 2,400 feet. The hinterland supplies coffee, and São Paulo transacts nearly all the business pertaining to the distribution of that product and serves as an *entrepôt* for the area (Fig. 188). It is one of the most progressive and enterprising cities in all South America. It is well served by a radiating system of railways and highways.

FIG. 189.—Butantan Institute ("snake farm").

Near the city is the famous Butantan Institute ("snake farm") where serums are prepared to counteract the effect of bites of the many poisonous snakes of the country (Fig. 189).

Santos is the world's greatest coffee port and is one of the chief export cities of Brazil. It is situated on an island which is protected by a higher island from storms on the Atlantic. It is the all-important port for the State of São Paulo, the richest, busiest, and second most populous of the states of Brazil (Fig. 190). It is connected with the city of São Paulo by a good railway and a good highway. It is well equipped for handling the coffee; it has special equipment for movement of the bags, and the berths are fitted with large warehouses. Although primarily noted for its coffee, Santos has considerable local fame as a resort and has some splendid beaches and good hotels. In northeastern Brazil are three port cities of importance. In order of size, they are Pernambuco (510,000), Bahia (370,000), and Pará (350,000). All are on well-protected harbors connected with points in the immediate hinterland by one or more railroads. Bahia (in Brazil called São Salvador) is the cacao-shipping port, Pernambuco (Recife) is the sugar-shipping port, and Pará (Belém), near one of the mouths

Fig. 190.—View overlooking Santos.

of the Amazon, has been the principal rubber-shipping port. The most important city in the far south of Brazil is Porto Alegre (350,000), in Rio Grande do Sul.

CONCLUSIONS

In attempting to evaluate the economic strength of Brazil, these outstanding elements must be taken into account:

1. The large size and great producing power of the country. Nearly three-fourths of the land has a tropical climate, however, and about one-half is covered by tropical vegetation, which man would have to fight endlessly if he tried to bring the land under cultivation. At present, only 20 per cent of the land of Brazil is divided into farms, and only about 1½ per cent is under cultivation. The agricultural exports are much less valuable than those of Argentina, which has only one-third as much land and less than one-third as many people.

2. More than half of the population lives in a continuously hot climate, and the majority of these are colored people of small producing and small buying power. They contribute relatively little to the economic upbuilding of the nation.

3. In the south and east is an elevated region several times as large as the British Isles, possessing a mild and stimulating climate, occupied by an energetic people, supplied with great potential water power and enormous reserves of high-grade iron ore, but seriously deficient in coal. This section must largely dominate the nation, whose destinies it controls.

4. The high degree of self-rule formerly accorded to the individual states, the heavy foreign debt of the country, and the tendency toward extravagance, waste, and graft in expending public revenues have brought about a critical financial condition which is embarrassing the government.

5. The export duties collected by the individual states and the high import tariff imposed by the federal government restrict interstate and international commerce and yet do not supply sufficient revenues.

6. Means of transportation are inadequate; scarcely one-eighth of the country is served by railways, and on these the rates are high. Only a few of the present lines are profitable, and it is difficult to secure the funds with which to build new lines. Good transportation, it must be remembered, is the key to economic development.

7. Under a stimulus arising from conditions created by the World War and a high import tariff, manufacturing. mainly in the southeast, has recently made excellent progress.

8. Both because of the high degree of self-sufficiency of the country and because of the low average buying power of half the people, the foreign commerce of the country is small in the total and small in proportion to the population. It is an impressive fact that Argentina exports almost twice as much as Brazil.

9. The future of Brazil depends mainly upon the human factor. Size, location, surface, natural resources, and even climate offer far more assets than liabilities and make possible a great nation, if man does his part.

Chapter XVIII. South America as a Whole and Some of Its External Relationships

SOME CONTRASTS

In studying the economic development of South America, it is scarcely possible to avoid comparisons with North America, and a North American writer is not an impartial judge. The North American is likely to be proud of the achievements of his country and to feel that these achievements are due mainly to the qualities of his countrymen and of his government. For the typical American of the United States, the interests and values in life are powerfully influenced by the materialistic civilization in which he lives. His estimate of the kinds of achievement that are most to be coveted, the kinds of success that are most to be desired, is warped. It cannot be otherwise. To him, the Brazilian, using a half hour in sipping coffee in a *café* in the middle of the morning or afternoon, seems trifling and wasteful of time; and the poetic effusions that delight the young manhood of Bogotá seem a pitiable substitute for baseball or football. It is hard for the hustling, aggressive business type of American to understand that other men may hold a different point of view and yet may not necessarily be wrong.

Contrasts in Attitudes.—As a whole, the Latin American's attitude in certain respects is quite unlike that of the American of the northern United States. The latter loves activity; he must be doing; he must be accumulating; he must be winning at the great game of business. The educated Latin American prefers leisure, enjoys spending money more than making it, places great store on being well dressed and well groomed, and finds it more agreeable to put off doing things than to do them promptly. In short, his ideal kind of life, the kind of life from which he gets most satisfaction, is not the business life. He loves more than the

North American the ease and luxury that wealth may afford, but he does not enjoy the self-discipline, the personal devotion to the details of business, or the hard work by which wealth is ordinarily acquired. This essential difference of attitude toward affairs that characterizes the two peoples partly accounts for the different stages of economic progress that the two continents have reached and partly accounts for some of the misunderstandings that arise.

Understanding the reasons why the Latin Americans entertain the attitude toward work and business that they usually do requires an examination of the direct and indirect effects of inheritance and of climate upon their social institutions and economic development. The men who came from Spain and Portugal to conquer and rule these vast dominions in the New World were soldiers, adventurers, and fortune seekers. Few of them were agriculturists; few came to do the hard work of developing a wilderness; most of them came for "gold, glory, and the gospel"; for priests and missionaries as well as soldiers and adventurers came. Neither Spain nor Portugal is well endowed with agricultural land. In both countries, the rocky and stubborn land yielded a scanty return, and the agricultural laborers lived a hard and pinched existence. There was nothing attractive about such a life; and, knowing only such agriculture, few Spaniards or Portuguese cared to go to far distant colonies to adopt or continue such drudgery.

Conversely, in England, the gentlemen, the aristocracy, the most honored and respected people were the holders of agricultural land. Farming was a genteel occupation and carried with it an air of respectability. The English colonists in North America were mostly people who desired to engage in agriculture and who regarded work on the land as thoroughly honorable for men of standing and substance. In short, the North American colonists came to make their homes on the land and to build up communities founded upon agriculture, in which they themselves actively worked. Gradually the difference in climate developed differences in the type of agriculture in the North and South, made slavery profitable in the South but not in the North, and created quite different attitudes toward actual labor by white men in the two sections of the United States. Wherever manual labor is done by slaves or by people of an inferior race, it becomes ignoble, and the upper class of society looks down upon it. This is precisely what occurred in Latin America, as it did to a degree in the warmer part of the United States. In a hot climate, white men—notably those of north European descent—find strenuous outdoor labor disagreeable. Consequently, they seek workers who are able to do this labor for them, and in the past they at times resorted to slavery. In the United States, the people of the South were not less humane or of their own choice less industrious than those of the North. They lived in a different climate, and their social institutions and attitudes yielded to the climate.

In a similar but more extreme way, the white colonists of tropical South America avoided manual labor and imposed it upon the native Indian or the imported Negro slave. They created a social order in which white men occupied the chief offices, filled the professions, held the land, and treated as inferiors those who worked. This attitude still persists but is less marked in Argentina and southern Brazil where large numbers of white laborers from Europe now work on the land and in the cities. Many of these immigrants have acquired wealth and social standing and have overcome the caste barrier between the gentleman and the man who works. But this barrier still exists, strong where Indians and Negros are numerous, but weakened in the lands of temperate climate. Without question, the attitude of the Latin Americans toward labor is due partly to climate and partly to their Spanish and Portuguese inheritance.

Into the present age, dominated by machinery, commerce, industry, and money making, the typical Latin American of good family has, in the past, fitted imperfectly. Even today, there are still parts of South America where the life of genteel leisure is esteemed; but, in the more progressive areas, the Latin American is taking an active interest in developing railways, factories, and mines and in the advancement of agriculture.

Contrasts in Development.—Economic progress in Latin America has been much less rapid than in Anglo-America (Figs. 191 and 192). In the acquisition of wealth and in the perfecting of means for creating new wealth, the part of America lying north of Mexico has advanced more rapidly than has the rest of the New World. So rapid has been the material growth of the United States, so widespread and unprecedented has been its material progress that the national life and ideals have become, or appear to the outsider to have become, highly materialistic.

Probably to a higher degree than elsewhere, making a fortune has become in the United States the popular ambition. Living in a country of great natural resources, stimulated by an invigorating climate, supplied with ample streams of immigration, and endowed with unlimited stores of mechanical energy, the people of the United States have found irresistible the challenge to go forth and achieve material things in a big way. Such has been

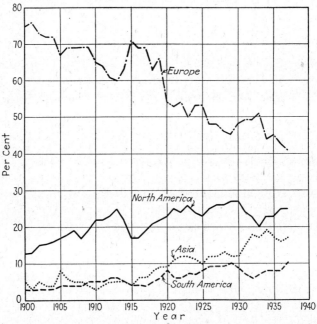

Fig. 191.—Percentage of total exports from the United States to continents receiving more than 5 per cent of total exports.

the stimulus and so great have been the financial rewards that the American people have found the conquering of forests, the cultivation of the soil, the developing of mines, the building of railroads and factories absorbing occupations. In such a country and in such a climate, they have come to regard material achievements, business successes, as the most challenging activities of life. Coupled with these conditions has been the heritage of Anglo-Saxon traditions and standards which have guided the political development of the country and have given it a liberal and at the same time a strong government.

With the changes in attitude noted above, there have come about very notable and rapid advances in economic development in South America. This development promises to be startling in its nature, for changes in time have been paralleled by rapid changes in mechanical means. The airplane, the movies, and other devices have brought about a new orientation of interests. Already this has produced notable results, and it is evident that the aroused interest in all phases of economic development will continue.

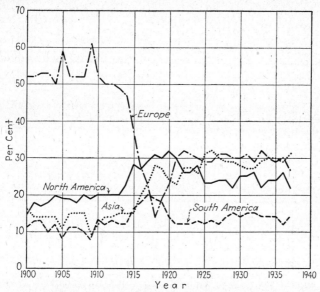

FIG. 192.—Percentage of total imports into the United States from continents supplying more than 5 per cent of total imports.

SOME COMPARATIVE MEASURES

Area.—In area, South America is smaller than its northern neighbor by 1 million or more square miles of land surface. This difference in size is not enough, however, to account for the much greater differences in economic development and in numbers of people.

Population.—South America is believed to have a population of 80 to 90 million people. This is less than half the population of North America. About one-half of these live in Brazil, one-seventh in Argentina, and one-third in the Andean countries.

Three distinct races form the foundation of this population: (1) The Indians, who occupied the entire continent when the conquering Europeans arrived, and most of whom are now found in the Andean countries. There are probably about 10 million pureblood Indians left in all South America. (2) Whites of European birth or descent who now form 30 to 35 per cent of the popula-

FIG. 193.—Value of exports from South American countries, 1927–1929.

tion and constitute the governing and property-holding class. (3) Negroes whose ancestors were brought as slaves from Africa. Decidedly more than half of the population of South America is Indian, Negro, or a mixture of these races with each other and with whites. In Venezuela, Colombia, Ecuador, Peru, Bolivia, and Paraguay, it is estimated that 80 to 90 per cent of the people have Indian blood. There are considerable numbers of Negroes in the lowlands of Colombia, Venezuela, and the Guianas, and they are especially numerous in Brazil. Argentina, southeastern

Brazil, Uruguay, and, to a lesser extent, Chile are peopled mainly by whites.

It is noticeable that the economic progress of the various countries is closely related to the make-up of the population, which, in turn, is intimately related to climate (Figs. 193 and 194). In those countries where Indians and mestizos are numerous, they are the cultivators of the land, the manual laborers,

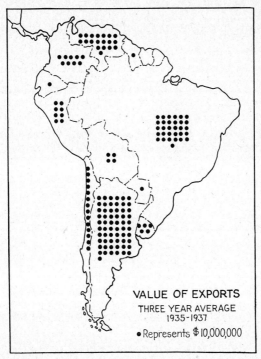

FIG. 194.—Value of exports from South American countries, 1935–1937.

domestic servants, and small tradesmen. The same is true of the Negroes and mulattoes in regions where they are found. As a class, the colored and mixed races get little education, own little property, have small purchasing power, and live on a low economic plane. The immigrants into South America have been mainly Spanish, Portuguese, and Italians; but there are important German colonies in southern Brazil and Chile, and most of the countries receive some immigration from various European countries. However, few white immigrants go to the west coast.

to the north coast, or to northern Brazil, regions where labor is done by the colored peoples. One of the great needs of all South American countries is industrious European immigrants, but in the past most of them have gone to the River Plata lands and to the more temperate parts of Brazil and Chile. South America needs efficient workers, real farmers, and industrial leaders. An unduly large proportion of the important business enterprises is controlled by foreigners.

Urban Development.—South America has three great cities of world importance: Buenos Aires, with over 2.3 million people; Rio de Janeiro, with upward of 1.8 millions; and São Paulo, the great coffee center, with over 1.2 millions. These are beautiful, modern cities that take rank among the finest in the world.

Next in rank are four cities with populations between $\frac{1}{2}$ million and 1 million: Santiago, the beautiful capital of Chile; Montevideo, the capital and thriving port of Uruguay; Recife, an important port of northeastern Brazil; and Rosario, the chief Paraná River port of Argentina.

In the third group are six commercial cities and ports each with upward of $\frac{1}{4}$ million people: Bahia, outlet for an important agricultural area of Brazil; Porto Alegre, rapidly developing port of southeastern Brazil; Bogotá, capital, commercial city, and educational center of Colombia; Córdoba, important inland city of Argentina; Pará, chief outlet of the Amazon valley; and Lima, the political and commercial center of Peru.

The capitals of all the west- and north-coast countries are inland cities. In every South American country, the capital is also the largest city. Four of these capitals are situated high in the mountains to get the coolness that altitude brings—Caracas, Bogotá, Quito, and La Paz. Lima is only a few miles back from the coast, for this coast is rendered cool by the Humboldt Current. The ports of the west coast are all small cities, with the exception of Valparaiso which approaches 200,000. Antofagasta, Arica, Mollendo, Callao, and Guayaquil are coastal termini of important railways. With these may be grouped Cartagena and Barranquilla on the north coast of Colombia.

INTERNAL ECONOMIC DEVELOPMENT

Agriculture and Grazing.—Agriculture and stock raising together constitute the leading occupation of the people of South

America. However, probably not more than 5 per cent of the land
of the continent is under cultivation. Because of their large size
and population, Brazil and Argentina together have over nine-
tenths of the land actually in crops in any one year. Colombia,
Peru, Chile, and Uruguay are estimated to have under cultivation approximately 2 million acres each, and the remaining
countries less than 1 million acres each. These figures can be regarded only as reasonably close approximations.

More than half the cultivated land is devoted to four crops:
corn, coffee, wheat, and alfalfa. The leading agricultural exports
are corn, coffee, and wheat. The coffee goes largely from Brazil,
and the corn and wheat go from Argentina. Corn is grown in
every country, but the only important corn-exporting country
is Argentina. The alfalfa is practically all grown in Argentina
and is used for feeding livestock.

A small fraction of the world's cotton and sugar is grown in
South America, mainly in Brazil, Argentina, and Peru. From
Brazil, Ecuador, and Venezuela comes nearly one-fourth of the
world's cacao, and Argentina stands as the leading producer and
exporter of flaxseed. Other agricultural crops of South America
are of minor importance in international trade and are used
chiefly for local consumption. The two outstanding agricultural
countries are Argentina and Brazil. Brazil is, of course, the
dominating country in the world's coffee trade, and Argentina
plays an important part in supplying Europe with foodstuffs.
Aside from these two countries, South America produces scarcely
as much in the form of agricultural foodstuffs as its own people
require.

The greater part of South America has a tropical climate;
and tropical lands, of course, are not well suited to the raising of
livestock. Cattle raising is concentrated in the River Plata
lands and is also important in the plateau of Brazil. Both of these
are regions of warm temperate and mild tropical temperatures.
In all South America, there are 100 million cattle, or a somewhat
greater number than in North America. Only one South American
country is a large exporter of beef, namely, Argentina. Brazil
and Uruguay, also, export important amounts. Colombia, Chile,
and Venezuela raise considerable numbers of cattle, but they are
distinctly inferior in quality to the improved breeds of Argentina
and Uruguay. Extensive areas in the Andean countries and in

interior Brazil are given over to cattle raising, but hides are practically the only products of these cattle that are an item in international trade. Dairying as a specialized industry has attained some growth in the Argentine Pampa and in southeastern Brazil—regions of large cities.

As a future source of meat for Europe and other importing lands, South America offers great promise. Argentina is already the largest exporter of beef in the world, exporting, in fact, as much as all other countries combined. The great success of alfalfa in the Pampa, the mild climate, and the nearness of the cattle lands to the ports are all favorable conditions. Unquestionably, the River Plata lands and southern Brazil can produce beef more cheaply than the United States, and the time may not be far off when the United States will import increasingly from those countries.

Sheep are even less well suited to living in the tropics than are cattle. The only country in the tropics of South America that raises many sheep is Peru, where they are raised at high altitudes in the Andes. In the bleak lands of the far south of Chile and Patagonia, sheep thrive and yield heavy fleeces. This development of sheep raising is largely due to British initiative, as it is in other sections of Patagonia. On the level lands of the Pampa and of Uruguay, sheep still are numerous, but less so than they were formerly. However, about 65 per cent of all the sheep in South America are in Argentina and Uruguay, and Argentina alone exports about 300 million pounds of wool, which is more than all the rest of the Western Hemisphere exports. Only Australia sends abroad more than Argentina. Moreover, the exportation of hides and skins from Argentina is greater than that from any other country in the world. The United States is a heavy purchaser of wool, hides, and skins from the River Plata lands.

Mineral Resources and Products.—Regarding mineral production in South America, seven facts stand out prominently:

1. The great importance of Spanish America in the production of gold and silver during the colonial period. The Spanish conquerors centered their efforts in the quest for the precious metals, and the forced labor of the Indians was inexpensive. The yield of gold in Spanish America during this period reached well into the billions of dollars.

2. The dominance of the Andean region in mineral production in South America, due to the high mineralization of these young, volcanic mountains (Fig. 195).

3. The preponderance of petroleum, which constitutes the leading item in value of all the minerals produced in South America.

FIG. 195.—Principal mineral-producing regions of South America.

Only a short time ago, Chilean nitrate held first place, but this is no longer true.

4. The very small production and small deposits of coal, the most essential industrial mineral. This, of course, is due to geological causes.

5. The vast deposits of iron ore, especially in the ancient rocks of Brazil, and the very small amount that is mined, owing partly to the lack of coal for smelting it.

6. The large extent to which the principal mineral workings are controlled by foreign capital, owing both to the shortage of capital in South America for investment and the insufficiency of trained and experienced mining men within the countries.

7. The small production of minerals in South America in comparison with North America and Europe and with what the continent probably will produce in the future.

For three centuries, Spanish America was the synonym for gold and silver; and, for a time, Brazil also yielded much gold and most of the world's supply of diamonds. Today, South American production of all these together amounts to only a small sum, say $30,000,000 to $40,000,000, which is generally less than the value of the copper from the single mine at Chuquicamata, Chile. The decline of gold mining is mainly due to two causes: (1) the exhaustion of the richer and more accessible deposits, and (2) the lack of adequate transportation facilities in the Andes, where most of the gold-bearing veins exist. In short, it costs too much to mine and market the gold. Although increased prices in recent years have stimulated gold-mining activity somewhat, nothing corresponding to the old level of production has been attained. Most of the silver that is mined is obtained in connection with other minerals, especially in association with the copper of Cerro de Pasco, Peru, and the tin of Bolivia.

Copper follows petroleum and leads nitrate in value of output, and most of it comes from properties in the Andes, namely, the Cerro de Pasco and associated mines in Peru, the Chuquicamata mines, the Braden mines, and the Andes mines, all in Chile and all American-owned. The total yield of copper in South America is only about one-half that of the United States; yet Chile ranks next to the United States in copper production and rose rapidly on account of the low cost of mining and reduction. The known copper deposits of the Andes are enormous, and it cannot be doubted that other deposits will be found. The cheap copper from South America will force mines in the United States either to close, in many cases, or to find cheaper methods of production.

Virtually all the tin mined in the Americas comes from the lofty plateau of Bolivia. The output constitutes about one-fifth of the world's supply.

South America has become an important producer of petroleum. Venezuela is yielding about 200 million barrels a year and Colombia about 20 million. A smaller quantity is obtained from Peru and Argentina, but the entire oil production of the continent was about 250 million barrels in 1937, or only about one-fifth as much as the United States. There is a belief, however, that the western and northern parts of South America have very large oil reserves yet to be tapped.

The small production of minerals in South America as contrasted with North America and Europe reflects the economically backward condition of the continent. The shortage of capital, of skilled labor, and of transportation and, to a certain extent, the character of some South American governments retard all forms of development. These conditions are improving, and the improvement is shown in the steadily mounting output of minerals. In all the Andean countries except Ecuador, mining is even now the most important industry so far as export products are concerned. In the case of Bolivia and Chile, minerals constitute the preponderance of exports, in Bolivia amounting to over nine-tenths of all and in Chile to over three-fourths of the total. In contrast, in all the east-coast countries, mineral exports are of scarcely any consequence. Petroleum and a small quantity of tungsten are the only mineral products of Argentina worth mentioning. Uruguay and Paraguay yield practically no minerals; even in giant Brazil, mining is a very minor industry. The platinum of Colombia deserves mention. The production of vanadium in Peru is extremely variable, but these mines have been a main source of this valuable alloy used in making vanadium steel. The diamonds of Brazil and British Guiana and the emeralds of Colombia have some potential value but yield only a small annual return.

It is significant that the total annual value of mineral production in all South America is less than the yearly value of coal produced in Pennsylvania alone.

Forest Resources and Products.—It is estimated that 44 per cent of the area of South America is forested, the highest percentage found in any of the continents.[1] More than one-quarter (28 per cent) of all the forest land of the world is in South America; yet the forest products exported from South America have

[1] Zon and Sparhawk, "Forest Resources of the World," vol. 1, p. 3, give the

a value of only $40,000,000 to $60,000,000 annually. At one time, the annual value of rubber alone from the Amazon valley reached $80,000,000 to $90,000,000. The total annual value of forest products of South America is unknown, for those products which are used locally are not reported. They doubtless exceed the forest exports in value.

The following figures represent an approximate average value, but there are wide variations from period to period.

ANNUAL VALUE OF EXPORTS OF FOREST PRODUCTS FROM SOUTH AMERICA

Quebracho wood and extract.	$15,000,000 to	$20,000,000
Rubber and balata..........	5,000,000 to	10,000,000
Yerba maté...............	5,000,000 to	10,000,000
Paraná pine...............	3,000,000 to	5,000,000
Brazil nuts...............	2,000,000 to	4,000,000
Vegetable wax.............	3,000,000 to	6,000,000
Ivory nuts...............	1,500,000 to	3,000,000
Cabinet woods.............	500,000 to	1,000,000
Miscellaneous.............	1,000,000 to	2,000,000
Total..................	$36,000,000 to	$61,000,000

By way of comparison, it may be pointed out that the single item of lumber exported by the United States has a value of about $100,000,000, and that from Sweden $60,000,000.

The small present production of rubber is, of course, due to the successful competition of plantation rubber grown in the Far East. The relatively large value of quebracho extract is due partly to the accessibility of the forests in northern Argentina and still more to the fact that this excellent tanning material is found nowhere else.

Yerba maté is obtained partly from wild forests and partly from plantations, and the relatively large output is due to the great demand for this stimulating and harmless beverage by the people of southeastern South America.

following ratio of forests to the total area of the continents:

South America...............................	44.0 per cent
Europe.......................................	31.0 per cent
North America...............	26.8 per cent
Asia...	21.6 per cent
Australia and Oceania.......................	15.1 per cent
Africa..	10.7 per cent
Total for world.............................	22.5 per cent

In spite of the abundance of such valuable woods as mahogany, ebony, rosewood, and Spanish cedar in the tropical forests, the great expense involved in getting the logs out of the jungle prevents any large extension of this industry.

The forests of southern Chile are of importance to that country, but very few of their products are exported.

Throughout South America, hardwoods predominate. The only large area of softwood (conifers) is the Paraná pine region. It is an impressive fact that the value of nitrates formerly exported from Chile was nearly double the value of all forest products exported from all South America. The forest industries of this continent are merely in their infancy. They will increase in importance as the continent develops.

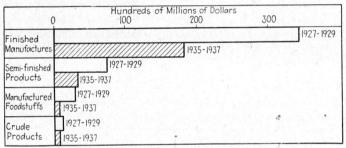

Fig. 196.—Comparison of United States exports to South America by classes in 3-year periods, 1927–1929 and 1935–1937.

Manufacturing.—As was shown in the discussion of the various countries in the preceding chapters, manufacturing is of importance in only a few South American cities. These are Buenos Aires, São Paulo, Rio de Janeiro, and Santiago; yet all of these together manufacture less in value than a city like Chicago. South American cities owe their growth chiefly to commerce or to the political and social attractions of the capitals. Smoking chimneys and great factories are few in South America. The seven leading cities of the continent have an aggregate population about equal to that of New York or London.

However, it must be emphasized that a pronounced trend toward industrialization has been on the way in South America in recent years and many commodities, formerly imported, are now manufactured in sufficient amounts to meet local requirements (Fig. 196). This is particularly true of Argentina and Brazil, and these countries produce some manufactured goods for export to their neighbors. Lack of local markets and insufficient coal were deterrent factors for many years, but increased purchasing power and recently developed hydroelectric power have made it possible to extend manufacturing operations, even in the fabrication of iron and steel products.

Transportation.—In only four sections of South America are railways sufficiently numerous to serve the needs of the regions even fairly well. These are (1) the Argentine Pampa, (2) the coffee-growing section of Brazil, (3) Uruguay, and (4) the Central Valley of Chile. To these might be added the Nitrate Belt of Chile, where the railroads have little traffic except that arising from the nitrate operations and from two large copper camps.

Argentina has the largest mileage and the best system. Most of the lines were built and are operated by British companies. The railroad mileage of Argentina (nearly 25,000) is about 40 per cent of that of all South America. This railway leadership possessed by Argentina is the outgrowth of the levelness and productivity of the Pampa. Other parts of the country are not well equipped with railways because there is not sufficient traffic to support them. The excellent progress of Argentina is due in no small measure to its network of railroads in its most productive section.

Railway building in Uruguay, also, has been relatively easy and reasonably remunerative. This little country has more miles of line in proportion to area and population than any other South American country. Most of these roads, also, were built and are operated by British companies.

In the coffee-growing section of Brazil, a rather complete network of lines, terminating at Santos and Rio de Janeiro, has been built. Elsewhere in Brazil, detached lines (with a few feeders) extending to a port are the rule. Some of the lines are corporation-owned, some are state-owned, and others are government-owned. The total mileage of about 20,500 is almost wholly in the states on the eastern side of the country. A few of the lines are excellent, especially the British-owned line from the coffee region of São Paulo to the port of Santos. Many are poorly built and equipped and yield an annual deficit. In proportion to area and population, Brazil has a small railway mileage. This fact is both a cause and a result of the undeveloped condition of the greater part of the country.

The Longitudinal Railway of Chile, extending nearly 1,600 miles from north to south, has many crosslines reaching to the ports, and these give a larger proportion of the country railway service than almost any other in South America has. Chile is also well served by steamship lines along the coast.

All the Andean countries north of Chile have little railway mileage and very few highways suited to wheeled vehicles. The massive ranges of the Andes make railway building in these countries almost prohibitive in cost. Few of the expensive mountain railways can return any profit on the investment, and most of them must have government assistance. In no other way does the great Andean barrier make itself more felt than in holding back the development of transportation, which in turn holds back all other forms of development.

It should be emphasized that in South America, as well as in some other parts of the world, the railway net is not always an indication of good transportation. In many parts, railway service is infrequent even where lines are fairly numerous.

In only a few places in all South America are there good highways. One of our smaller states has more miles of modern highways than all South America. Yet the country roads of the United States were poor until recently. Good roads are expensive to build and maintain, and most of South America cannot yet afford them. There are several times as many miles of railway in the continent as there are of good roads. In five countries, Venezuela, Colombia, Ecuador, Peru, and Bolivia, and in parts of several other countries, pack animals do a large part of the carrying not done on rivers or on the sea. Tropical climate, mountainous topography, and insufficiency of capital are all reasons for the conditions that exist. Many of the bonds issued for railway construction have not turned out well for investors, and the securing of foreign capital for this purpose is not easy. Increase in highway mileage has gone on so rapidly in South America in the last decade that it is difficult to give any accurate statistics. Many of the countries had started building roads before the general depression, and construction was temporarily suspended. In the last four or five years, however, activity has again begun, and road building is progressing rapidly.

Rivers are much used in three regions: (1) the Amazon valley, which has upward of 25,000 miles of navigable waterways; (2)

the River Plata system consisting of the River Plata estuary, the Uruguay, the Paraná and the Paraguay, which forms an outlet for Paraguay and southern Brazil; (3) the Magdalena, which is the chief means of reaching interior Colombia. All these serve large regions that either are not served at all or are poorly served by railroads; yet the tonnage of traffic that they carry is not great. The Orinoco in Venezuela carries only a small traffic. The rivers are used mainly because there are no better means of transportation but also because they carry certain heavy products more cheaply than railroads can.

INTERNAL POLITICAL AND SOCIAL CONDITIONS

It is frankly recognized by many South Americans that the majority of their 10 republics have been republics only in name.[1] Although the general trend is toward improvement, there are frequent setbacks. During the last two decades there have been serious and successful revolutions in several countries, including Argentina and Brazil, two of the most advanced. A strong president is very likely to develop into a dictator, and it is frequently said that the best governments in the backward countries are the enlightened dictatorships. Far too commonly, public office is treated as an opportunity for personal profit, as it has been and still is in places in the United States.

A very unfortunate condition in most of the countries is the diversion of funds appropriated for public improvements into the pockets of a large staff of officials, superintendents, inspectors, and others, with the result that a high proportion of the funds does not go into the authorized improvements. Several of the countries are so heavily in debt and administer their finances so badly that their credit is impaired and they must pay high rates of interest on foreign loans. In the matter of national credit as in other respects, the countries differ widely as between the best and the worst. These countries greatly need foreign capital. The people of large wealth have the greater part of it in land. They either cannot or will not use this wealth freely in the purchase of bonds or stocks of railways and industrial enterprises. Very large sums of foreign capital have been invested in South American railways, mines, port works, and other enterprises,

[1] See Calderon, F. Garcia, Dictatorship and Democracy in Latin America, *Foreign Affairs*, vol. 3, pp. 459–477, 1925.

with all degrees of success. Some of the ventures have paid handsomely, and others have resulted in heavy losses to the investors. It is undoubtedly true that one chief hindrance to the economic development of several South American republics has been the foreign capitalists' lack of confidence in the governments concerned.

In the matter of schools,[1] South America as a whole is deficient, for two main reasons: (1) the lack of funds and (2) the general attitude of the educated classes. As a rule, the latter are but little interested in education for the lower classes. In regions where the colored and mixed races predominate, illiteracy predominates.[2] Outside the cities, schools, as a rule, are few and poor. This is most general in the Andean countries north of Chile and in tropical Brazil. School conditions are best in cities of Argentina, Uruguay, central Chile, and southeastern Brazil. Whereas appropriations for schools in cities in the United States are $40 to $60 per pupil annually, in many South American cities they are only 20 to 25 per cent as much. Where there is a preponderance of uneducated people, real republican institutions cannot exist, earning power and buying power are low, sanitary and health conditions are bad, and general economic backwardness prevails.

SOUTH AMERICA'S EXTERNAL RELATIONSHIPS

Foreign Investments in South America.—From the foregoing section, it might be inferred that South American countries have not been able to attract foreign capital to any large extent. They have attracted such capital to the extent of over $9,000,000,000, a large sum, but wholly insufficient for the development of these countries. British investments are probably the largest and approximate $4,000,000,000.[3] Before the World War, France was the next heaviest investor in South America with a total of about $1,600,000,000. Since the World War, the United States has greatly increased its investments in the southern continent,

[1] See Lucky, George W. A., Outline of Educational Systems and School Conditions in Latin America, U.S. Bureau of Education, *Bull.* 44, Washington, D.C., 1923.

[2] In Brazil, Colombia, Venezuela, Ecuador, Peru, Bolivia and Paraguay, 75 to 80 per cent of the people are illiterate; in Chile, Argentina, and Uruguay, about 30 per cent.

[3] Halsey, F. M. Investments in Latin America, *Special Agents Series* 169, p. 20, U.S. Dept. of Commerce, 1918.

and the U.S. Department of Commerce estimated the total in 1924 at $1,300,000,000.[1] German and other investments bring the grand total in 1930 to $9,000,000,000 or more.

The largest investments are in the railways of the east-coast countries. They are supplied mainly by British and French capital. Large sums of United States capital are invested in meat-

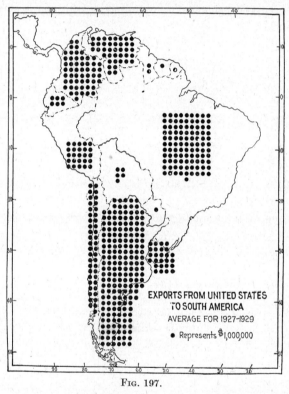

EXPORTS FROM UNITED STATES
TO SOUTH AMERICA
AVERAGE FOR 1927-1929
● Represents $1,000,000

FIG. 197.

packing plants in the River Plata lands and southeastern Brazil. Still larger sums are invested in mining operations in the west-coast countries. Americans are the largest owners of telegraph cables reaching South America; excellent and frequent American steamship and air lines connect South American ports with those of the United States. A large majority of the banks in South America are foreign-owned. The United States has only recently entered the foreign banking field. In comparison with the British,

[1] This amount was increased every year until 1930.

the Americans have been only moderate suppliers of capital to South America. Since the World War, European countries have not been able to furnish much capital, and the United States is increasingly doing this. Often these loans are partly expended in the purchase of machinery, equipment, or other materials from United States manufacturers. Undoubtedly, South American countries will buy more goods from the United States if American

EXPORTS FROM
UNITED STATES
TO SOUTH AMERICA
THREE YEAR AVERAGE
1935-1937
• Represents $1,000,000

Fig. 198.

investors will lend them the money with which to do it. With some of these countries, borrowing is a pleasant process, but paying is disagreeable and horribly inconvenient.

Trade Relations.—The annual foreign trade (exports plus imports) of the 10 South American countries is about $2,000-000,000, or about $25 per capita. This is creditable, but not large. Cuba, for example, has a per capita foreign trade nearly three times as large. About one-third of the external commerce of South America is with the United States, which is much more than the share of Great Britain. Exports from the United States to that continent rose from approximately $120,000,000 a year, just before the World War, to nearly $500,000,000 in the decade following the war. At present, it amounts to around $300,000,000 (Figs. 197 and 198). United States imports from South America increased from $200,000,000 to $550,000,000 in the immediate

IMPORTS INTO UNITED STATES
FROM SOUTH AMERICA
AVERAGE FOR 1927-1929
• Represents $1,000,000

FIG. 199.

postwar period and have since declined to around $400,000,000 (Figs. 199 and 200). This growth is just about the normal rate of increase in the total of United States foreign trade. The growth of United States commerce with Canada, Asia, and Africa has been considerably more rapid. In fact, United States trade with the 10 or 11 million people of Canada is larger than with the 80 to 90 millions of South America. The producing power and the purchasing power of half the people of South America is so low that it pulls down the general average of the continent, for the average in the temperate part of South America is high. Almost half the foreign commerce of South America is carried on by Argentina.

When one considers the tremendous growth of the foreign trade of Cuba, he is convinced that tropical lands are capable of great development if favorable economic and political conditions can be maintained.

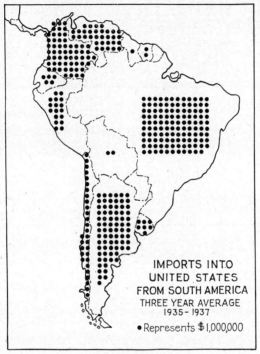

IMPORTS INTO
UNITED STATES
FROM SOUTH AMERICA
THREE YEAR AVERAGE
1935-1937
• Represents $1,000,000

FIG. 200.

South American exports are almost exclusively products of ranch, plantation, mine, and forest. This is to be expected in a continent in the stage of development that South America now occupies. The largest single export is petroleum, coming mainly from Venezuela, but also from Colombia and Peru. The two largest items exported from the west coast are copper and nitrates, together valued at over $150,000,000 a year, with copper far in the lead. Wool exported principally from the River Plata lands frequently exceeds $25,000,000 a year. Every country of

South America exports hides and skins. The United States commonly takes $20,000,000 to $25,000,000 worth of these annually, the largest part coming from Argentina. Flaxseed, sent from Argentina to the United States, reaches $20,000,000 to $30,000,000 a year. Cacao from Brazil, Ecuador, and Venezuela exceeds $10,000,000. Rubber from the Amazon valley, once a leading import into the United States, declined to $2,000,000 or $3,000,000 a year but increased during the higher prices that prevailed in 1924 to 1925. The large exports of cereals and meats go mainly to Europe.

The location of South America, largely in the tropics, and of the United States, in the intermediate zone, would be expected to stimulate a very large exchange of products. Of the four leading United States imports, three are tropical products, cane sugar, coffee, and rubber. The United States' chief source of cane sugar is Cuba; of rubber, southeastern Asia. Of the three leaders, only coffee comes from South America. Bananas come into the United States mostly from Central America and Jamaica. The largest source of cacao is west Africa, although large quantities also come from South America. All these products are grown in South America; yet, for one reason or another, the United States depends mainly upon that continent for only one of the five. However, the United States buys more from South American countries than it sells to them.

Many years ago Great Britain and, in a lesser degree Germany and France supplied South America with most of its needed manufactures. The United States has only recently been a serious competitor for this trade. European exporters had developed the trade and could usually undersell American exporters. The United States, however, has built up an active trade in certain articles that Europe is not well prepared to supply, such as lumber and timber, petroleum products, agricultural and mining machinery, and, more recently, machine tools and automobiles. American automobiles almost monopolize the South American markets. The United States' enormous production for home demand enables it to manufacture automobiles more cheaply than any other country. Railway materials and special machinery are exported from the United States to South America in increasing quantities; but United States sales of textiles, hardware, and general merchandise are not large. These still come mainly from Europe and

especially from Great Britain and Germany. There is some doubt
as to the ability of the United States to meet European competition in this field of general manufactures.

Beginning in the early 1930's and particularly after 1934,
German imports increased rapidly in South American countries.
By 1937, German products had assumed large proportions sur-
passing Great Britain in most countries and exceeding the United
States in at least two—Brazil and Chile. Recent events in Europe
have, of course, brought to an end temporarily this rapid rise in
German imports to Latin American countries.

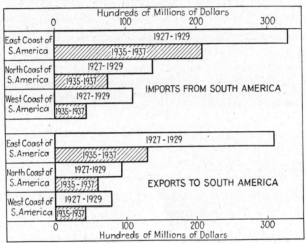

Fig. 201.—Comparison of United States trade with South America in 3-year
periods, 1927–1929 and 1935–1937.

About 60 per cent of the United States trade with South
America is with the three east-coast countries, Brazil, Argentina,
and Uruguay; about 25 per cent is with the north-coast countries;
and 15 per cent with the west coast. Ordinarily the balance of
trade is against the United States in every South American
country with the exception of Bolivia (Fig. 201).

The Panama Canal and South American Trade.—The opening
of the Panama Canal in 1914 has had a favorable effect upon the
commerce between the United States and the west coast of South
America. The effect, however, does not show itself in any great
increase in the actual volume of goods sold to the west coast,
although the percentage of increase is considerable. It is to be

remembered that the total population of the west-coast countries (omitting Colombia) is less than 20 million, the majority of whom earn very low wages and hence have very low purchasing power. So far as the consumption of goods from the United States is concerned, probably half or more of these people may almost be

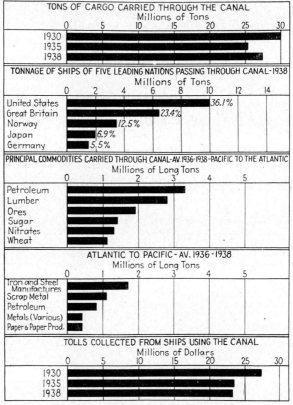

FIG. 202.—The use of the Panama Canal.

dropped from consideration. The opening of the canal greatly increases the ease with which United States exporters can send goods to the west coast of South America. It does not, however, have very much effect upon the buying power of the Indian and mestizo people who live in the mountains and on the high plateaus.

The canal is performing a valuable service, however, in making possible direct and frequent steamship service between the eastern United States and the west coast of South America. The excellent steamship service through the canal is attracting an ever-increasing stream of tourists, educators, businessmen, and others, whose visits to South America are doing much to inform North Americans and to correct misapprehensions and misunderstandings. Though trade between the United States and the west coast increased 160 per cent in value during the first 10 years following the opening of the canal, this represents a total increase of only $120,000,000 in a total increase of United States foreign trade during that period amounting to more than $4,000,000,000.

The canal has greatly facilitated the shipment of three mineral products from the west coast to the eastern United States, namely, nitrate, copper, and iron ore (Fig. 202). The greater part of these come from Chile, and total United States importations from Chile increased 300 per cent in value during the decade following the opening of the canal. The value of exports from the United States to Ecuador and Peru nearly doubled during this decade. This is a little below the ratio of the growth of the general foreign trade of the United States. The direct effect of the canal upon United States commerce with the west coast may be expressed thus: The canal has permitted a normal growth in United States trade with western South America. This normal growth would not have been possible if the barrier at Panama had not been cut through.

It is evident that increased intercourse of the United States with the west coast is leading to the increased investment of United States capital and to a steadily growing interest in the development and stability of these republics.

TOWARD IMPROVED RELATIONS

In the past, the relations of South American countries with several countries of Europe were closer than those with the United States. Culturally, France has occupied first place in the minds of South Americans. Commercially and financially, Great Britain has stood closest, for British capital has done more to develop these countries than has that of any other nation. Until quite recently, the United States devoted its capital and energy to developing its own resources and its own internal commerce. Only since the opening of the present century has the United States entered vigorously upon a policy of financial and commercial expansion. The acquisition of territory in the Caribbean region in 1898, the development of close relations with Cuba, the building of the Panama Canal, the establishment of United States banks in Latin America, the accumulation of large sums of money for investment, the severe setback that European countries received from the World War, and the great improvement of steamship service to both coasts of South America have all favored the expansion of American interests in the southern continent (Fig. 203).

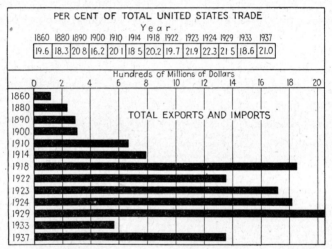

FIG. 203.—Trade of United States with Latin America, 1860–1937. The above figures are those of all Latin America, which includes Mexico, Central America, the West Indies, and South America.

Partly owing to advantages derived from the World War, United States trade with South America far exceeds that of any European country. But that increase has not been purely accidental. It is due also to more intelligent and more energetic efforts. The United States Departments of Commerce and of State have sent to South American countries well-trained, high type men as commercial *attachés*, consuls, trade commissioners, and special financial investigators. No European nation has found itself able to send so many men to study South American conditions and report upon them so thoroughly as the United States has done. The publications included in the United States *Consular Reports*, *Special Agents Series*, *Trade Promotion Series*, *Tariff Series*, *Trade Information Bulletins*, and others, make available to exporters and to the American people at large a vast body of information. The fine type of men who have been sent to South America to fill responsible official positions and to represent leading business houses promises well for the future. The strong place held by the British in South American business affairs is due in no small degree to the substantial and able men who represent British interests abroad.

Complaints of defective packing, unduly short credits, failure to send the exact goods ordered, and other shortcomings of United States exporters have greatly decreased. If the prices and quality of goods offered by American firms are as favorable as those offered by other firms, they get their share of the orders. One important difficulty is that of selling American-made goods as cheaply as European-made goods can be sold.

Tens of thousands of American visitors are now going to South America yearly, and large numbers of South American students are attending schools and universities in the United States. Increasingly, these universities are establishing courses that deal with South American political and social institutions, history, and geography. In recent years, there has been a tremendous increase in the study of Spanish in the United States. All these influences are helping to clear away past misunderstandings on both sides, and a genuinely cordial feeling is growing up. However, the Latin American is more sensitive and temperamental than the Anglo-American. He is prompt to resent any assumption of superiority on the part of the North American; he resents any air of condescension, objects to haste or high-pressure business methods, and attaches much weight to good manners, to fastidious dress, and to the social graces generally.

Many American firms have found the South American market unprofitable, because the cost of doing business exceeded the profits. This must often be true where orders are small. Unless the value of sales is considerable or the selling costs are largely assumed by local selling agencies, there is little profit in much South American business. But when the astonishing commerce that the United States has built up in the Caribbean region, especially in Cuba and Puerto Rico, is considered, there is reason for believing that something similar may be accomplished in other parts of Latin America. If one-half of the population of South America were to purchase as many American products per capita as the Cubans buy, the commerce of the United States with South America would be over $3,000,000,000 a year.

Bibliography

ACKERMAN, RALPH E. Forest Resources and Lumber Industry of Chile, *Trade Information Bull.* 324, U.S. Dept. of Commerce, Washington, D.C., 1925.

AGASSIZ, PROFESSOR and MRS. LOUIS. A Journey in Brazil, Boston, 1868.

AKERS, C. E. History of South America, New York, 1912.

ALBES, EDWARD. Rio de Janeiro, *Bull. Pan-Am. Union,* vol. 44, pp. 693–717, 1917.

———. Santiago, Chile's Charming Capital, *Bull. Pan-Am. Union,* vol. 46, pp. 141–172, 1918.

———. Tagua-Vegetable Ivory, *Bull. Pan-Am. Union,* vol. 37, pp. 192–208, 1913.

Anuario Estadistico de la Republica del Paraguay, Asunción, Annual.

Anuario Estadistico de la Republica del Uruguay, Montevideo, Annual.

ARANJO, OSCAR D'. Le Climat du Brazil, *Revue Scientifique,* vol. 52, Paris, 1914.

Argentina, Ministerio de Agricultura, Official Publications:

El Cultivo del Maiz, *Circular* 640, 1926.

El Rendimiento de Trigo, *Circular* 623, 1926.

Los Porcinos, *Circular* 618, 1926.

Plantas Forrajeras, *Circular* 562, 1926.

Sistemas y Máquinas para Cosecha de Trigo, *Circular* 489, 1925.

Argentina, Official Publications:

Anuario del Comercio Exterior de la Republica Argentina, Annual.

Anuario Estadistico, Buenos Aires, Annual.

Argentine Republic, Agricultural and Pastoral Census, 3 vols., Buenos Aires, 1909.

BABSON, R. W. Future of South America, New York, 1915.

BAIN, H. FOSTER, and MULLIKEN, H. S. The Cost of Chilean Nitrate, Part I of the Nitrogen Survey, *Trade Information Bull.* 170, U.S. Dept. of Commerce, Washington, D.C., 1924.

———, and READ, THOMAS T. Ores and Industry in South America, New York, 1934.

BANCROFT, HOWLAND. Bolivian Tin and Its Relation to the United States, *Proc. Sec. Pan-Am. Sci. Cong.,* Washington, D.C., 1915–1916, vol. 8, pp. 294–309, Washington, D.C., 1917.

BARCLAY, W. S. The Geography of South American Railways, *Geog. Jour.*, vol. 49, pp. 161–201, 241–282, 1917.

———. The River Paraná, an Economic Survey, *Geog. Jour.*, vol. 33, pp. 1–10, 1909.

BARRETT, ROBERT and KATHARINE. A Yankee in Patagonia, Edward Chace, New York, 1931.

BARTH, E. Petroleum Resources of Bolivia, *Bull. Pan-Am. Union*, vol. 62, pp. 468–474, 1928.

BARTHOLOMEW and HERBERTSON. Atlas of Meteorology, Edinburgh, 1899.

BELL, P. L. Colombia. A Commercial and Industrial Handbook, *Special Agents Series* 206, U.S. Dept. of Commerce, Washington, D.C., 1921.

BELTRAN, G. G. La Geografía de la Argentina, Buenos Aires, 1917.

BENNETT, FRANK. Forty Years in Brazil, London, 1914.

BENNETT, H. H. Some Geographic Aspects of Western Ecuador, *Annals Asso. Am. Geographers*, vol. 15, pp. 126–147, 1925.

BEORO, J. A. Geografía de la Nación Argentina, Buenos Aires, 1914.

BINGHAM, HIRAM. Across South America, Boston, 1911.

———. Across Venezuela and Colombia, New Haven, 1909.

———. Inca Land, New York, 1922.

———. The Wonderland of Peru, *Nat. Geog. Mag.*, vol. 24, pp. 387–574, 1913.

———. Further Explorations in the Land of the Incas, *Nat. Geog. Mag.*, vol. 29, pp. 431–524, 1916.

BLACK, WILLIAM SPENCE. Problem of Life at High Altitudes, *Engineering and Mining Journal Press*, vol. 114, pp. 800–804, 1922.

BLAKESLEE, G. H. The Adaptability of the White Man to Tropical America, Addresses on Latin America, pp. 360–386, Clark University, 1913.

BLANCHARD, W. O. Foreign-trade Routes of Bolivia, *Jour. of Geog.*, vol. 22, pp. 341–345, 1923.

BLAND, J. O. P. Men, Manners, and Morals in South America, New York, 1920.

Blue Book of Colombia, New York, 1918.

BOLLO, LUIS CINCINATO. South America, Past and Present, translated from the Spanish, New York, 1919.

BOURNE, EDWARD G. Spain in America, 1450–1580, New York, 1904.

BOWMAN, HEATH, and DICKINSON, STERLING. Westward from Rio, New York, 1936.

BOWMAN, ISAIAH. Desert Trails of Atacama, *Am. Geog. Soc.*, New York, 1924.

———. The Andes of Southern Peru, *Am. Geog. Soc.*, New York, 1916.

———. Geographical Aspects of the New Madeira-Mamoré Railroad, *Bull. Am. Geog. Soc.*, vol. 45, pp. 275–281, 1913.

———. Man and Climatic Change in South America, *Geog. Jour.*, vol. 33, pp. 267–278, 1909.

———. The Andes of Southern Peru, *Am. Geog. Soc.*, New York, 1916.

———. The Distribution of Population in Bolivia, *Bull. Geog. Soc. Phila.*, vol. 7, pp. 74–93, 1909.

———. The Highland Dwellers of Bolivia: An Anthropological Interpretation, *Bull. Geog. Soc. Phila.*, vol. 7, pp. 159–184, 1909.

———. Trade Routes in the Economic Geography of Bolivia, *Bull. Am. Geog. Soc.*, vol. 42, pp. 22–37, 90–104, 180–192, 1910.

BRADY, GEORGE S. Argentine Road Development, *U.S. Commerce Reports*, pp. 247–255, Apr. 13, 1920.

————. The Comodoro Rivadavia Petroleum Fields, *U.S. Commerce Reports*, pp. 602–608, Aug. 1, 1921.

————. Railways of South America—Argentina, *Trade Promotion Series 32*, U.S. Dept. of Commerce, Washington, D.C., 1926.

BRANDT, D. Kulturgeographie von Brasilien, Stuttgart, 1923.

BRANNER, JOHN C. Out ines of the Geology of Brazil, to accompany the geologic map of Brazil; includes large map in color and extensive bibliography, *Bull. Geol. Soc. Am.*, vol. 30, pp. 189–338, 1920.

Brazil, Official Publications:
Annuario Estatistico do Brasil, no. 1 (1908–1912), 2 vols., Rio de Janeiro, 1917.
E azilian Yearbook, only 1908, 1909, Rio de Janeiro.
Commercio Exterior do Brasil, Rio de Janeiro, Anpual.
Directoria Geral de Estatistica, Rio de Janeiro, Annual.
Recenseamento do Brasil, Three vols., Introduction, 1922; Agr., 1923; Agr. and Ind., 1924; Agr., 1925, Ministerio do Agr., Ind., and Com., Rio de Janeiro.

British Department of Overseas Trade. *Economic and Financial Conditions in Argentina*, London, Annual.

————. *Economic Conditions in Bolivia*, London, Annual.

————. *Economic and Financial Conditions in Brazil*, London, Annual.

————. *Economic Conditions in Chile*, London, Annual.

————. *Economic Conditions in Colombia*, London, Annual.

————. *Economic Conditions in Ecuador*, London, Annual.

————. *Economic Conditions in Paraguay*, London, Annual.

————. *Economic Conditions in Uruguay*, London, Annual.

————. *Report on the Finances, Industries, and Trade of Peru*, London, Annual.

BROWN, H. R. and MACE, B. M. Cost of Transportation and Handling of Argentine Wheat, *Trade Information Bull. 439*, U.S. Dept. of Commerce, Washington, D.C., 1926.

BRUCE, G. J. Brazil and the Brazilians, New York, 1914.

BRYCE, JAMES. South America; Observations and Impressions, New York, 1912.

BULEY, E. C. North Brazil; South Brazil, 2 vols., New York, 1914.

BUNGE, ALEJANDRO E. Ferrocarriles Argentinos, Buenos Aires, 1918.

————. Las Industrias del Norte, Buenos Aires, 1922.

————. Analisis del Comercio Exterior Argentino en los Años 1910–1922, Buenos Aires, 1923.

CALDERON, F. GARCIA. Latin America, Its Rise and Progress, New York, 1913.

CARLSON, FRED A. Geography of Latin America, New York, 1936.

CARPENTER, FRANK G. Chile and Argentina, New York, 1923.

————. Lands of the Andes and Desert, New York, 1924.

CARVALHO, C. M. D. DE. Meteorologie do Brasil (bibliography), London, 1917.

————. Geografía do Brasil, Rio de Janeiro, 1913.

————. The Geography of Brazil in Relation to Its Political and Economic Development, *Scot. Geog. Mag.*, vol. 34, pp. 41–55, 1918.

Cattle Industry in Colombia. *Special Circular 12*, Foodstuffs Division of U.S. Dept. of Commerce, Washington, D.C., pp. 1–9, 1928.

Cerballos, Pedro F. Geografía de la Republica del Ecuador, Lima, 1888.

Chalmers, Sir David P. British Guiana, *Scot. Geog. Mag.*, vol. 12, pp. 125–139, 1896.

Chamberlain, E. T. Shipping of the West and East Coasts of South America, *Trade Information Bull.* 304, U.S. Dept. of Commerce, Washington, D.C., 1925.

Chile, Official Publications:

Anuario Estadistico de la Republica de Chile, Santiago, Annual.

Oficina Central de estadistica; *Statistical abstract of Chile*, Santiago, Annual.

Chile Economico, Santiago, 1914.

Estadistica Comercial de la Republica de Chile, Valparaiso, Annual.

Estado actual de la Agricultura en Chile, Dirección General de los Servicios Agricolas, Santiago, 1919.

Sinopsis Estadistica y Geografica de Chile, Santiago, Annual.

Church, Col. George E. Aborigines of South America, London, 1912.

———. South America: An Outline of Its Physical Geography, *Geog. Jour.*, vol. 17, pp. 333–406, 1901.

Clapp, E. G. Review of the Present Knowledge Regarding the Petroleum Resources of South America, *Bull. Am. Inst. Mining Engrs.* 130, pp. 1739–1791, 1917.

Clemenceau, G. E. B. South America Today (Argentina, Brazil, Chile), New York, 1911.

Coker, R. E. Peru's Wealth-producing Birds, *Nat. Geog. Mag.*, vol. 37, pp. 537–566.

———. The Fisheries and Guano Industry of Peru, *Bull. U.S. Bureau of Fisheries*, vol. 28, pp. 333–365, Washington, D.C., 1908.

Colin, Elicio (sous la direction de). Bibliographie Géographique, Librairie Armond Colin, Paris, Annual.

Colonial Reports. British Guiana, London, Annual.

Commercial Traveler's Guide to Latin America. Part I, West Coast of South America, Part II, East Coast of South America, U.S. Dept. of Commerce Bureau of Foreign and Domestic Commerce, Washington, D.C., 1939, 1938.

Conway, Sir Martin. The Bolivian Andes, New York and London, 1901.

Cooper, Clayton S. The Brazilians and their Country, New York, 1917.

———. Understanding South America, New York, 1918.

Corthell, Elmer L. Two Years in Argentina as the Consulting Engineer of National Public Works, *Bull. Am. Geog. Soc.*, vol. 35, pp. 439–471, 1903.

Coxe, George R. The States of Brazil, *Trade Information Bull.* 148, U.S. Dept. of Commerce, Washington, D.C., 1923.

Crespo, Jorge B. Geografía Economica del Brasil (in Spanish), Buenos Aires, 1919.

———. Geografía de la Republica de Bolivia, La Paz, 1910.

Crist, Raymond. Life on the Llanos of Venezuela, *Bull. Geog. Soc. Phila.*, vol. 35, no. 2, April, 1937.

Cuevas, Enrique. The Nitrate Industry, *Proc. Sec. Pan-Am. Sci. Cong.*, Washington, D.C., 1915–1916, vol. 8, pp. 37–62, Washington, D.C., 1917.

Cunningham, R. B. The Conquest of the River Plate, New York, 1924.

CURRAN, FRANK B. Motor Roads of Latin America (with lists of sources, references and 10 maps), *Trade Promotion Series* 18, U.S. Dept. of Commerce, Washington, D.C., 1925.

DAVIES, HOWELL (ED.). *The South American Handbook*, Annual, London.
DAVIS, WALTER G. *Climate of the Argentine Republic, and Pastoral Census of 1908*, vol. 3, pp. 597–705, 44 plates (in English and Spanish), Buenos Aires, 1909; also published as a separate bulletin (in English), 1910.
DAWSON, E. R. British Guiana and its Development, *Jour. Royal Colonial Institute*, vol. 39, pp. 313–337, 1907.
DAWSON, THOMAS C. The South American Republics, 2 vols., New York, 1903.
DECOUD, H. Geografía de la Republica del Paraguay, Leipzig, 1911.
DENIS, PIERRE. Amérique du Sud, Géographie Universelle, vol. 15, Paris, 1927.
———. Brazil, translated by Bernard Miall, New York, 1911.
———. The Argentine Republic, translated from the French by Joseph McCabe, London, 1922 (excellent).
DESMOND, ALICE CURTIS. South American Adventures, New York, 1934.
DICKEY, HERBERT S. My Jungle Book, Boston, 1932.
DOBKIN, WILLIAM W. Petroleum Industry and Trade of Peru and Ecuador, *Trade Information Bull.* 178, U.S. Dept. of Commerce, Washington, D.C., 1924.
DOMVILLE-FIFE, C. W. Great States of South America, New York, 1910.
———. The Real South America, New York, 1922.
———. The United States of Brazil, London, 1910.
DUGUD, JULIAN. Green Hell, New York, 1931.
DUNN, W. E. Peru, A Commercial and Industrial Handbook (530 pp.), U.S. Dept. of Commerce, Washington, D.C., 1925.
———. The Cotton Industry of Peru, *Trade Information Bull.* 95, U.S. Dept. of Commerce, Washington, D.C., 1923.
———. Road Construction in Peru, *Trade Information Bull.* 198, U.S. Dept. of Commerce, Washington, D.C., 1924.

EDER, PHANOR J. Colombia, New York, 1913.
EIJKMAN, DR. C. Some Questions Concerning the Influence of Tropical Climate on Man, *The Lancet*, vol. 206, pp. 887–893, 1924.
El Ecuador (Guia Comercial Agricola e Industrial de la Republic), Quito, Annual.
ELLIOT, G. F. SCOTT. Chile, New York, 1907.
ELLIOTT, L. E. Brazil Today and Tomorrow, New York, 1917.
———. Chile Today and Tomorrow, New York, 1922.
———. The Argentina of Today, New York, 1926.
———. The Romance of Nitrate, *Bull. Pan-Am. Union*, vol. 62, pp. 1129–1138, 1928.
EMORY, LLOYD T. Bauxite Deposits of British Guiana, *Engineering and Mining Journal Press*, vol. 191, pp. 686–689, 1925.
ENOCK, C. REGINALD. Ecuador, London, 1914.
———. Peru, London, 1908.
———. The Andes and the Amazon, London, 1917.

————. The Republics of South and Central America, New York and London, 1913, 2d ed., 1922.

————. The Great Pacific Coast, New York, 1910.

————. Spanish America: Its Romance, Reality and Future, 2 vols., New York, 1920.

————. The Secret of the Pacific, New York, 1914.

————. The Tropics, New York, 1916.

ENRIQUE, N. M. The Magdalena River, *Bull. Pan-Am. Union*, vol. 51, pp. 248–265, 1920.

ESTABROOK, L. M. Agricultural Survey of South America (Argentina and Paraguay), *U.S. Dept. of Agr. Bull.* 1409, Washington, D.C., 1926.

FERGUSSON, ERNA. Venezuela, New York, 1939.

FILSINGER, E. B. Commercial Travelers' Guide to Latin America, *Miscellaneous Series* 89, bibliography by countries, pp. 705–722, U.S. Dept. of Commerce, Washington, D.C. Latest revision.

————. Exporting to Latin America, pp. 465–498, New York, 1916.

FINCH, V. C., and BAKER, O. E. Geography of the World's Agriculture, U.S. Dept. of Agr., Washington, D.C., 1917.

FLEMING, PETER. Brazilian Adventure, New York, 1934.

FORD, M. F. The Nitrate Region of Chile and Its Ports, *U.S. Commerce Reports*, vol. 4, pp. 212–215, Washington, D.C., 1926.

Foreign Commerce Yearbook. Annual, U.S. Dept. of Commerce, Washington, D.C.

Fortune Magazine:

South America (general), vol. 16, December, 1937.

Peru, vol. 17, January, 1938.

Chile, vol. 17, May, 1938.

Argentina, vol. 18, July, 1938.

Venezuela, vol. 19, March, 1939.

Brazil, vol. 19, June, 1939.

FOUNTAIN, PAUL. The River Amazon, New York, 1914.

FRANCK, HARRY A. Vagabonding down the Andes, New York, 1917.

————. Working North from Patagonia, New York, 1921.

FRASER, JOHN FOSTER. The Amazing Argentine, New York, 1914.

GODING, F. W. The Manavi or Panama Hat, *Bull. Pan-Am. Union*, vol. 39, pp. 685–693, 1914.

GOLDSMITH, P. H. A Brief Bibliography of Books in English, Spanish, and Portuguese Relating to Latin America, 107 pp., New York, 1916.

GORDON, IRELAND. Boundaries, Possessions, and Conflicts in South America, Cambridge, Mass., 1938.

GREGORY, J. W. Interracial Problems and White Colonization in the Tropics, *Bull. Am. Meteor. Soc.*, vol. 5, p. 113, 1924.

HAAS, WILLIAM H. Studies in the Geography of Brazil, *Jour. of Geog.*, vol. 22, pp. 285–317, 325–335, 1923; vol. 23, pp. 167–180, 1924; vol. 24, pp. 83–93, 165–183, 1925.

————. The South American Indian, *Sci. Monthly*, vol. 19, pp. 186–215, 1924.

HALSEY, F. M. Investments in Latin America and the British West Indies, *Special Agents Series* 169, U.S. Dept. of Commerce, Washington, D.C., 1918.
———. The Railways of South and Central America, New York, 1914.
———. Railway Expansion in South America, New York, 1916.
——— and SHERWELL, G. B. Investments in Latin America; I. Argentina, U.S. Dept. of Commerce, Washington, D.C., 1925.
HAMMERTON, J. A. The Real Argentine, New York, 1915.
Handbook of Bolivia. Bolivian Consulate General in London, 1924.
HANKE, LEWIS (ED.). *Handbook of Latin American Studies.* Annual since 1936 giving bibliography of recent publications on Latin America. Many articles listed were consulted by the junior author.
HANN, J. Handbuch der Klimatologie, 3 vols., vol. 1 translated into English by R. De C. Ward, 1903, 2d ed., Stuttgart, 1908.
HARING, CHARLES H. South America Looks at the United States, New York, 1928.
HARRISON, E. Below the Equator, Chicago, 1918.
HASKINS, HALFORD L. Guide to Latin American History, Boston, 1922.
HEWETT, EDGAR L. Ancient Andean Life, New York, 1939.
HIRST, W. A. Argentina, London, 1910.
———. Guide to South America, New York, 1915.
HOAR, H. M. Quebracho, Tanning Materials Survey, Part III, *Trade Information Series* 295, U.S. Dept. of Commerce, Washington, D.C., 1924 (bibliography).
HOLDICH, SIR THOMAS. The Countries of the King's Award, London, 1904.
HUNTINGTON, E. The White Man and Tropical America, *Jour. of Race Development*, vol. 5, no. 2, pp. 185–211, 1914.
———, and CUSHING, S. W. The Nature and Possibilities of Tropical Agriculture, *Bull. Geog. Soc. Phila.*, December, 1919.

INMAN, SAMUEL G. Latin America; Its Place in World Life, New York, 1937.

JAMES, H. G. Brazil after a Century of Independence, New York, 1925.
——— and MARTIN, PERCY. The Republics of Latin America, New York, 1923.
JAMES, PRESTON E. Geographic Factors in the Development of Transportation in South America, *Econ. Geog.*, vol. 1, pp. 247–261, 1925.
———. Industrial Development in São Paulo State, Brazil, *Econ. Geog.*, vol. 11, pp. 258–266, 1935.
———. The Changing Patterns of Population in São Paulo State, Brazil, *Geog. Rev.*, vol. 28, no. 3, July, 1938.
———. The Transportation Problem of Highland Colombia, *Jour. of Geog.*, vol. 22, pp. 346–354, 1923.
———. The Upper Paraná Lowland, *Bull. Pan-Am. Union*, vol. 58, pp. 265–277, 1924.
JÁUREGUI ROSQUELLAS, ALFREDO. Geografía General de Bolivia, La Paz, 1918.
JEFFERSON, MARK. New Rainfall Maps of Brazil, *Geog. Rev.*, vol. 14, pp. 127–135, 1924.
———. Peopling the Argentine Pampa, *Am. Geog. Soc.*, New York, 1926.
———. Recent Colonization in Chile, *Research Series* 6, *Am. Geog. Soc.*, New York, 1921.

———. The Rainfall of Chile, *Research Series* 7, *Am. Geog. Soc.*, New York, 1921.

———. The Distribution of People in South America, *Bull. Geog. Soc. Phila.*, vol. 5, pp. 182–192, 1907.

———. The Real Temperatures throughout North and South America, *Geog. Rev.*, vol. 6, pp. 240–267, 1918.

———. Actual Temperatures of South America, *Geog. Rev.*, vol. 16, pp. 443–466, 1926.

JONES, CHESTER LLOYD. Caribbean Interests of the United States, New York, 1916.

———. Supplying the World's Coffee, *Jour. of Geog.*, vol. 14, pp. 129–135, 1916.

JONES, C. F. Agricultural Regions of South America, *Econ. Geog.*, vol. 4, no. 1, January, 1928.

———. Commerce of South America, New York, 1928.

———. South America, New York, 1930.

JONES, GROSVENOR M. Ports of Chile, *Daily Commerce Reports*, U.S. Dept. of Commerce, pp. 1619–1627, Washington, D.C., June 27, 1919.

———. Ports of Peru, *U.S. Commerce Report*, pp. 585–591, Washington, D.C., Apr. 28, 1919.

JONES, W. R. Tin Fields of the World, Mining Publications, London, 1925.

JOYCE, T. A. South American Archaeology, New York, 1912.

KEAN, A. H., and MARKHAM, C. R. Central and South America, *Stanford's Handbook Series*, London, 1901.

KELTIE, J. SCOTT (ED.). *Statesman's Yearbook*, bibliography for each country, London and New York, Annual.

KENDREW, W. G. The Climates of the Continents, Oxford, 1927.

KERR, GEORGE A. The Quebracho Forests of South America, *Bull. Pan-Am. Union*, vol. 54, pp. 9–34, 1922.

KIRCHER, JOSEPH C. Paraná Pine Lumber Industry of Brazil, *Trade Information Bull.* 493, U.S. Dept. of Commerce, Washington, D.C., 1927.

KOEBEL, W. H. Anglo-South American Handbook for 1921, London and New York, later editions called The South American Handbook, London, Annual.

———. The Great Southland; the River Plate and Southern Brazil, New York, 1920.

———. South America, New York, 1918.

———. South Americans, New York, 1915.

———. Paraguay, London, 1917.

———. South America, an Industrial and Commercial Field, New York, 1918.

———. The New Argentina, New York, 1923.

———. The Great South Land: the River Plate and Southern Brazil Today, New York, 1920.

———. Uruguay, London, 1912.

KOETTLETZ, REGINALD. From Pará to Manaos: A Trip up the Lower Amazon, *Scot. Geog. Mag.*, vol. 17, pp. 11–30, 1901.

LA FOND, G. La République Argentine, Paris, 1927.

LANDOR, W. SAVAGE. Across Unknown South America, Boston, 1913.

LANGE, A. The Rubber Workers of the Amazon, *Bull. Am. Geog. Soc.*, vol. 43, pp. 33–36, 1911.

LARDEN, WALTER. Argentine Plains and Andine Glaciers, London, 1911.

LATANÉ, J. H. The United States and Latin America, New York, 1920.

LATZINA, FRANCISCO. Geografía de la Republica Argentina, Buenos Aires, 1890.

LAVARRE, WILLIAM G. Diamonds and Orchids, New York, 1935.

LEEUW, HENDRIK DE. Crossroads of the Caribbean Sea, New York, 1935

LEVINE, V. Colombia, London, 1914.

LINDGREN, WALDEMAR. Gold and Silver Deposits in North and South America, *Proc. Sec. Pan-Am. Sci. Cong.*, Washington, D.C., 1915–1916, vol. 8, pp. 560–577, Washington, D.C., 1917.

LLOYD, REGINALD. Twentieth Century Impressions of Chile, London, 1915.

LONG, R. C. Brazil: An Economic Survey by States, *Trade Information Bull.* 349, U.S. Dept. of Commerce, Washington, D.C., 1925.

LONG, W. R. Railways of South America, *Trade Promotion Series* 39, U.S. Dept. of Commerce, Washington, D.C., 1927.

MAITLAND, FRANCIS J. G. Chile: Its Land and People, London, 1914.

MARKHAM, SIR CLEMENTS. The Incas of Peru, New York, 1910.

MARSTERS, V. F. Peru and Its Oil Field, *Bull. Pan-Am. Union*, vol. 52, pp. 590–594, 1921; also in *Petroleum Age*, April, 1921.

MARTIN, CARL. Landeskunde von Chile (contains extensive bibliography), Hamburg, 1923.

MARTIN, F. O. Explorations in Colombia, *Geog. Rev.*, vol. 19, pp. 621–637, 1929.

MARTIN, PERCY F. Peru of the Twentieth Century, London, 1911.

MARTINEZ, A. Colombia Yearbooks, 1925–1927, New York.

———— and LEWANDOWSKI, MAURICE. The Argentine in the Twentieth Century, New York (no date).

MATHER, KIRTLEY F. Along the Andean Front in Southeastern Bolivia, *Geog. Rev.*, vol. 12, pp. 358–374, 1922.

McBRIDE, GEORGE M. Chile: Land and Society, *Am. Geog. Soc.*, New York, 1936.

————. The Agrarian Indian Communities of Highland Bolivia, *Am. Geog. Soc. Research Series* 5, New York, 1921.

————. The Galapagos Islands, *Geog. Rev.*, vol. 6, pp. 229–239, 1918.

McCONNELL, I. W. Irrigation in Brazil (map), *Bull. Pan-Am. Union*, vol. 56, pp. 16–30, 1923.

McCREERY, W. G. and BYNUM, MARY L. The Coffee Industry of Brazil, *Trade Promotion Series* 92, U.S. Dept. of Commerce, Washington, D.C., 1930.

MEEHAN, M. J. The Ecuadorian Market, *Trade Information Bull.* 468, U.S. Dept. of Commerce, Washington, D.C., 1927.

————. The Guianas: Commercial and Economic Survey, *Trade Information Bull.* 516, U.S. Dept. of Commerce, Washington, D.C., 1927.

MERRIMAN, R. B. Rise of the Spanish Empire in the Old World and the New, vol. 4, New York, 1918.

MILLER, B. L., and SINGEWALD, J. T. Patiño Tin Mines, *Bull. Pan-Am. Union*, vol. 43, pp. 490–496, 1916.

———— and ————. The Fuel Situation in the Andine Plateaus, *Proc. Sec. Pan-Am. Sci. Cong.*, Washington, D.C., 1915–1916, vol. 8, pp. 709–717, Washington, D.C., 1917.

———— and ————. The Mineral Deposits of South America, extensive bibliography for each country, New York and London, 1919.

MILLER, G. M. The 1927–1928 Peruvian Expedition of the American Geographical Society, *Geog. Rev.*, vol. 19, pp. 1–37, 1929.

MILLS, J. G. Chile, New York, 1914.

MILSTEAD, H. P. Bolivia as a Source of Tin, *Econ. Geog.*, vol. 3, pp. 354–360, 1927.

————. Distribution of Crops in Peru, *Econ. Geog.*, vol. 4, pp. 88–106, 1928.

Minister of Agriculture. Naciones Utiles sobre La Republica Argentina, 2d ed., Buenos Aires, 1924.

Ministry of Foreign Affairs, Brazil, Annual, Rio de Janeiro.

MOSES, B. Spanish Dependencies in South America, New York, 1915.

MOSSMAN, R. C. Notes on the Rainfall of Chile, *Jour. Royal Meteor. Soc.*, vol. 44, pp. 294–302, 1918.

————. The Climate of Chile, *Jour. Scot. Meteor. Soc.*, vol. 15, pp. 313–346, 1911.

————. The Climate of São Paulo and Ceará, *Quart. Jour. Royal Meteor. Soc.*, vol. 45, pp. 53–63, 69–79, 1919.

MURPHY, ROBERT CUSHMAN. Bird Islands of Peru, New York, 1925.

————. The Guano Industry of Modern Peru, *Brooklyn Museum Quart.*, vol. 7, pp. 244–269, 1920.

————. The Sea Coast and Islands of Peru. *Brooklyn Museum Quart.*, vol. 7, no. 2, 1920; vol. 9, no. 4, 1922.

————. The Oceanography of the Peruvian Littoral with Reference to the Abundance and Distribution of Marine Life, *Geog. Rev.*, vol. 13, pp. 64–85, 1923.

————. The Most Valuable Birds in the World, *Nat. Geog. Mag.*, vol. 46, pp. 279–302, 1924.

————. Oceanic and Climatic Phenomena along the West Coast of South America during 1925, *Geog. Rev.*, vol. 16, pp. 26–54, 1926.

NASH, ROY. Brazilian Forest Policy, *Bull. Pan-Am. Union*, vol. 53, pp. 688–706, 1924.

————. The Conquest of Brazil, New York, 1926.

NESBITT, L. M. Desolate Marches, New York, 1936.

NILES, BLAIR. Casual Wanderings in Ecuador, London, 1923.

————. Colombia, Land of Miracles, New York, 1924.

————. Peruvian Pageant, New York, 1937.

The Nitrate Industry of Chile, *Latin-Am. Circ.* 67, *Commerce Reports*, vol. 2, p. 1093, 1920.

OAKENFULL, J. C. Brazil, London, several editions.

OGILVIE, ALAN G. Geography of the Central Andes, *Am. Geog. Soc.*, New York, 1922.

OSPINA, JULIO. Geologia Generally Economica de Colombia, *Proc. Sec. Pan-Am. Sci. Cong.*, Washington, D.C., 1915–1916, vol. 8, pp. 322–347, Washington, D.C., 1917.

Pan-American Union. Buenos Aires: Metropolis of the Southern Hemisphere, *Bull. Pan-Am. Union*, vol. 44, pp. 277–300, 1917.

———. List of Publications Issued or Distributed by the Pan-American Union, Washington, D.C., Annual.

———. The Magdalena River, vol. 51, pp. 248–265, 1920.

Parker, C. S. The Development of British Guiana, *United Empire*, vol. 4, pp. 422–429, 1913.

Parker, W. B. Chileans of Today, London, 1920.

———. Paraguayans of Today, Buenos Aires, 1920.

———. Uruguayans of Today, New York, 1921.

Paxson, F. L. The Independence of the South American Republics, Philadelphia, 1903.

Pearse, Arno S. Brazilian Cotton, *Report of the British Cotton Mission of 1921*, Manchester, England, 1921.

———. Cotton in North Brazil, Report of a Journey in 1923 by the British Cotton Mission, Manchester, England, 1923.

———. Colombia, with Special Reference to Cotton, London, 1928.

Peck, Annie S. Industrial and Commercial South America, bibliography, pp. 477–488, New York, 1922.

———. The South American Tour, bibliography, pp. 383–389, New York, 1924.

Pennington, A. Stuart. The Argentine Republic, New York, 1910.

Peru Official Publications:

Estadistica del Comercio Especial del Peru, Callao, 1920.

La Mineria en el Peru, Lima, 1908.

Los Carácteres Agrologicos de las Tierras Cultivadas en la Costa del Peru.

Reseña Historica de los Ferrocarriles del Peru, 1908.

Statistical Abstract of Peru, Annual.

Phoebus, M. A. Economic Development of Argentina since 1921, *Trade Information Series* 156, U.S. Dept. of Commerce, Washington, D.C., 1923.

Platt, Raye R. Present Status of International Boundaries in South America, *Geog. Rev.*, vol. 14, pp. 622–638, 1924.

———. Railroad Progress in Colombia, *Geog. Rev.*, vol. 16, pp. 82–97, 1926.

———. The Millionth Map of Hispanic America, *Geog. Rev.*, vol. 17, pp. 301–308, 1927.

Platt, Robert S. Coffee Plantations of Brazil: A Comparison of Occupance Patterns in Established and Frontier Areas, *Geog. Rev.*, vol. 25, pp. 231–239.

———. Items in the Chilean Pattern of Occupance, *Bull. Geog. Soc. Phila.*, vol. 32, pp. 33–41.

———. Patterns of Occupance in the Maracaibo Basin, *Annals Asso. Am. Geographers*, vol. 24, pp. 157–173.

———. Six Farms in the Central Andes, *Geog. Rev.*, vol. 22, no. 2, pp. 245–259.

Proceedings Second General Assembly Pan-Am. Inst. Geog. and Hist., Washington, D.C., 1937.

Rand, E. B. Coal Mining in Colombia, *U.S. Commerce Reports*, 1929, vol. 2, pp. 230–231.

Redfield, A. H. Brazil, A Study of Economic Conditions Since 1913, *Miscellaneous Series* 86, U.S. Dept. of Commerce, Washington, D.C., 1920.

Reed, W. G. South American Rainfall Types, *Quart. Jour. Royal Meteor. Soc.*, vol. 36, pp. 49–59, 1910.

Reid, William A. La Paz, the World's Highland Capital, *Bull. Pan-Am. Union*, vol. 46, pp. 574–597, 1918.

————. Lima: The City of the Kings, *Bull. Pan-Am. Union*, vol. 46, pp. 281–312, 1918.

————. Navigation on South American Rivers, *Bull. Pan-Am. Union*, vol. 43, pp. 13–32, 1916.

————. Ports and Harbors of South America, rev. ed., paper, Pan-American Union, 1923.

————. South American Port Improvements, West Coast *Bull., Pan-Am. Union*, vol. 14, pp. 141–165, 1917.

————. Ports and Harbors of South America, Washington, D.C., 1929.

Reyes, Rafael. The Two Americas, translated from the Spanish, New York, 1914.

Robertson, William S. History of the Latin American Nations, New York, 1922.

————. Rise of the Spanish American Republics, New York, 1918.

Robinson, William A. Voyage to Galapagos, New York, 1936.

Rodway, James. Guiana, British, Dutch and French, New York and London, 1912 (bibliography).

Roosevelt, Theodore. A Journey in Central Brazil, *Geog. Jour.*, vol. 45, pp. 97–110, 1915.

Root, Elihu. Latin America and the United States, Cambridge, Mass., 1917.

Rosenfeld, A. H. The Sugar Industry of Peru, *Tropical Plant Research Foundation, Sci. Contribution*, no. 6, Washington, D.C., 1926.

———— and Jones, C. F. The Cotton Industry of Peru, *Tropical Plant Research Foundation, Sci. Contribution*, no. 9, Washington, D.C., 1927.

Ross, E. A. South of Panama, New York, 1915.

Ross, H. J. Gordon. Argentina and Uruguay, London, 1917.

Roush, G. A. The Mineral Production of Latin America, *Proc. Sec. Pan-Am. Sci. Cong.*, Washington, D.C., 1915–1916, vol. 8, pp. 191–208, Washington, D.C., 1917.

Royal Institute of International Affairs. The Problem of International Investment, Oxford University Press, New York, 1937.

————. The Republics of South America—A Political and Cultural Survey, Oxford University Press, New York, 1937.

Rudolph, W. E. The River Loa of Northern Chile, *Geog. Rev.*, vol. 17, pp. 553–585, 1927.

Schleh, Emilio. La Industria Azucarera en su Primer Centenario, Buenos Aires, 1921.

————. La Industria Algodonera en La Argentina, Buenos Aires, 1923.

Schmidt, E. W. Die Agrarisch Exportwirtschaft Argentiniens, Jena, 1920.

Schmieder, O. (In *University of California Pubs. in Geog.*):
Alteration of the Argentine Pampa in the Colonial Period, vol. 2, pp. 303–321.
The Historical Geography of Tucuman, vol. 2, pp. 359–386.
The Pampa: A Natural or Culturally Induced Grassland, vol. 2, pp. 255–270.

SCHURZ, W. L. Bolivia: A Commercial and Industrial Handbook, *Special Agents Series* 208, U.S. Dept. of Commerce, Washington, D.C., 1921.

————. International Communications in South America, *Foreign Affairs*, vol. 3, pp. 624–636, 1925.

————. Paraguay: A Commercial Handbook, *Special Agents Series* 199, U.S. Dept. of Commerce, Washington, D.C., 1920.

————. The Brazilian Iron and Steel Industry, *Trade Information Bull.* 6, U.S. Dept. of Commerce, Washington, D.C., 1922.

————. Brazilian Sugar Industry, *U.S. Commerce Reports*, pp. 44–45, Jan. 7, 1924.

SCHURZ, W. L., and others. Rubber production in the Amazon Valley. *Trade Promotion Series* 23, U.S. Dept. of Commerce, Washington, D.C., 1925.

SHANAHAN, E. W. South America, New York, 1927.

SHEPHERD, W. R. Central and South America (brief), New York, 1914.

————. The Hispanic Nations of the New World, New Haven, 1919.

————. Historical Atlas, New York, 1911.

SHERWOOD, F. A. Glimpses of South America, New York, 1920.

SIEVERS, WILHELM. Süd und Mittclamcrika, Leipzig, 1914 (leading work in German).

SINGEWALD, J. T. Across the Peruvian Andes on Mule Back, *Bull. Pan-Am. Union*, vol. 52, pp. 250–252, 1921.

————. Among Bolivia's Highest Tin Mines, *Bull. Pan-Am. Union*, vol. 52, pp. 217–235, 1921.

———— and MILLER, B. L. The Genesis of the Chilean Nitrate Deposits, *Proc. Sec. Pan-Am. Sci. Cong.*, Washington, D.C., 1915–1916, vol. 8, pp. 873–879 (bibliography), Washington, D.C., 1917.

Sintesis Estadistica de la Republica Oriental del Uruguay, Montevideo.

SKOTTSBERG, CARL. The Islands of Juan Fernandez, *Geog. Rev.*, vol. 5, pp. 362–383, 1918.

SMITH, H. H. The Rubber Industry of the Amazon, London, 1916.

SMITH, H. L. and LITTELL, H. Education in Latin America, New York, 1934.

SMITH, J. RUSSELL. The Economic Geography of the Argentine Republic, *Bull. Am. Geog. Soc.*, vol. 35, pp. 130–143, 1903.

————. The Economic Importance of the Plateaus of Tropic America, *Bull. Am. Geog. Soc.*, vol. 43, pp. 36–45, 1911.

SNETHLEGE, EMILIE. Nature and Man in Eastern Pará, *Geog. Rev.*, vol. 4, pp. 41–50, 1917.

STARK, MABEL C. Geographical Regions of South America, bibliography, pp. 40–42, Normal, Ill., 1922.

Statistical Year-Book of the League of Nations. League of Nations Intelligence Service, Geneva.

STEWART, G. H. The Tacna-Arica Dispute, *World Peace Foundation Pamphlets*, vol. 10, no. 1, Boston, 1927.

STRODE, HUDSON. South by Thunderbird, New York, 1937.

STUART, GRAHAM H. Latin America and the United States (diplomatic and commercial relations), New York, 1922.

SUTTON. C. W. Irrigation and Public Policy in Peru, *Proc. Sec. Pan-Am. Sci. Cong.*, Washington, D.C., 1915–1916, vol. 3, pp. 840–850, Washington, D.C. 1917.

SYCKES, D. C. Cattle Raising in Argentina, *Trade Information Bull.* 647, U.S. Dept. of Commerce, Washington, D.C., 1929.

TAYLOR, M. M. Development of the Petroleum Industry in Colombia, *U.S. Commerce Reports*, vol. 2, pp. 706–708, 1927.

Tercer Censo Nacional de la Republica Argentina, 10 vols., Buenos Aires, 1917.

TORNQUIST, ERNESTO. The Economic Development of the Argentine Republic in the Last 50 Years (in English), Buenos Aires, 1919.

———. Business Conditions in Argentina, booklet published quarterly by Ernesto Tornquist & Co., Bankers, Buenos Aires.

TOWER, WALTER S. A Journey through Argentina, *Bull. Geog. Soc. Phila.*, vol. 12, pp. 89–113, 1914.

———. The Pampa of Argentina, *Geog. Rev.*, vol. 5, pp. 293–315, 1918.

———. Notes on the Commercial Geography of South America, *Bull. Am. Geog. Soc.*, vol. 45, pp. 881–901, 1913.

———. The Andes as a Factor in South American Geography, *Jour. of Geog.*, vol. 15, pp. 1–8, 1916.

TREWARTHA, GLENN T. An Introduction to Weather and Climate, New York, 1937.

TROLL, K. An Expedition to the Central Andes, 1926–1928, *Geog. Rev.*, vol. 19, pp. 234–247, 1929.

U.S. Dept. of Agriculture. Peruvian Cotton, *Foreign Crops and Markets*, vol. 13, pp. 53–66, Washington, D.C., 1926.

U.S. Dept. of Commerce. Bolivia, *Supplement to Commerce Reports*, Washington, D.C., Annual.

———. Chile: Trade and Economic Review, *Supplement to Commerce Reports*, Washington, D.C., Annual.

———. Markets of Southern Chile, *Trade Information Bull.* 274, Washington, D.C., October, 1924.

———. Colombia, Commerce and Industries, *Trade Information Bull.*, Washington, D.C., Annual.

———. Colombia, *Supplement to Commerce Reports*, Washington, D.C., Annual.

———. Ecuador, *Supplement to Commerce Reports*, Washington, D.C., Annual.

———. Fuel and Power in Latin America, Washington, D. C., 1931.

———. Motor Roads in Latin America, Washington, D. C., 1925.

———. Paraguay, *Supplement to Commerce Reports*, Washington, D.C., Annual.

———. Peru, *Supplement to Commerce Reports*, Washington, D.C., Annual.

———. Tariff Systems of South America, *Tariff Series* 34, Washington, D.C., 1916.

———. Trade and Economic Review, Brazil, *Supplement to Commerce Reports*, Washington, D.C., Annual.

———. United States Trade with Latin America, Washington, D.C., Annual.

———. Uruguay, *Supplement to Commerce Reports*, Washington, D.C., Annual.

———. The Valorization of Coffee, *Trade Information Bull.* 73, Washington, D.C., 1922.

URIEN, CARLOS M., and COLOMBO, EZIO. Geografía Argentina, Buenos Aires, 1905.

VAN CLEEF, EUGENE, and WEITZ, B. O. Rainfall Maps of Latin America: Illustrative of Types of Latin-American Rainfall, *Monthly Weather Rev.*, vol. 49, pp. 537–543, Washington, D.C., 1921.

VAN DYKE, H. W. Through South America, New York, 1912.

VEATCH, A. C. Quito to Bogotá, New York, 1917.

VISHER, S. S. Variability vs. Uniformity in the Tropics, *Sci. Monthly*, vol. 15, p. 22, 1922.

VIVIAN, E. CHARLES. Peru, New York, 1914.

WALKER, PERCY H. Rubber, *Proc. Sec. Pan-Am. Sci. Cong.*, Washington, D.C., 1915–1916, vol. 8, pp. 367–384, Washington, D.C., 1917.

WALLE, PAUL. Bolivia, translated from the French by Bernard Miall, New York, 1914.

WARD, R. DE C. Outline of the Economic Climatology of Brazil, *Bull. Geog. Soc. Phila.*, vol. 7, pp. 53–66, 135–144, 1909.

———. A Visit to the Brazilian Coffee Country, *Nat. Geog. Mag.*, vol. 22, pp. 908–931, 1911.

———. The Southern Campos of Brazil, *Bull. Am. Geog. Soc.*, vol. 40, pp. 652–662, 1908.

———. The Hygiene of the Zones, *Bull. Geog. Soc. Phila.*, vol. 4, pp. 29–55, 1906.

———. The Climate of South America, *Bull. Am. Geog. Soc.*, vol. 35, pp. 353–360, 1903. Contains list of other papers on related subjects by same author.

———. The Hygiene of the Zones, chap. 7 in Climate, New York, 1918.

———. Some Problems of the Tropics, *Bull. Am. Geog. Soc.*, vol. 40, pp. 7–11, 1908.

———. The Life of Man in the Tropics, chap. 9 in Climate, New York, 1918.

WARSHAW, J. The New Latin America, New York, 1922.

WEDDELL, ALEXANDER W. Introduction to Argentina, New York, 1939.

WELCH, M. M. Bibliography on the Climate of South America, *Monthly Weather Rev. Supplement*, no. 18, U.S. Dept. of Agr., 42 pp., Washington, D.C., 1921.

WHITBECK, R. H. Adjustments to Environment in South America, *Annals Asso. Am. Geographers*, vol. 16, pp. 1–11, 1926.

WHITE, I. C. Coals of Brazil, *Proc. Sec. Pan-Am. Sci. Cong.*, Washington, D.C., 1915–1916, vol. 8, pp. 176–190, Washington, D.C., 1917.

WHYMPER, EDWARD. Travels among the Great Andes of the Equator, London, 1892.

WILCOX, EARLEY V. Tropical Agriculture, New York, 1916.

WILCOX, MARRION. Encyclopedia of Latin America, 887 pp., New York, 1917.

WILLIAMS, FRANK E. Crossing the Andes at 41° South, *Bull. Geog. Soc. Phila.*, vol. 32, no. 1, January, 1934.

WILLIS, BAILEY, DIRECTOR. Northern Patagonia: Character and Resources, vol. 1 (in English), Ministry of Public Works, published in New York, 1914.

WILSON, LUCY L. W. Climate and Man in Peru, *Bull. Geog. Soc. Phila.*, vol. 8, pp. 79–97, 135–171, 1910.

WILSON, OTTO. South America as an Export Field, *Special Agents Series* 81, U.S. Dept. of Commerce, Washington, D.C., 1914.

WINTER, NEVIN O. Argentina and Her People Today, Boston, 1911.

———. Brazil and Her People of Today, Boston, 1910.

———. Chile and Her People of Today, Boston, 1912.

WRIGHT, JOHN KIRTLAND. Aids to Geographical Research (best guide in English to geographical bibliographies and sources), *Am. Geog. Soc. Research Series* 10, New York, 1923.

WRIGLEY, G. M. Fairs of the Central Andes, *Geog. Rev.*, vol. 7, pp. 65–80, 1919.

YEATMAN, POPE. Mine of the Chile Exploration Company at Chuquicamata, Chile, *Proc. Sec. Pan-Am. Sci. Cong.*, Washington, D.C., 1915–1916, vol. 8, pp. 922–1004, Washington, D.C., 1917.

ZON, RAPHAEL. South American Timber Resources and Their Relation to the World's Timber Supply, *Geog. Rev.*, vol. 2, pp. 256–266, 1916.

——— and SPARHAWK, WILLIAM N. Forest Resources of the World, vol. 2, chap. 6, references on each South American country, New York, 1923.

Index

A

Aconcagua, Mount, 14, 295
Acre, Territory, Brazil, 384
Agricultural colonists, Argentina, 261
    Brazil, 359
Agriculture, Argentina, 254, 257–275,
    286–287, 289–291, 298–300
    Bolivia, 161–164
    Brazil, 334–336, 352–373, 376–382
    Chile, 199–209
    Colombia, 44, 55, 59
    Guiana colonies, 91–93
    Paraguay, 314–318
    Peru, 118–126, 129–131, 139–142
    South America, summary, 414–416
    Uruguay, 302–306
    Venezuela, 69–72, 76–79
Aguardiente, 47
Airways, 143, 169, 220, 236, 395
Alagôas, state of, Brazil, 376, 381
Alfalfa, Argentina, 265–266
Alpacas, 133, 134, 163
Amazon Basin, 21, 22, 24, 383, 391
Amazon River, 21, 124, 128, 141, 142,
    148, 324–326, 383–385, 405
Ambalema, Colombia, 48
Andes Copper Company, Chile, 197
Andes Mountains, 10, 13, 17, 20, 21,
    24, 99, 109, 110, 115, 116, 119,
    124, 128, 130, 132, 133, 136, 137,
    140, 144, 152, 153, 157, 173, 183–
    187, 191, 199, 213, 234, 239, 240,
    243, 245, 291, 292, 296, 300, 312,
    383

Andes Mountains, climatic influences,
    16
    transportation difficulties, 15, 99
Anopheles, 28
Antioquia, department, Colombia, 47,
    50–52, 60
Antofagasta, Chile, 192
Antofagasta and Bolivia Railway, 15,
    156, 168, 192, 195, 219
Araucanians, 188, 214
Arequipa, Peru, 133, 144, 148
Argentina, 223–300
    agricultural colonists, 261
    agriculture, 254, 257–275, 286–287,
    289–291, 298–300
    alfalfa, 265–266
    Bahía Blanca, 237, 243, 258, 259,
    281
    Buenos Aires, 21, 23, 168, 218–220,
    223, 226, 227, 233, 234, 236–240,
    243, 245, 249, 251, 266, 271–273,
    275–282, 293, 308, 312, 319, 320,
    332, 364, 391, 393
    Buenos Aires, Federal District, 255
    Buenos Aires, Province, 237, 259,
    261, 265, 268, 281
    cattle, 268–273, 286, 290–291, 297–
    298
    Chaco, 235, 249, 267, 287–291
    Chubut, Territory, 241, 242, 249
    coal, 241–242
    Córdoba, Province, 259, 261, 265,
    281
    corn, 261–263
    Corrientes, Province, 285

M